Robin Jenner has had a varied career, being a musician, songwriter, accountant and community worker, and now works as a volunteer at Gloucester Cathedral. He also buys and sells Wedgwood pottery. He has previously brought out a book featuring famous people from the 18th century as although interested in history generally, it is the 18th century that is his main level of expertise.

In loving memory of Kathleen 'Olive' Jackson, Sylvia 'Joan' Base and Linda Jane Base.

Robin Jenner

EDWARD JENNER – THE ORIGINAL VACCINATOR

AUSTIN MACAULEY PUBLISHERS™

LONDON * CAMBRIDGE * NEW YORK * SHARJAH

A CIP catalogue record for this title is available from the British Library.

ISBN 9781528993241 (Paperback)
ISBN 9781528993258 (Hardback)
ISBN 9781528993265 (ePub e-book)

www.austinmacauley.com

First Published 2022
Austin Macauley Publishers Ltd®
1 Canada Square
Canary Wharf
London
E14 5AA

I have no specific acknowledgements other than the many who were thanked in my first book, but I am deeply grateful to them all and they know who they are.

Table of Contents

Introduction

This book has been written in an attempt to go some way to right a wrong to one of Britain's forgotten heroes, namely Doctor Edward Jenner.

I have the same surname as Jenner and became interested in the man and his work many years ago when a distant cousin and myself worked on his family tree. Like other people with the same name, we thought that we may well be related. However, on completing work on his tree as well as our own, we realised that we were not as he had two sons, neither of whom married and had issue, whilst the third child, a girl named Catherine, married but her surname altered and that particular branch of the Jenner line was closed. However, some people with the same surname may be linked via Edward's brother Henry as he married and the name was continued.

However, despite my disappointment, my interest in the man continued and I have spent many years researching his life, both professionally and personally and my interest has increased due to my work at Gloucester Cathedral where there is a statue of him. Unfortunately, it has but one word on it – 'JENNER' and nothing else. Many visitors to the cathedral have either scant knowledge of the man or none at all and as the Jenner Museum which used to be the house that he and his family lived in at Berkeley making him more or less a local man, I spend as much time as I can explaining who he is and what he achieved when I am at the cathedral.

Edward Jenner (1749–1823) was a man who was a victim of his own success because what he achieved in his work against the dreaded disease of smallpox was so monumental that the people who commissioned his statue in the cathedral thought that his name would live forever. However, the opposite occurred because smallpox was officially deemed to have been eradicated by the announcement of the World Health Organisation in 1980. Now that there is no more smallpox, it has rarely been discussed and therefore neither has Edward Jenner's name and his involvement with it.

Jenner would have been considered a well-known doctor even if he hadn't worked on the smallpox disease as he involved himself in other projects such as the nesting habits of the cuckoos, the launching of the first hot air balloon in Britain, the annual migration of birds, and the causes of angina to name but a few.

In writing this book, I have tried to not only show his incredible work but also to go into a little more depth in describing some of the people that he worked with and socialised with along with a chapter on the monarchs who ruled in Jenner's time. I have also written about Cheltenham and Bath, two places which figured in his life along with a little information on the Napoleonic wars in order to give a more rounded picture of the man and the age in which he lived.

With the 200th anniversary of his death approaching in 2023, I felt that the time was right in bringing a new book on him out and I hope that this book will give the reader interesting information of the man, his family and friends, in a way that readers will enjoy.

Robin Jenner
Gloucester, March, 2019

Chapter 1

Early Family Life, Death of Parents, Early Education and Subsequent Treatment Against Smallpox

Edward Jenner, the little child that was to become an eminent country doctor who cured the world of smallpox, was born on 17 May, 1749 to the Rev Stephen Jenner and his wife, Sarah (nee Head) in the Gloucestershire village of Berkeley.

When he eventually reached adulthood, he grew away from a long line of male Jenners in terms of the career that he chose, as many of them earned their living by being bakers. When he eventually grew older, Jenner made a friend by the name of the Rev Thomas Dudley Fosbroke (1770–1842) who was a local historian and who wrote about the histories of Cheltenham and Berkeley. Fosbroke was born in London and studied at St Paul's school and then Pembroke College, Oxford, where he gained his MA in 1792. He attempted Edward's family tree and did rather well, managing to trace back to Jenner's great-great-grandfather, Stephen Jenner (1610–1667) who lived in Standish, about eight miles from Berkeley and who was a baker by trade. He married a lady by the name of Mary (1626–1707). Unfortunately, Fosbroke was unable to find her surname or the date of the marriage, although it was likely to be around 1644 as their son, also called Stephen, was born in 1645. We have to assume that if they had produced more children which was highly likely, then they would have been born after Stephen, because as it was, Mary could only have been around 19 years of age when she gave birth to Stephen. Stephen (1645–1727) was Edward's great-grandfather and, like his father, was also a baker by trade. He too lived in Standish but moved to Slimbridge and lived there until his death in 1727. He married Deborah Davies (?–1683) in 1669 and they produced at least six children, one of which was again named Stephen (1672–1728) and who married

Mary Davies (1676–1758) in 1697. This Stephen followed the same trade as his father and grandfather, he too making a living as a baker. By dying in 1728 as he did, he outlived his father by only one year. Mary's father was Thomas Davies (?–1679) and if Thomas was the brother of Deborah Davies (?–1683), who had married Stephen (1645–1727), it would make Stephen (1672–1728) and Mary (1676–1758) first cousins. It was quite common in the 18th century and even later for first cousins to marry because with limited means of travel, people often spent their entire lives in the same village or town and so their choice of partner was much more limited than it is today.

Moving on with Jenner's forbears, Stephen (1672–1728) and Mary (1676–1758) who were Edward's grandparents, produced at least three children that we know of, one of which was a son once again being called Stephen (1702–1754) and who married Sarah Head (1708–1754) in 1729 and it was this couple who were Edward's parents. This Stephen broke away from several generations of bakers and went to Pembroke College, Oxford to study Theology. Both Stephen and Mary had connections with the church as Mary was the daughter of the Rev Henry Head (?–1728) and his wife, Mary (?–1739). Henry Head was the prebend of Bristol Cathedral and later on became the vicar of Berkeley. In 1725, Stephen who would one day become Edward's father, was appointed by the Most Rev Joseph Wilcocks (1673–1756), the Bishop of Gloucester as the curate of the parish church of Coates which was in the Cotswolds and was between Stroud and Cirencester. The Most Rev Joseph Wilcocks was appointed Chaplain to the British Embassy in Lisbon in 1709 and on his return was made Chaplin-in-Ordinary to King George I who ruled between 1714 and 1727. On 11th March, 1721, he was installed a Prebendary of Westminster and on 3rd December, 1721, he was consecrated Bishop of Gloucester, a position he held for ten years before being installed as the Dean of Westminster on 21st June, 1731. He died on 28th February, 1756 and is buried in Westminster Abbey where a monument was erected in his memory in 1761.

Returning to Stephen, however, the position he now held as Curate would have only given him a limited income given that he would soon have a family to support as he married Sarah Head in 1729. However, misfortune for Sarah's father, the Rev Henry Head who died in 1728 but would have been Stephen's father-in-law had he lived another year ended as good fortune for Stephen (1702–1754). In 1728, the Rev Head's position as Vicar of Berkeley came into the hands of a gentleman named Ralph Webb. However, Webb's tenure at Berkeley lasted only a year and in 1729, Stephen, who in twenty years' time would be Edward's father, was appointed as Vicar of Berkeley.

And now the family tree reaches Edward. He was born in Berkeley on 17th May 1749 and he was one of nine children. Stephen (1702–54) and Sarah (1708–54) sadly lost three of the children who failed to reach adulthood. Although it was common in the 18th century for some children to die young, it was still a tragedy and the sadness that it caused the parents during those times should not be underestimated, and of course it was always a terrible tragedy when the mother died giving birth as is the case of Jenner's mother, who died the day after giving birth to Thomas in 1754. The children that Stephen and Sarah lost were Edward (1743–49), Henry (1734–36) and Thomas (1754–54). Thomas lived just one day. He was christened on 8th October and buried on the 9th whilst Sarah, his mother, died one day after that, on the 10th October. The six who survived were Mary (1730–1810), Stephen (1732–97), Henry (1736–98), Sarah (1738–80), Anne (1741–1812), and, of course, Edward (1749–1823).

If losing his beloved mother, Sarah, in October 1754 wasn't enough for the young Edward to cope with, there was worse to come which would devastate the family, young Edward in particular. Only two months after losing his mother, Stephen, Edward's father, died on 9th December leaving Edward an orphan at just five years of age. This was a devastating blow to the whole family, but they somehow had to rally and support their young brother. It was his brother Stephen who, although only twenty-two years old, was now considered the head of the family and who became Edward's guardian although, of course, he was helped a great deal by his sisters, Mary, Sarah and Anne.

Despite the tragic death of both his parents, Edward seemed to be a happy child. He loved the simple things in life and particularly loved nature and loved to explore the surrounding countryside, but naturally after a few years, the subject of his education came up. Stephen and his sisters decided to send him to a Grammar school in Wotton-under-Edge and he was put in the care of the headmaster, the Rev Thomas Clissold with whom he was to board. We cannot be certain as to quite how the young Edward reacted to being sent away from his home as by now, he would have thought of Stephen as his father, brother and friend. He was just eight years old when he left Berkeley to go to school and although we think that he was happy there, we cannot be sure as he would have got used to the trauma of losing his parents at the age of five years and would have become used to the stability that being cared for by his elder brother, Stephen, had been given him during that period of three years.

It was during his time at the Grammar School at Wotton-under-Edge that Edward was subjected to the horrific treatment against smallpox that was to haunt him for the rest of his days and that was to drive him later on in his life when he was attempting to effect a cure for this dreaded disease. Smallpox was a dreadful and much feared illness that affected millions of people across the world and it was felt that it had been responsible for the hideous deaths of people as far back as 10,000 BC. We will look at it in more detail when we reach Jenner's work on it in the latter part of the century but at this stage, we will examine only the cure that was available at the time of Jenner in his youth. Before Edward effected a cure for this disease much later in his life, the standard treatment for smallpox was to give a healthy patient a small dose of the disease in the hope that the person would catch a very mild dose of the disease, recover, and then lead a normal life being immune against the full blown disease for life. It was called Variolation which was a derivative of the Latin word for smallpox which was called Variola. The person who has generally been given the credit for introducing this cure was Lady Mary Wortley Montagu (1689–1765) in 1721. Lady Mary came across the treatment several years before and had one of her children inoculated against smallpox at that time. Lady Mary was born in London in 1689 and she was a daughter of Evelyn Pierrepoint, the 5th Earl of Kingston-Upon-Hull and who was the younger brother of William, the 4th Earl. Lady Mary was a long-standing friend of Anne Wortley Montagu who was the grand-daughter of the 1st Earl of Sandwich and through Anne, came to know her brother, Edward Wortley Montagu. Mary and Edward became close after his sister Anne died in 1709 and wished to marry. However, Lady Mary's father, the 5th Earl of Kingston-Upon-Hull, for some reason wanted Mary to marry another man and he refused permission for the couple to wed. Mary and Edward were determined, however, and in 1712 they eloped, living quietly in the country until Edward became a Member of Parliament in 1715 and they moved to Istanbul when Edward was made Ambassador there, the following year.

Lady Mary learned of the practice of inoculation with smallpox when she was in the Ottoman Empire. She and her brother had both contracted the disease and although she survived, her looks were badly marred whilst her brother died. At this time, inoculation or variolation was the only cure for smallpox and to a degree it worked. However, this treatment was thought to have two major faults.

18

The first was that it was risky as sometimes people died who were in good health before they were inoculated, especially when administered by people who were not properly qualified. This couldn't possibly happen with cowpox as the disease was mild and never fatal. The second fear was that even if the person was successfully variolated, it was thought that it could be that the disease was still being spread as the people who were cured could possibly become carriers. This second reason proved unfounded but the first point about cowpox being non-life threatening was sound enough for Jenner to wish to pursue the possibility of its use during his later career.

As mentioned earlier, Edward was subject to inoculation when he was at Wotton-under-Edge and reading it today, it looks barbaric and caused him harm for the rest of his life. He was inoculated by Mr Holbrow who was a surgeon in the area. Edward's future friend, Thomas Dudley Fosbroke (1770–1842) described it in a very factual manner, leaving the reader to judge for him or herself as to how bad it was. Fosbroke wrote the following:

"He was bled, to ascertain whether his blood was fine; was purged repeatedly, till he became emaciated and feeble; was kept on a very low diet, small in quantity, and dosed with a diet-drink to sweeten the blood. After this…he was removed to one of the then inoculation stables, and haltered up with others in a terrible state of disease, although none died. By good fortune, the Doctor escaped with a mild exhibition of the disease."

This whole treatment seems utterly bizarre and it would seem highly unlikely that Lady Mary Wortley Montagu had this in mind when she introduced inoculation to this country some thirty-six years earlier. It is impossible to imagine that she would have put her own child through this torture and bearing in mind that the young Edward Jenner was just eight years old when subjected to it, it must be concluded that it was British doctors who thought this preparation up. In any event, it had a terrible effect on Edward and it took him a very long time to get over it. For many years following this treatment, he suffered from painful headaches and was very nervous at sudden noises.

It had such an effect on the young Edward that not surprisingly, he wanted to leave the school in Wotton-under-Edge and go home, or at the very least attend another school. This he did the following year, 1758, when Edward was nine years old. He went to school as a boarder in Cirencester and came under the tutelage of the Rev Dr Washbourne whose main interest seemed to be in the classics, namely Latin and Greek. Dr John Baron (1786–1851), Jenner's future biographer, a clever man who went to Edinburgh at the age of fifteen years to study medicine and graduated M.D. four years later in 1805 aged just nineteen, described Dr Washbourne as a man who 'respected proficiency in the classics'. Jenner had little interest in either Latin or Greek and whilst he learned just enough to get by, he was still much more interested in nature and every spare moment that he had was spent collecting fossils from the countryside that surrounded the beautiful little Cotswold town. Although studying Latin and Greek did not inspire Edward, it wasn't all bad at Cirencester. He made good friends there, some of whom stayed with him for life, the three that he was especially close to were Caleb Hillier Parry, Charles Brandon Trye and John Clinch.

Caleb Hillier Parry (1755–1822) was the son of a Presbyterian Minister named Joshua Parry and his wife Sarah, the daughter of Caleb Hillier of Upcott and would later become a doctor in the fashionable town of Bath. Parry was born in Cirencester on 21st October, 1755 and was the eldest son of the afore mentioned Joshua Parry (1719–66). Caleb lost his father very early in his life, being only eleven years old at the time. Soon after that trauma, he went to school in Cirencester until leaving in 1770. He then entered Warrington Academy at the age of just fifteen years where he met and fell in love with Sarah Rigby, the lady who would eventually become his wife. In 1773, he became a student of Medicine at Edinburgh University where he came under the tutelage of William Cullen (1710–90), the Professor of Medicine. Cullen deviated from the normal practice of lecturing in Latin and instead took the unusual route and lectured in English. After two years Caleb moved to London to continue his studies and returned to Edinburgh in 1777 and graduated M.D. in June, 1778 before marrying Sarah. The couple went on a tour of Northern Europe before returning to Cirencester and for a short while moved in with Caleb's widowed mother before finally settling in Bath in 1779 where Parry set up in practice as a physician. In the eighteenth century, Bath was a fashionable city and there were a large number of doctors there so his practice was slow to progress but eventually it did and the couple became quite wealthy. This was because Parry began to get well known and was visiting patients as far north as Gloucester and as far south as Warminster. They were wealthy enough indeed for them to purchase a very grand townhouse in the Circus in Bath and on top of that, they had a large country house built on the lower slopes of Lansdown, north of the city centre. In 1800, Parry was elected to the Royal Society but in 1816, he suffered a severe stroke and lost the use of his right side and his speech was also badly affected. It was clear that he could no longer run his practice in any meaningful way and he spent the last six years of his life dictating parts of his life story and supervising the work on his gardens. His health greatly deteriorated over a period of years until he died on 9th March 1822. He is buried in Bath Abbey where the medical contingent of the city had a monument erected in his memory.

Jenner also made friends with Charles Brandon Trye F.R.S. (1757–1811) who was the eldest son of John Trye, his father being the rector of Leckhampton which is close to Cheltenham, like Bath, a fashionable spa town, and his wife, Mary, daughter of the Rev John Longford of Haresfield near Stroud. Charles was born on 21st August 1757. In March 1773, he was apprenticed to Thomas Hallward who was an apothecary in Worcester and in 1778, he became a pupil of William Russell, the surgeon with whom he stayed for two years before becoming a pupil of the famous Dr John Hunter (1728–93) whose life and work we shall look at later. Trye was later appointed House Surgeon at the Westminster Hospital. Hunter greatly influenced Charles's career as he worked for Henry Watson as a dissector at the Royal Academy. Trye eventually returned to Gloucester and was admitted to the Royal Society on 17th December 1807. He was a great friend of Edward Jenner and was later to promote vaccination as a cure for smallpox, the method having been taught to Charles by his friend sometime during or after 1798 when Jenner became confident of how much better it was than the previous method of inoculation or variolation. Trye showed great loyalty to his friend Jenner during this time, as the new method of curing smallpox, namely the vaccination of a healthy patient with cowpox, came in for heavy criticism from senior members of the medical world and could have damaged Trye's career. Charles Brandon Trye died on 7th October 1811 and was buried in the Mary de Crypt church in Gloucester. There is a memorial to him in Gloucester Cathedral where there is also a statue of Jenner, and because Jenner and Trye were lifelong friends and worked together, it is probably worth writing the words of the latter's monument which is in the west end of the north side of the nave in the cathedral.

SACRED TO THE MEMORY OF CHARLES BRANDON TRYE, ESQUIRE, F.R.S., SURGEON TO THE GLOUCESTER INFIRMARY, DESCENDED FROM THE ANCIENT FAMILY OF TRYE OF HARDWICK COURT IN THIS COUNTY, WHO DIED ON THE SEVENTH

DAY OF OCTOBER, A.D. MDCCCX1, AND LIES BURIED IN THE CHURCH YARD OF ST MARY DE CRYPT IN THIS CITY.

HIS EXTENSIVE MEDICAL AND ANATOMICAL KNOWLEDGE,

HIS EMINENT SKILL IN THE MORE HAZARDOUS OPERATIONS OF SURGERY, HIS ATTENTION AND BENEVOLENCE TO THE POOR, HIS STRICT INTEGRITY AND HIS GENUINE PIETY,

FOUNDED ON A FIRM BELIEF IN THE TRUTHS OF CHRISTIANITY, GAINED FROM THE GENERAL CONFIDENCE AND RESPECT OF AN EXTENSIVE DISTRICT AND INDUCED HIS FRIENDS TO ERECT THIS MONUMENT AS A GRATEFUL TRIBUTE TO HIS MEMORY.

There is a medallion bust of Trye at the top of the monument by Charles Rossi, R.A., (1762–1839) which was engraved by J. Nagle from a drawing by the painter Richard Smirke (1753–1845).

John Charles Felix Rossi, normally known as Charles Rossi, was born on 8th March 1762 and entered the Royal Academy of Schools in 1781 and in that year won the silver medal and in 1784, the gold medal for his 'Venus Conducting Helen to Paris'. Rossi became an Associate of the Royal Academy in 1798 and a full Academician in 1802. He had a long and distinguished career but suffered from declining health in his later years eventually dying on 21st February 1839 aged 76 years.

Richard Smirke (1753–1845), meanwhile, was an English painter and illustrator who was born on 15th April 1753 in Wigton near Carlisle. In 1791, he was elected to the Royal Academy and four years later became a full academician in 1795. In 1804, he was nominated to take over from Joseph Witton as Keeper to the Royal Academy but the appointment was blocked by King George III who was unhappy with Smirke's radical political views and Henry Fuesli (1741–1825) was appointed instead. If Smirke's political views were the reason that his appointment was blocked, it would seem strange as Fuesli had had a relationship with Mary Wollstonecroft (1759–97) who was a radical feminist before the term was invented. However, George III's mind may have been put at rest due to the relationship between Fuesli and Wollstonecroft being of short duration with Fuesli saying, "I hate clever women, they are always troublesome." Which is not exactly a comment expected of someone who has positive views as to the rights of women. Richard Smirke, meanwhile, enjoyed a good career and died on 5th January 1845 at the age of 92 years and is buried in Kensal Green Cemetery.

The third boy who came into Jenner's life at Cirencester was John Clinch (1749–1819), who went on to become a clergyman and who eventually became a missionary to the indigenous population of Newfoundland.

John Clinch was a clergyman-physician who as far as we can tell, was the first man to practice vaccination in North America. He was born in Cirencester on 9th January 1749, the same year that Jenner was born and he attended the same school in Cirencester as Jenner did and at the same time as the two boys were the same age. In 1770 both young men moved to London to study under the great Dr John Hunter (1728–93) and Clinch eventually went on to study medicine in Dorset where he gained a knowledge of Newfoundland from Benjamin Lester who was a merchant of Poole and of Trinity in Newfoundland, Trinity being a small town located on Trinity Bay in Newfoundland and Labrador. Clinch moved to Newfoundland in 1775 and set up as a doctor and Lay Reader in the Anglican Church. In 1783, he moved to Trinity where he married Hannah Hart who bore him six children. The first three children had learning difficulties but the fourth eventually became a doctor like his father whilst the youngest became an Anglican Clergyman in Boston, Mass. John and Hannah's only daughter married a William Bullock in 1823 and he succeeded his father-in-law at the Trinity Mission that Clinch had set up in the way that Robert Raikes (1735–1811) had done in England at that time. Raikes had set up the first Sunday Schools in England after he had witnessed the misery and poverty that so many children lived in. Clinch was an Evangelist and welcomed all faiths and took his children to the Congregational Chapel in Poole. He suffered a stroke and died on 22nd November 1819 after a long illness.

This then is a brief summary of Edward's early life, the schools that he attended, his brush with smallpox as a little boy and the effect that it had on him, and a very brief summary of three of the many friends that he made. We can now move on and look at his education as an adult where we will meet the famous Dr John Hunter (1728–93) who he was to study with from 1770 until 1773, and the lifelong friendship that grew up between the two men during that time.

-oOOo-

Chapter 2

Dr John Hunter. Jenner Refuses Offer to Set Up a Lucrative Practice in London and Also Refuses a Trip 'Round the World with Captain Cook and Joseph Banks

In the first chapter, we have looked at Edward's childhood and early education, so we must now look at his adult education.

It was now 1761 and Edward had been to school at Wotton-under-Edge and then to the school in Cirencester but both Edward and his family were unsure of where he should go at this time of life. Edward still loved nature but Stephen and the rest of the family were unclear as to whether that interest alone could lead to a career that would allow him to make a living. We do not know who made the final decision that he would train to be a doctor; it could have been Stephen, one of his sisters, or even Edward himself but in the end the decision was made that he would enter the world of medicine. Whoever thought of this, it was a decision that would eventually have repercussions for the whole world and would affect all of us, even those of us that are alive today.

It was decided to send Edward to Daniel Ludlow of Chipping Sodbury. Ludlow was a surgeon-teacher and had a practice in Chipping Sodbury which was a small market town in Gloucestershire. Here was where Edward became Mr Ludlow's apprentice and stayed with him from 1761 until 1769 by which time Edward was twenty years old and had almost as much knowledge as was needed for him to become a surgeon. However, when he returned home at the end of his six years with Ludlow, little did the young adult Edward Jenner, born and bred in the country, know what was in store for him for the next three years.

In the autumn of 1770, Jenner went to London to study under the famous Dr John Hunter (1728–93). It was a huge move for Jenner, as he had always lived in Gloucestershire and it must have been a huge culture shock for him to see London with its varied sights, the beautiful Georgian houses that Hunter's wealthy patients lived in along with the filthy streets and houses that the poor inhabited. London was a mixture of huge wealth and grinding poverty that Edward had never seen before as all he had seen was the beautiful county of Gloucestershire with towns like Cirencester nestled within it. Now, at the age of twenty, he had known academia but it was nestled within lovely countryside, or at worst small towns, but he was now going to experience life as he had never done before.

The young Edward Jenner had several options as to which surgeons he could apply to learn from including Dr Percival Pott (1714–88), of St Bartholomew's Hospital, Dr Caesar Hawkins (1711–86), who was the surgeon to King George III, and Dr William Bromfield (1712–92), who was surgeon at the new Hospital of St George's. However, in the end, Edward and probably his elder brother and guardian, Stephen, chose Dr John Hunter who was working with his elder, and at that time, probably better-known brother, Dr William Hunter (1718–83) who ran his own anatomy school in Windmill Street, in the heart of the city centre. William's school was better equipped than any other of its type and it is probably worth noting its prospectus here which read:

"The whole comprehends a full course of Anatomy, Physiology, and Midwifery: illustrated by a greater number of elegant and curious anatomical preparations than ever were brought together or used in any School of Anatomy. The honorarium paid by students is ten guineas to be perpetual, seven guineas for attending one complete course, or four guineas for the first half and three for the second. There is likewise a School of Practical Anatomy kept open and much frequented through the whole winter. Here students see everything that is going on, both dissections and all the arts of examining diseases and making preparations; and with their own hands dissect as many bodies, make for themselves as many preparations, and perform as many operations of surgery as they please. In this School so many subjects are dissected in the course of a winter, so many diseases examined, and occasional demonstrations of all parts of the body so often repeated, that for acquiring substantial knowledge it is reckoned preferable to any other kind of study and to be the finishing part of the education. The honorarium for this part through the whole winter is five guineas."

William Hunter had been born at Long Calderwood which is now a part of East Kilbride, South Lanarkshire on 23rd May 1718. He went to the University of Glasgow in 1737 at the age of nineteen years and studied Divinity but decided his future lay in medicine and went to the University of Edinburgh and studied under the Scottish Physician, Dr William Cullen (1710–90). In 1741, he travelled to London and became a pupil of Dr William Smellie (1697–1763) from 1741 until 1744 and was trained in anatomy at St George's Hospital. Hunter specialised in obstetrics and in 1746, started to give courses in dissecting, operative procedures and bandaging. Unlike his younger brother, John, he had nice manners and dressed accordingly, again, unlike his younger brother. Eventually he was to become the leading obstetrician in London and open his famous anatomy school, the prospectus of which we have already seen.

It may also be worth noting in detail the contents of William's lectures, because although Jenner was to become the pupil of William's brother John, Jenner would draw on the contents of them during his three years in London, from 1770 until 1773. Although the source of this information stems from the 'European Magazine' dated 1782, nine years after Jenner had finished studying with John Hunter, it was almost certainly the same as when Jenner returned to Berkeley. The syllabus was as follows:

This course of lectures has now been given for thirty-six years, and till the last three years two Courses were read every winter, one from the beginning of October to the middle of January, the other from the end of January to the middle of May.

1. The first lectures give the history, the uses, and the best method of conducting the study of anatomy.
2. Then the nature and uses of the similar and constituent parts of the body are explained, to convey a general knowledge of the body, and of its operations in this order: blood, arteries, veins, lymphatics or absorbents, glands, nerves, muscles, bones, and their appendages. After which the particular anatomy is taken up in the following order:
3. The bones.
4. The muscles in a fresh subject.
5. The male organs in the same.
6. The different fresh joints in the same.
7. The viscera and female organs in a fresh subject.

8. The organs of sense and integuments in a fresh subject.
9. The brain and nerves in a fresh subject.
10. The diseases of bones.
11. The diseases of the viscera.
12. Chirurgical diseases more particularly, and the operations of surgery explained and performed upon a fresh subject.
13. The anatomy and physiology of the gravid uterus and foetus.
14. The diseases peculiar to the sex.
15. Of pregnancy and parturition.
16. Of the disorders and management of women in childbed.

The advantages of this school are various:
1) The long experience of the lecturer.
2) The great convenience of the several apartments, which were planned and built on purpose for anatomical studies.
3) But above all the inestimable treasure of preparations, and especially of diseases, which the museum contains, and which are introduced into the lectures, such as no teacher was ever possessed of before.

Hunter had an interesting hobby that had little to do with his medical career, he was an antique coin collector of some renown, and his collection is in the Hunter Coin Cabinet at the Hunterian Museum. He collected coins from many different sources, but no doubt the coin that had pride of place in his heart was that of the Athenian gold piece donated by King George III. He also had a large collection of books which he purchased at an auction from the British Museum, who in turn had bought them when the owner, Dr Anthony Askew (1722–1774), an English Physician died in 1774.

In 1748, William's younger brother, John, left Scotland to work in London and work with, and learn from his elder brother. We know that John was born in 1728, but it is not altogether certain of the exact day when he was born but it is believed to be either the 13th or 14th July although some sources quote 13th February, so we can be sure of the year but unfortunately not the month. John Hunter was born, like his elder brother William, in Calderwood. Three of his would-be siblings died before John was even born, sadly, a normal occurrence in the 18th century when it happened but it was nonetheless a tragedy especially for the mother. John did not show any interest or aptitude for anything in particular and had a scruffy appearance. He was completely unlike William who was always very smartly dressed and was very focussed on his career as a physician. In complete contrast, John was a troublesome young man to his family, he had no idea what he wanted to do in the way of a career and seemed only interested in nature. Later in his life after becoming a successful surgeon, he once wrote:

"When I was a boy, I wanted to know all about the clouds and grasses, and why the leaves changed colour in the autumn; I watched the ants, bees, birds, tadpoles, and caddis-worms; I pestered people with questions about what nobody knew or cared about."

As his elder brother was now head of the family, William felt that he should do something that would steer his younger brother John into something that would give the younger brother a direction in life. As William's life was dedicated to being an anatomist and surgeon, he sent for John to make his way down to London where he could possibly become a surgeon as well as his elder brother.

So with a great deal of encouragement from William, in 1748, when John was twenty years old, he left Scotland and travelled to London to join William and assist him in his dissections. Once he had arrived in London, William gave his younger brother an arm to dissect which was not an easy undertaking. Surprisingly perhaps, he took to this work very well and was soon running his own classes because he was soon to become an expert in dissections.

The way he did this was to procure freshly dead bodies, and he wasn't altogether too fussy about the way he went about it. In more recent times, it has been said that William along with his former tutor, Dr William Smellie (1697–1763) were in some way responsible for the deaths of pregnant women, and as his younger brother John, was William's assistant, he too was implicated. Neither of the Hunter brothers were saints, certainly not John, but many feel that this theory is totally implausible as it implies that some of the pregnant women that they attended to were in effect, murdered. This cannot be the case as William was one of the leading obstetricians of his day and he had a high reputation to guard. However, his younger brother John was far more of a maverick than his brother William and he, John, was almost certainly breaking the law on many occasions as to how he managed to get his hands on bodies after the people died. However, we can certainly exclude pregnant women in this matter. At a general level, then certainly dubious methods were used as surgeons were strictly limited as to the number of dead bodies they were allowed to experiment on and John Hunter certainly exceeded those numbers. There were certainly places that could be used for obtaining newly buried bodies and these were of course graveyards. John Hunter wouldn't necessarily go himself, but there were always groups of body snatchers who would willingly raid local graveyards, and one of these was St George's churchyard in Bloomsbury to name but one, although there would certainly be others. Looking out of the dissecting room in Covent Garden one can see the churchyard of St Paul's and this too would be a target for body snatchers or even Hunter's students. Another source were hospital patients and an entry into Hunter's notes proves this:

"In 1759, I stripped the bones of an old woman that died in St George's Hospital," Hunter added: "I knew nothing of her history."

This makes clear that it was not one of Hunter's patients and doubtless there were many more.

In 1760, John Hunter became an Army Surgeon and the following year travelled to the French island of Belle Ile before serving with the British Army in 1762. Hunter had what was at the time, an interesting take as to how to treat gunshot wounds. The usual practice was for the field surgeon to deliberately widen the bullet hole to make it easier for the bullet to be removed, but in this period of ignorance concerning the spread of germs, as often as not, the wound would become infected, often leading to death. Hunter was a great believer in nature healing itself and he would often not touch the wound unless it was absolutely necessary and fewer men died as a result.

1763 saw Hunter leaving the army and returning to London and he went into partnership with a well-known London dentist called James Spence. Working with his brother, William, again was out of the question. The brothers had fallen out over the ownership of John's preparations that he had left under his brother's care and turning to somebody else to work with was the only solution. However, working in dentistry was a good way of expanding his medical knowledge. Dentistry was in its infancy, but Spence was well known for extracting healthy teeth from the poor and transplanting them into the mouth of a well-to-do person, allowing the donor to receive money for his or her pains.

Hunter Junior went on to have a great career as a surgeon teacher having many pupils, his star pupil being Edward Jenner who studied and worked with him for three years, from 1770 until 1773. Hunter was a workaholic and he would start at 6am when he would spend his time until 9am dissecting bodies and he would then stop for breakfast. After breakfast, he would then tend to his patients until mid-day although he would often carry on until the middle of the afternoon should the need arise. He had dinner at 4pm whereupon he would work with his students often until midnight and beyond. It was a punishing schedule by any standards and often his students would not know when they were starting or ending their day, as it all depended on what Hunter expected of them given his own timetable which to say the least, tended to be flexible.

John Hunter was elected to the Royal Society in 1767 and not only did he do well professionally, being appointed as a surgeon to St George's Hospital in 1768 and surgeon to King George III in 1786, he was fortunate in his personal life as well. Despite the fact that he was a workaholic and scruffy in his manners and appearance, he married a very cultured woman in July, 1771 by the name of Anne Home (1742–1821). The record of their marriage is entered into the register of St James's Church, Piccadilly: "John Hunter of this Parish and Anne Home of the Parish of St Martin in the fields were married in this church by licence from the Bishop of London this twenty Second day of July in the year 1771 By me W Parker, Rector.

This marriage was Solemnized between us

John Hunter Anne Home

In the presence of Robt. Home, Mary Home."

Although they loved each other, neither had been in a hurry to get married, but when they did, on 22nd July 1771, it was after a long courtship which had lasted seven years.

Anne was the eldest daughter of the surgeon Robert Boyne Home and was the sister of another surgeon, Everard Home F.R.S. (1756–1832) who spent many years working with his brother-in-law. John and Anne were completely different characters because she was very much the artistic type, being a gifted poet. She penned many lyrics, some of which were put to music by none other than the great Austrian composer named Franz Joseph Haydn (1732–1809), the most famous being 'My mother bids me bind my hair'. If the reader looks up who wrote this song, they will almost certainly find that it is credited to Franz Joseph Haydn (1732–1809), but no writing credit ever seems to go to Anne Home. These are the lyrics that Anne Home wrote for Haydn for this particular song:

MY MOTHER BIDS ME BIND MY HAIR

My mother bids me bind my hair
With bands of rosy hue,
Tie up my sleeves with ribbons rare,
And lace my bodice blue. "For why," she cries, "sit still and weep,
While others dance and play?"
Alas! I scarce can go or creep,
While Lubin is away.
'Tis sad to think the days are gone,
When those we love were near,
I sit upon this mossy stone,
And sigh when none can hear.
And while I spin my flaxen thread,
And sing my simple lay,
The village seems asleep or dead,
Now Lubin is away.

The reason that Anne Home receives little or no credit is because she was the lyric writer. Even in the year 2018, it is still happening. Elton John never wrote the lyrics to his songs; the lyric writer was Bernie Taupin but he rarely gets a mention. According to just about every armchair critic, all the songs in the wonderful film 'West Side Story' that came out in the 1950s were written by Leonard Bernstein but again no one mentions, or gives much credit to the great lyrics by Stephen Sondheim. Getting nearer to the present day, Brian Wilson of the Beach Boys is always credited for the beautiful songs that he wrote, especially the wonderful 'God Only Knows' from the Pet Sounds album. No one should want to take away the beauty of that lovely song but Wilson didn't write the lyrics and it is doubtful whether hardly anybody can name the person who did. In fact it was Tony Asher and without his haunting lyrics, the song would never have become the beautiful love song that we have today. If all these male lyric writers have problems getting their deserved recognition in the 21st century, it is not surprising that a woman, Anne Home, doesn't get a credit for the work that she produced two centuries ago.

However, to return to Haydn, he was loved and respected by many and he is credited with the development of chamber music, much of which was played by a piano trio. He is also given credit for the introduction of the string quartet, a much-loved way of interpreting classical music to this day and which is normally made up of two violins, one viola and one cello. Anne Hunter (Home) was a highly intelligent person and living in an age where women were denied the vote must have been frustrating for her and the other women in her set, Mary Delany (1700–88), the English lady of letters and conversationalist, Elizabeth Montagu (1720–1800), the English writer and society leader, and Elizabeth Carter (1717–1806), the English scholar and poet and later on, women such as Fanny Burney (1752–1840), the writer who would one day influence Jane Austen (1775–1817) whose books are still enjoyed today as well as being turned into television series and films. Initially idolising Fanny Burney, Austen's popularity would eclipse that of her mentor. Mary Delany had set up the famous 'Blue Stocking Club' which would meet for evenings of good conversation which, while dismissed as pretentious by some, was a good outlet for women with strong views but no outlet such as Parliament to express them. Looking back, we can view them as feminists before the word was coined.

Although Anne's husband, John, kept well away from these gatherings, he respected his wife's views and artistic talents and their marriage worked well and was a happy one, producing four children.

During the course of his dissections, Jenner had learned about angina and the dangerous illness that it was. He didn't pass on his knowledge to Hunter as he felt that if Hunter knew what he had, then it would hasten the latter's death. It was strange that Edward thought that Hunter was unaware of it and given his sometimes-volatile nature, Hunter knew that a fierce argument with one of his colleagues could well trigger a fatal attack, and sadly, he was proven correct in this. On 16th October 1793, he went to St George's Hospital for a meeting in order to argue the case for two Scottish young men who wanted to be Hunter's students but who did not have the necessary experience as they had not served the necessary apprenticeships. Hunter knew that the meeting would be confrontational, and he was right. No sooner had he started to argue the case for accepting them, he found himself in an argument with one of the other surgeons in the room and after a short squabble between them, he suddenly groaned, sank into the arms of one of the other surgeons present, and died aged sixty-five years.

This book is about Edward Jenner, but is also about the friends and colleagues that he had throughout his career and as nobody else ever made the same impression on Jenner as Hunter did, it has been necessary to look at his life in more detail than in other books about Jenner. Jenner not only studied under John Hunter, the two men remained lifelong friends and continued to work together for many years. There is still so much that hasn't been spoken about Hunter in this chapter, that readers interested in learning more about this great man, Dr John Hunter, will find no shortage of material if the they wish to conduct their own research on this man who was way ahead of his time in his ideas and methods of surgery.

This then is a small portrait of the man that the young Edward Jenner was to meet in London in the autumn of 1770. Not only did Edward soon grow to love John Hunter as his teacher and mentor, but he also got on very well with Anne Hunter. Because of the very nature of his work, Jenner was heavily involved in the sciences which, of course, dominated Hunter's every waking hour, but Jenner was also a poet and musician, playing both the violin and the flute, which consequently drew him in to Anne's world and the two had a strong connection which far from making Hunter jealous, drew the two men, Hunter and Jenner, together even more, resulting in a lifelong friendship that only ended when Hunter died.

From the very beginning, Jenner threw himself into the lectures often attending other lectures in medicine over and above that which Hunter asked him to do – he was a most diligent pupil and always eager to learn. He would often attend extra lectures that were given by a Scottish physician by the name of Dr George Fordyce (1736–1802) who at the time was posted at St Thomas's Hospital. The lectures were on chemistry, physics, and materia medica, which is the Latin name for the plants and minerals that were used to make medicines in the 18th century. Jenner studied so hard that on 15th May, 1772, Hunter signed a Certificate stating, "That Mr Edward Jenner, Surgeon, hath diligently attended Four Courses of my Anatomical and Chirurgical Lectures." Jenner also studied 'The theory and Practice of Midwifery' along with two other well-respected midwives, Thomas Denman (1733–1815) from Bakewell in Derbyshire and William Osborne. Denman was the senior partner out of the two and had learned his surgical skills at St George's Hospital in London and had received his M.D. from Aberdeen in 1763. Like Dr William Hunter, he had studied under Dr William Smellie (1697–1763). Osborne had lived in London all his life and like Denman, had also studied at St George's Hospital. The two men began working together in 1770 which as it so happened, was the year that Jenner joined Hunter in London. Denman and Jenner stayed friends and Denman would turn out to be a staunch supporter of Edward's vaccination theories in later years.

Jenner picked up on John Hunter's way of teaching which was to follow him all his life. Up until the mid-eighteenth century, medical practices were used that had been handed down from the Greeks for centuries, were unchallenged by doctors and some of them such as bleeding patients and applying leeches to them were often quite useless. Patients often recovered from their illnesses despite being treated by these methods rather than because of them. Hunter took a completely opposite view to those which 18th-century doctors took. Far from accepting the practices of the day, he always questioned them and encouraged his pupils to do the same. Hunter would often experiment on live animals in the days where there were no anaesthetics while several men would hold the squealing animal down while Hunter cut it open, but he felt he had no choice. It sounds horrific to us today which of course it was, but what Hunter really wanted was dead human bodies but he had to resort to illegal means to get them as surgeons were only allowed a very meagre number. The small number of dead bodies that surgeons were allowed to perform on were not enough and he would spend hours day after day cutting open and performing autopsies on bodies which had been illegally brought to him. The problem was: where to get them from? The Company of Surgeons were allowed only six bodies a year which for Hunter to use and learn from was wholly inadequate. He needed far more than this so that he could learn more and pass on his acquired knowledge to his pupils such as Edward Jenner. The gallows were one source but people in Georgian society were none too fussy about newly buried bodies being taken away and used so this did not give Hunter nearly enough to work on. Hunter used unscrupulous undertakers who for payment would let newly buried bodies go whilst gangs of body snatchers were also used. They would roam London for recently buried bodies so that they could dig up the body before morning. Hunter dissected thousands as a result of this and his knowledge of the human anatomy was vast as a result. It seems ironic that a man should have to resort to such a degree in order to gain knowledge not just for himself, but for people who were coming behind him such as Jenner and by definition mankind as a whole.

Edward Jenner and his family had chosen well to choose John Hunter to learn from. In 1773, he completed his training and returned to Berkeley, the little village in Gloucestershire that he loved. Although he learned so much from Hunter and spent three years in London, Jenner made two decisions concerning his immediate future that show us so much about the man and his love of nature and the countryside along with his great modesty and lack of interest in fame.

The first decision was in 1772 when he refused an offer from the great botanist, Joseph Banks (1743–1820) to sail round the world with him as one of his party on board the HMS Resolution on Captain Cook's great second world voyage. This offer came about because Joseph Banks had returned to England on HMS Endeavour with Captain Cook on the latter's first round the world trip that had lasted three years, from 1768 until 1771. Banks and his assistant, Daniel Solander (1733–82) had brought back at least 1,000 specimens of Australian flora and these needed to be catalogued. Jenner was Hunter's favourite pupil and Hunter had no hesitation in recommending Banks asking the young Edward Jenner to undertake this huge task for him. This Jenner did with great care and diligence and Banks was so impressed with Jenner's work that he offered Edward a place on Cook's second trip. Had he accepted and had the trip taken place in the way it was originally planned, it would have given him, Edward Jenner, everlasting fame and wealth. They would have visited the beautiful South Sea islands such as Tahiti, a once in a lifetime chance for Jenner. However, Jenner politely refused; he simply wanted to return to the countryside and use his skills there for the benefit of the local people, rich or poor. Another man who was very supportive of Jenner until his death in 1815 was a London physician by the name of John Coakley Lettsom (1744–1815). He was born in the Virgin Islands and was brought up a Quaker, and when he had his practice in London, he enjoyed a reputation for being one of the best physicians in the city. He asked Jenner if he would travel with Banks but Lettsom said that Jenner had told him that he was turning the offer to sail with Banks and Cook down because of his 'deep and grateful affection…for his elder brother…and partly by an attachment to the rural scenes and habits of his early youth'. If neither Hunter nor Lettsom could persuade Jenner, then nobody could have. There was another motive, however. Since 1768, Jenner had had in the back of his mind the lingering thought that he may have found the answer to the curing of the dreaded disease of smallpox that killed thousands of people round the world and in his own country. He had heard the story that was circulating in the countryside that milkmaids who caught cowpox never seemed to catch smallpox and he wanted to investigate further, although it would be many years before he was able to look into this. However, with regard to Cook's second voyage that Jenner was offered, it wouldn't have been possible for him to go because as it happened, there was a huge row between the Admiralty and Banks concerning the type of ship that Cook insisted upon and Banks withdrew, but it says everything about the modest Edward Jenner that he turned down the proposed trip of a life time.

The second occasion was in 1773 when he had ceased his learning in London and Hunter offered his favourite pupil, as Jenner undoubtably had been, a chance of a very lucrative opening to practice his surgical and medical skills in the capital city. Again, Jenner would have had the support of two very eminent men, John Hunter, and John Coakley Lettsom but still Jenner politely refused for the same reason that he turned down the first offer. London had little attraction for him whatever the rewards, and again he preferred the countryside.

In December, 1772, Jenner received his final certificates. He had attended three courses each of the practice of physic, chemistry and materia medica, as we know, the latter being the Latin name for the use of plants and minerals for making medicines in the 18th century. The certificate that confirms these courses was signed by William Fordyce (1736–1802) F.RS., M.D. Fordyce was a distinguished Scottish physician who lectured on medicine and he had spent many years working with Hunter. Jenner had also attended courses on midwifery allowing him to practice these essential skills in Berkeley and these certificates were signed by Thomas Denman and William Osborne, and like the other courses, were signed in December, 1772. We don't know much about Dr Osborne, but Thomas Denman (1733–1815) M.D. was an English physician and midwife and like many others had studied under Dr William Smellie (1697–1763).

All through his studies between 1770 and 1773, Jenner lived with Hunter, and after he had been there a year, the household then included Anne Hunter (nee Home) who we have read about before. Although he was sad to leave the Hunters, Edward was pleased to return to his beloved Berkeley where he would be re-united with his brother, Stephen (1732–97) who had more or less brought Edward up when their parents died in 1754. In any event, Edward had established a firm friendship with Hunter and the two would continue to work together over the years until Hunter's death in 1793.

And so it was that Edward Jenner was now free to do what for so long was his ambition, and that was to return to Berkeley and set up his own practice which he gladly did in 1773. He had learned much from his friend, Dr John Hunter, and now at the age of twenty-three, it was time for him to do it alone.

-oOOo-

Chapter 3

Berkeley Castle and the Berkeley Family – A Story of Two Marriages Between the Same Couple, the 5th Earl and Mary Cole

Jenner had a slow start in his new practice, but it was not long before word got around that he was back in Berkeley and people slowly began to appreciate his knowledge and skills as a physician/midwife. After that, he was never short of work until the day he died.

On his return to Berkeley, one of the families who Jenner looked after was the Berkeley family who had lived in Berkeley Castle for hundreds of years. The castle was famous amongst other things, for the murder of Edward 11 on 21st September 1327. Edward was born on 25th April 1284 and was knighted in an elaborate ceremony at Westminster Abbey in 1300 and became king in 1307. He lost the battle of Bannockburn in 1314 to Robert the Bruce and was eventually forced to relinquish his crown in January 1327. He was taken captive and eventually imprisoned in Berkeley Castle where the story has it that he was murdered on 21st September 1327. The popular story that has circulated for many years has been that he was brutally killed by inserting a red-hot poker into him so that no outer signs on his body would show, but in recent times, many modern historians have come to the conclusion that he was probably suffocated.

Returning to the 18th century, it was an interesting time for the family which had repercussions for many years afterwards so that we should look a little closely at what happened to them.

The family can trace its beginnings back to Saxon times but its present form started when Charles 11 who reigned from 1660 until his death in 1685 made George Berkeley (1628–98) the first Earl in 1679. The fact that the Berkeley family can trace its beginnings back to Saxon times is due to John Smyth who recorded everything that he knew about them until he died in 1641. He managed to get all their records together and his book 'Lives of the Berkeleys' is extraordinary reading. It doesn't just chronicle dates, but gives details about their characteristics both good and bad in great detail.

However, to write the whole history of the family here would take us too far off the main subject of the book which is Edward Jenner, so we will concentrate on the 5th Earl of Berkeley (1745–1810), as he was the head of the family at the time that Edward Jenner looked after their medical needs and the family was the subject of a scandal that called into question who the 5th Earl's rightful heir should be when he died in 1810.

Frederick Augustus Berkeley was born in 1745 and became the 5th Earl in 1755 on the death of his father, Augustus Berkeley, the 4th Earl. Frederick was involved in a huge scandal that the rather gentle, God fearing Christian like physician, Edward Jenner would hardly be likely to approve of, but as he was concerned only with their medical health, he kept his opinions to himself.

The 5th Earl was having a relationship with a young woman named Mary Cole (1767–1844). Mary was the third child of William Cole and his wife Susannah and was born in 1767, the entry of her christening being in the register of the church of St Mary de Lode and she attended a school in Lower Northgate Street, Gloucester. William, her father, was the proprietor of the Swan Inn, Wotton which was fairly near Gloucester. Her mother, Susannah, ran the house and earned a little extra money by looking after sick children or by looking after someone's newly born child. Mary and her siblings, Ann, Susan, and William were looked down upon by their neighbours and it was felt that they were subject to very little discipline from their parents and were accused of having ideas above their station, although it may be that the family were simply not ready to cow tow to their so-called betters. Mary seemed to be slightly different from her sisters who were considered quite beautiful but rather ostentatious in their mode of dress. She was quiet, loved nature, and was more subdued in her dress and did not seem to aspire to being upper class like her sisters did which as it turned out for her, was supremely ironic.

It was with some surprise therefore, that this rather shy well-behaved girl should end up having a relationship with someone such as the 5th Earl, a close friend of the Prince of Wales who in 1811 became the Prince Regent when his father, George III became too ill to carry out his duties. Then in 1820 when George III died, the Prince Regent became King George IV. The Prince of Wales was a man of loose morals both in his wild spending sprees, if you can call them spending sprees because as it turned out, he rarely paid his debts, and also his many affairs with women. Whether they were married or not didn't concern him too much although the one good thing that we can give him credit for are the beautiful Regency buildings that are so admired to this day. The behaviour towards women by the 5th Earl was hardly better than that of the Prince of Wales. At one time the 5th Earl had a Miss Bayley living with him at the castle and in 1773 the two of them were caricatured in the Town and Country Magazine. However, as with any liaison he had with a woman it petered out when he tired of her and he would look elsewhere. Miss Bayley did not escape his loss of interest and like all the others, she was dropped. He had no intention of marrying any of them as women were seen as playthings that he could discard like an unwanted toy. He is quoted once as saying, "They shall never get the marriage chain around my neck."

From the time that he first saw Mary serving in the butcher's shop in Westgate Street, Gloucester, he seemed to view her in the same way as he would any other young women who had crossed his path and seemed to assume that she would become just like many others, fall at his feet and feel honoured that he had chosen her as his mistress. However, although inexperienced and rather shy, Mary did not go along with the Earl's little games, and whether it was a case of the Earl wanting what he couldn't have, or whether he really liked her, he continued to pursue her and they seemed to enter into some sort of relationship, but Mary would not give in to the Earl's advances unless she was married. In order for the Earl to consummate this rather strange relationship with Mary a marriage was arranged and carried out on the morning of 30th March 1785. In getting married in this way, the 5th Earl was not going back on his desire not to be married, because he thought that he was setting up what would later be seen as a sham marriage and one that would be found to be illegal if challenged in years to come. The then Vicar of Berkeley, the Revd Augustus Thomas Hupsman was totally in awe of the 5th Earl and he took little persuading to carry the marriage service out although it was made clear to him that it was to remain a complete secret although it's almost certain that the Revd Hupsman thought it to be legal. The reason that he thought that the 5th Earl wanted it to be a secret would have been the class structure. Marrying between different classes was looked upon with distaste in the 18th century and the 5th Earl was determined that it should be kept quiet. Despite this secrecy, over the next decade, it seemed that the Earl had begun to be genuinely fond of Mary. His fondness for her stayed with him, and it was clear in later years that he never wished to let her go completely out of his life and these feelings endured until his death in 1810 when he argued that the 1785 marriage was in fact legal. It has to be said too, that he did change as he got older and became a more considerate and kinder person.

On 26th December 1786, their first child was born and was a boy to be named William Fitzhardinge and he was baptised by the Revd John Chapeau. It shows in the Register of Baptisms of the parish as follows:

January 23rd, 1787.
William Fitzhardinge, sone of the
Earl of Berkeley, by Mary Cole

It is not known whether Mary saw the entry which would shock her into realising that the 5th Earl did not actually recognise her as his legal wife especially as William's father was not at the ceremony.

Over the years, this so-called marriage remained a secret but Mary was a good wife and organised the homes that they lived in very well but all of the time, the maids and servants were kept in the dark and were told to call Mary 'Miss Tudor'. She was also to be treated with the utmost respect and any orders that she gave were to be obeyed.

Maurice Frederick (1788–1867), the second child was born on 3rd January 1788 and Augustus, the third child, the following year, 1789. Although Augustus lived until adulthood, we do not know the actual date that he was born nor the year that he died. In total, Mary and the 5th Earl produced four children who lived until adulthood, the fourth and final one in this so-called marriage being Francis Henry, (1794–1870). In between the other births, Mary bore the 5th Earl three more children, Maria (1792–94), Francis (born and died in 1792), and Henrietta (born and died in 1793) but although it was very common in those days, the latter three dying so young caused Mary great sadness. By this time, Mary had had enough and she wanted to be married legally, in fact she had been broaching the subject for some time. Apart from her own feelings of wanting to be a wife that was recognised as such, both she and the Earl were concerned about the succession as it was by no means certain that William Fitzhardinge, their first-born and therefore the eldest son would necessarily inherit his father's title when his father died. The couple's seven children had all been registered as illegitimate and Mary and the 5th Earl both decided that a second and legitimate marriage should take place. They had both grown attached to each other and the Earl was at last coming round to the notion of a legal marriage as by now he was very fond of Mary and was recognising how well she ran the places that they lived in.

A second marriage, this time to be an open and legal one was arranged for 16th May, 1796, virtually eleven years since the first one at Lambeth Parish Church and they were married by licence by the Revd John Cole, curate. This time, Lord Berkeley kept to his word that the marriage was to be totally legal and so it was. However, in order for the ceremony to be licenced, the 5th Earl had to make an affidavit. It read as follows:

COMMISSARY OF SURREY 6th May, 1796.

Appeared personally, the Right Honourable Frederick Augustus Berkeley, Earl of Berkeley, and made Oath that he is of the Parish of Saint Martin in the Fields, in the county of Middlesex, a Batchelor, of the Age of Twenty-one years and upwards, and intendeth to inter-marry with Mary Cole, of the Parish of Saint Mary Lambeth, in the County of Surrey, a Spinster of the Age of Twenty-one years and upwards; and that he knoweth of no lawful impediment by reason of any Pre Contract, Consanguinity, Affinity, or any other lawful Means whatsoever, to hinder the said Intended Marriage, and prayed a Licence to solemnise the same in the Parish Church of Saint Mary Lambeth, and further made Oath, that the usual Place of Abode of her, the said Mary Cole, Spinster, hath been in the Parish of Saint Mary Lambeth for the space of Four Weeks last past.

BERKELEY. Sworn before me

Th. Ch. Crespigny
Surrogate

So now the marriage between the couple was legal and the couple were delighted when on 19th October 1796, the couple's fifth child but the first under the second marriage was born. Mary didn't mind whether it was a boy or a girl so long as the baby was healthy, but Earl Berkeley was delighted that it was a boy as he assumed that it would take his title as the 6th Earl when he died. The boy was named Thomas Moreton and there were two baptisms, the first, a private service, being at London and a second at Berkeley Castle. The London ceremony was registered at St Martin in the Fields on 19th November 1796, exactly one month after his birth.

In the first marriage, the couple produced four children who lived into adulthood, and after the birth of Thomas Moreton, the first child of the second, there followed five more which made a total of six in all, three sons and three daughters. After Thomas Moreton, these were:

George Charles b:10th February 1800
Mary Henrietta b: 4th October 1801
Caroline Fitzhardinge b: 12th April 1803
Craven Fitzhardinge b:? May 1805
Emily Elizabeth b1807

The year 1810 brought matters to a head as to whether the first marriage was legal or not as it was the year that the 5th Earl died. On 27th October 1810, William Fitzhardinge presented his formal petition to King George III, that he be recognised as the 6th Earl of Berkeley and that he be summoned to Parliament as such. The question that had to be answered was which of the sons would succeed the 5th Earl and become the 6th Earl. Would it be William Fitzhardinge who was born on 26th December, 1786 and who was the couple's first child or would it be Thomas Moreton, who was born on 19th October, 1796, their fifth child but who was the first child of the Berkeley's second marriage. The Earl had originally intended that the first marriage was illegal which is why he had kept it so quiet for so many years but as he was aware that he was approaching death he was having a change of heart. There were two main reasons for this, the first being that he wished his first born, William Fitzhardinge, to succeed to his title and the second was for Mary herself. For many years past, he had grown more fond of her and wanted her to have the dignity of all her children being legitimate.

The case went to the House of Lords and the proceedings commenced in March 1811 and finished on 28th June, three months later. The case relied heavily on the statements made by Mary, the late Earl, and her brother William. It was always going to be difficult to argue the case that the marriage that had taken place twenty five years earlier but had been kept secret for that time was in fact legal, but another devastating piece of evidence against it being legal was due to the fact that the dubious entries that had been made in the Berkeley parish registers of 1784 and 1785 looked suspiciously like the writing of the late Earl himself. Lord Buckingham on being questioned about the handwriting in the Register of Marriage of 1785 replied reluctantly that it did indeed greatly resemble that of the late Earl's, in other words, the entry was a forgery committed by the late Earl. It was not only the entry to the first marriage that didn't look good for William Fitzhardinge but the entries for the second which were puzzling to say the least. The Lambeth marriage register of 1796 (the second marriage) described William Fitzhardinge, Earl of Berkeley as a bachelor and Mary Cole as a spinster which didn't put the claim that they had been married since 1785 in a good light. Even Dr Jenner, although naturally sympathetic to the Berkeley family as they were his patients as well as friends, gave evidence that would favour Mary in terms of her character, but like other witnesses who did the same, that alone was nowhere near enough for Mary to prove that the first marriage was legal. Edward had been in a state of nervous tension for weeks before he had to give his evidence as he knew the path that it would lead the Lords to. Even the Prince Regent, as the Prince of Wales had now become due to George III's grave illness, gave evidence in favour of the Countess but in the end, it was to no avail, the Countess lost the case which made her first four children illegitimate and took away the title of the 6th Earl that William Fitzhardinge, (born 26th December, 1786) the couple's first child thought was his. Instead the title was given to the late Earl's and Mary's fifth child but first in the second marriage which was Thomas Moreton (born 19th October, 1796).

The Lords gave their decision with the following words:

"It was resolved and adjudged by the Lords Spiritual and Temporal in Parliament Assembled, that the Claimant has not made out his claim to the Title Dignity and Honour of Earl of Berkeley, Viscount Dursley and Baron Berkeley. It was further ordered that the said Resolution and Judgement be laid before his Royal Highness the Prince Regent by the Lords with White Staves."

In case there was any doubt about the status of everyone concerned, especially the children of the first marriage, The Times bluntly reported the result of the case as follows:

"By the decision of the Committee of Privileges of the House of Lords on the Berkeley Peerage, the four eldest sons of the late Earl and present Countess of Berkeley are declared illegitimate, and the title devolves upon the fifth son, who is the first born in wedlock, viz., Thomas Moreton Fitzhardinge, now Earl Berkeley, born the 19th of October, 1796."

Now that was all at an end, one can only wonder if the outcome of this case would have been different if it had been conducted ten years later, when the Prince Regent would have been King George IV as he was from 1820 until his own death in 1830. Throughout the whole of the Georgian period of rule, Hanoverian Kings and their sons never got on and we can only speculate that whilst King George III was more favourably disposed towards Thomas Moreton Fitzhardinge, the Prince Regent might have favoured William Fitzhardinge. We will never know, but this was the outcome of the case that so troubled Edward Jenner, whose work we can concentrate on from the following chapter onwards.

We can summarize all the children born to Mary Cole of Gloucester and Frederick Augustus, Fifth Earl of Berkeley, whether they lived into adulthood or died young as follows:

The children of the first marriage:

William Fitzhardinge (1786–1857), later Baron Segrave and Earl Fitzhardinge
Maurice Frederick Fitzhardinge (1788–1867), later Baron Fitzhardinge
Augustus Fitzhardinge born 1789–?
Francis Ducie Fitzhardinge (born and died 1792)
Maria Fitzhardinge (1792–94)
Henrietta Fitzhardinge (born and died 1793)
Francis Henry Fitzhardinge (1794–1870)

Children of the second marriage:

Thomas Moreton, sixth Earl of Berkeley (1796–1882)
George Charles Grantley Berkeley (1800–81)
Mary Henrietta Berkeley (1801–73)
Caroline Berkeley (1803–86), (married 1829 James Maxse Esq.)
Craven Berkeley (1805–55)
Emily Elizabeth Berkeley (1807–95) married Colonel Sydney Capel.

-oOOo-

Chapter 4

Return to Berkeley and Setting Up Practice. Meets Edward Gardner. Writes Light Verses. Abolition of Slavery. John Hunter Offers Jenner Partnership

In 1773, Edward Jenner returned to Berkeley from London after an absence of three years. He loved the countryside and in particular Berkeley itself where he was born and grew up. Not only was he returning to the village that he loved, he was also returning to Stephen (1732–97), his elder brother who had been his father, friend and mentor since they had lost their parents within two months of each other in 1754 when Edward was only five years old and Stephen was twenty-two. Edward loved all his brothers and sisters but it was always Stephen who was his favourite. Now back in Gloucestershire as a qualified physician aged twenty-four years, Edward could enjoy the company of his elder brother on more equal terms, although he was always respectful of Stephen and what he had done for Edward before he went to London. The big city had put Jenner into the company of some great medical men but whilst he appreciated just what they had given him in terms of knowledge, he was delighted to be back to the place where he considered that he belonged. Edward Jenner was definitely a country boy and remained so for the rest of his life. Jenner also made a new friend quite soon after his return to Berkeley. His name was Edward Gardner (1752–1823) and he was a wine merchant based in Frampton-upon-Severn and was just three years younger than Edward. Edward Gardner became a lifelong friend of Jenner's, both in fact died in the same year, and Jenner would confide in Gardner about very personal matters. It was Gardner who described Jenner to Dr John Baron, (1786–1851) Jenner's future friend and biographer and he described him in the following way:

"His height was rather under the middle size, his person was robust but active, and well formed. In dress he was particularly neat, and everything about him showed the man intent and serious, and well prepared to meet the duties of his calling. When I first saw him it, was on Frampton Green... He was dressed in a blue coat and yellow buttons, buckskins, well-polished jockey boots with handsome silver spurs, and he carried a smart whip with a silver handle. His hair, after the fashion of the times, was done up in a club, and he wore a broad brimmed hat."

Although Edward Gardner earned his living as a wine merchant, poetry played a big part in his life, and that was one of the reasons why he and Jenner stayed lifelong friends because Jenner was also a poet as well as a musician. In those days where there was no television or radio or any other gadgets to keep people amused, much of the entertainment was carried out at home, so anyone with talent such as Jenner possessed, meant that he was always welcome in the houses of the bourgeoning middle classes shown so beautifully in the works of Jane Austen. This first piece was a ballad written by Jenner:

> Come all ye bold Britons who love to be jolly
> And think that Starvation's a very great folly,
> Let's sing of the thing which so much we admire,
> A good foaming pot, Boys, of Ladbrokes Entire.
> Derrydown
>
> 'Tis bright as a ruby, and brown as a berry,
> It makes the Heart light, and the countenance merry
> From eve until morn one might quaff and not tire;
> A Feast that neer cloys us is Ladbroke's Entire.
> Derrydown.

This was clearly a rousing musical ballad which was more likely to be performed in a pub, but this next piece is pure poetry which would suit in someone's drawing room. It was named 'Address to a Robin'

> Come, sweetest of the feather'd throng,
> And sooth me with thy plaintive song;
> Come to my cot, devoid of fear,

No danger shall await thee here;
No prowling cat with whisker'd face
Approaches this sequester'd place;
No school-boy, with his will (ow) bow,
Shall aim at thee a murd'rous blow;
No wily lime-twig e'er molest
Thy olive wing or crimson breast;
Thy cup, sweet bird, I'll daily fill
At yonder cressy bubbling rill;
Thy board shall plenteously be spread
With crumlets of the nicest bread.
And when rude Winter comes and shews
His icicles and shivering snows,
Hop o'er my cheering hearth and be
One of my peaceful family.
Then sooth me with thy plaintive song,
Thou sweetest of the feather'd throng.

Jenner's talents for poetry and music were no doubt encouraged by his mentor, John Hunter's wife, Anne Hunter, nee Home, as we know, a very gifted poet who penned many beautiful lyrics that were put to music, one of the most famous being 'My mother bids me bind my hair', the music having been written by none other than the great Austrian composer, Franz Joseph Haydn (1732–1809). Jenner rarely expressed a political opinion that we are aware of, but another song that we know of concerns the slavery issue. It is called 'By a negro after being severely beaten for Stealing a bit of bread'.

If, when me nothing had to eat,
For stealing bit of bread,
Black Man you so severely beat,
And whip till almost dead;
What Punishment's to Massa's due?
From Guilt can he be free?
Who, when he bought poor Negro, knew
That white man steal me.

It makes for painful reading, and the great reformer, William Wilberforce (1759–1833), along with others such as Thomas Clarkson (1760–1846) and Hannah More (1745–1833), the great religious writer and playwright, conducted a long an arduous campaign to get slavery abolished. In 1807 the anti-slavery group succeeded in getting a bill passed through Parliament halting the trafficking of slavery and it was finally abolished by the passing of the Abolition of Slavery Bill of 1833 on 26th July. William Wilberforce died just three days after the act was passed. He had campaigned for this day for nearly fifty years.

The previous poem was obviously dealing with a dreadful subject, so we should lighten the mood and add one of Jenner's that shows his romantic and affectionate nature. It was called 'To Mrs J on her dismal dream the night before she went to Bath'.

> When Fancy at midnight's disposed for a ramble,
> She will steal to our pillows to gambol.
> Then laugh my dear Kate at her Tale of the Hearse
> When she whispers in dreams happens just the reverse.
> And sure as you're there she has chosen this path
> To heighten the pleasures you'll meet with at Bath.

Jenner had quickly made a lifelong friend in Edward Gardner, because although they trod very different career paths, they had a shared interest in poetry. Here is a letter that Jenner wrote to his friend within a year or two of him returning from London to settle back in Berkeley. He was carrying out experiments on hedgehogs for his mentor John Hunter and his love of nature and working away from London meant that this was a very happy time for him. He wrote the following letter to Gardner, which was likely to be fairly shortly after his return from London to his beloved Berkeley, which would place it on or around the spring of 1774 or 1775. He was clearly buoyed up by being surrounded by the green fields of Berkeley after three years in the smoke and noise of London.

Dear Gardner,

Enclosed is the medley and the song I sang to the Gallant Bowmen, miserably scrawled, indeed you will hardly make it out. If your brain is not too much in a whirl, let me remind you of the Ranunculuses for Mr Nelmes. Did not you

promise me some, and some rose trees? These are the flowery subjects, and I
hope in harmony with your mind.

I have thrown in a few more stanzas to 'Ladbroke's Entire' it is my best song.
I wish I could give up, or at least suspend the little acquaintance I have made
with the Muses. Every time I begin a bagatelle I almost swear it shall be the last;
and hardly steer clear of perjury, you see. But when I see that the resolves of the
greatest philosophers can be set aside by the gentlest means in the world, I, who
am amongst the lowest of the order, should not repine at my lot. As I once told
you, we are certainly puppets danced about by wires that reach the skies. For
my own part, I rejoice at your thinking it wrong to dance without a partner, and
shall be among the first to congratulate you on the great Master of Ceremonies
indulging you with the hand of a fair one.

Sincerely yours,
E. Jenner.

John Hunter was a brilliant man who had made Edward Jenner a brilliant
doctor. However, all he saw in Jenner was a hard-working pupil who was intent
on learning as much as he could from his master. He knew the possibilities that
were before his pupil, but Jenner had in effect, flown the nest and was his own
man. He had already turned down a three year voyage with Captain Cook due to
leave in July, 1772, and he was now to be offered a place in a lucrative London
practice which would have enabled him to make a great deal of money, and also
for him to be a companion and assistant to his mentor John Hunter. Jenner would
always love John Hunter and the offer would have tempted just about anyone
else but Jenner was absolutely focussed on returning to Berkeley where he would
set his sights on removing smallpox from the world. Hunter did understand that
Jenner had always loved the countryside, and this can be seen in the following
letter, it's just that he didn't realise to what extent. Here is the letter that Hunter
wrote to Jenner in May, 1775:

Dear Jenner,

I have received many things from you, and will thank you in the lump; but
while I thank you let me know what I owe you. I have a great scheme to
communicate to you, and want you to take part in it; but remember it is as yet a
profound secret. My scheme is to teach natural history, in which will be included

anatomy, both human and comparative. The labour of it is too much for one man, therefore I must have some person to assist; but who that person shall be is the difficulty. When running over a variety of people you have come into my mind among the rest. Now if it is a scheme you would like, and a possibility of leaving the country, at the same time able and willing to lay down one thousand guineas, I will send you the whole proposals, but if you cannot leave the country upon any terms, then it is unnecessary to go any farther; and all I have to beg is to keep it a secret. I would not have you mention it to Ludlow &c. I proposed it to L**** before he left London; but his father objected, I believe to the money. I know the scheme itself will be to your taste. Before you consult with any of your friends, just consult with yourself and ask, can I go to London, and can I give one thousand guineas for any chance that can be worth it? Let me hear from you soon.

Yours,
London 24th May (1775) John Hunter

We cannot be sure of who L**** is, yet it cannot be much of a surprise that the father balked at putting in one thousand guineas up front. There was naturally no quarrel about Hunter's skill as a surgeon and as a teacher, but whether he was as competent concerning money would be open to question. The one thousand guineas that Hunter was asking for would translate into anything between £60,000 to £65,000 in today's terms, a huge sum for a project as yet untried. Jenner probably felt the same as after all, he was only twenty-four years old and the sort of money that Hunter wanted in what as yet was no more than an idea would be more than likely to make him question the project. To date, we have no record of any letters that Jenner sent to Hunter, only the other way round. Jenner clearly refused the offer as the first paragraph of Hunter's letter to him concerning the scheme showed an irritation that went further than the inevitable disappointment that he felt in being refused by his star pupil. It is not difficult upon reading Hunter's letter that he would have liked Jenner more than anyone else but he was also aware that Jenner's roots were deeply set in the countryside. Jenner was after all, a pupil of Hunter's when he was made the offer by Joseph Banks to accompany the famous botanist on Cook's second voyage round the world and Jenner had turned down the chance of travelling to these paradise islands in order to return to the English countryside. Much as Jenner loved

Hunter, he was unlikely to return to London to work as he hated the place so much. We do not have a copy of Jenner's refusal to Hunter, but we do have the letter that Hunter sent back by way of his response.

Dear Jenner,

I received yours in answer to mine, which I should have answered. I own I suspected it would not do; yet as I did intend such a scheme, I was inclinable to give you the offer.

I thank you for your experiment on the hedgehog but why do you ask me a question by the way of solving it? I think your solution is just, but why think why not try the experiment? Repeat all the experiments upon a hedgehog as soon as you receive this, and they will give you the solution. Try the heat. Cut off a leg at the same place; cut off the head and expose the heart, and let me know the result of the whole.

I am, dear Jenner, Ever yours John Hunter

This letter was written on August 2, 1775, and it is puzzling that Hunter asked Jenner to work out his own solutions by practicable means rather than ask questions. This was due to the fact that he would have spent from 1770 until 1773 repeating his philosophy again and again during the years that Jenner was his pupil, but it may have been just a little irritation on Hunter's part because Jenner had refused his partnership offer. Many people would probably have thought Jenner slightly mad at not going into partnership with John Hunter but as events turned out, Jenner going back to his beloved Berkeley was not only right for Jenner, but as it turned out, the whole world.

-oOOo-

Chapter 5

Introduction to John Howard, Prison Reformer (1726–90). Jenner Thinks About Cowpox as a Cure for Smallpox. Description of Smallpox. Artistic Side of Edward Jenner. Daniel Sutton and Variolation. Launch of Hot Air Balloon. Experiments on Hedgehogs for John Hunter. Migration of Birds. Marriage and Children

During the early part of the 19th century, Jenner's great friend, Dr John Coakley Lettsom (1744–1815) who was a loyal advocate of Jenner's vaccine ideas, suggested that a subscription be organised to erect a monument to John Howard, the great prison reformer. John Howard (1726–90), was a wealthy man due to the inheritance he received on the death of his father. In 1748, he left England to go on a world tour but was taken prisoner by the French in 1756 but was eventually exchanged for a French officer who was being held by the British. It was in that year that he was elected as a Fellow of the Royal Society. After being elected to the post of High Sheriff of Bedfordshire in 1773, he toured hundreds of prisons himself rather than delegate the task and was shocked by what he saw. He published a booklet 'On the State of the Prisons' in 1777 which was very detailed and explained how they could be reformed. It is said that he helped establish single cells in the United Kingdom and thereafter the United States of America. He died in 1790 and there is a statue of him in Bedford. Jenner wrote in his diary:

> Why Lettsom bid the sculpur'd Pillar rise
> To him whose name's familiar in the Skies,

And on the Earth will never be forgotten,
Until old TIME himself be dead and rotten?

So there we see another side of Jenner, the artistic and sometimes-humorous side of the man, and this somehow squares nicely with the scientific approach that Jenner had for his work as a physician, especially his single-minded search that would drive him on for his work in the elimination of smallpox.

Things were looking good for Jenner as by this time, his brother, Stephen, had been the rector of Rockhampton but had resigned the position which was taken by his brother Henry and Stephen was living in Berkeley, which allowed Edward to more or less make his home with his favourite brother.

Jenner had to build his practice up from scratch. He struggled a little at first, but word of mouth is the best advertisement and it was not long before he became known as the person to see if there was any illness in a family or whether a woman in the late stages of pregnancy needed a midwife to deliver a baby. Jenner's reputation spread far and wide in Gloucestershire and he would ride miles to see a patient, rich or poor and would often treat a person for free if he thought that they were in financial difficulties as many of them were. There was no benefit system to look after families if they were out of work, and some were starving but Jenner treated them all and soon was able to build his practice up.

Jenner had not long been in Berkeley when he started to think of the connection between the dreadful disease of smallpox and the much milder form of the same disease which was called cowpox. He had mentioned it to some medical men whilst he was in London but most were totally disinterested but Edward would not stop thinking about it. As mentioned earlier, Jenner had heard as far back as 1768 that dairymaids who caught cowpox never seemed to catch smallpox. There was nothing that Jenner could do about it then because he hadn't even started his training with John Hunter and even when he returned to Berkeley in 1773 as a qualified physician, there had been no recent outbreak of smallpox in the area which left him with nothing to work with. It's a little ironic that in order to work on the cure of this dreadful disease, he was left with the rather guilty hope that smallpox would rear its ugly head knowing that it would cause the death of thousands. He could only keep reassuring himself that any current suffering would be for the greater good of mankind in the future, because that was what he was aiming for, to get rid of the disease altogether by letting the whole world know about it.

A medical textbook published in 1803 painted a vivid picture of this dreadful disease – it reads as follows:

"There is no disease that the medical writer has to describe which presents a melancholier scene than the natural smallpox as it very frequently occurs.

"The symptoms bring on pain and debilitation, a terrible feeling of anxiety, high temperature, unquenchable thirst, inflammation of the eyes, violent sweating, and convulsions. Many speck like spots that resemble flea bites would appear becoming red and painful. These turn to pustules accompanied by throat inflammation, salivation, and diarrhoea. The eyelids would swell and stick together causing loss of sight by the seventh day. The eighth day would find the spots full of yellow pus or fluid which eroded the skin. Sleep was fitful and disturbed with each morning bringing a horrid scene of gore mingled with corruption. Death would relieve the sufferer between the 14th and 17th day. Those who survived would be left scarred for life and often blind. This dreadful disease was smallpox that was responsible for 10% of all deaths and up to 35% of child deaths when Edward Jenner embarked on a career in medicine towards the end of the 18th century."

This was the scenario that Edward Jenner was looking to cure when he returned to Berkeley in 1773. However, there was other work that he had to do before he was able to put all his endeavours into curing smallpox and much of this work was generated by his onetime teacher, but now friend, Dr John Hunter.

We have seen that besides medicine, there was another side of Jenner that was both fun loving and artistic. He joined a musical club where he played the violin and in 1779 also played a large part in forming a society for the improvement of medical science, and for the promotion of good fellowship amongst fellow medical practitioners. This group was named the Convivio-Medical Society which was often confused with the Medico-Convivial Society which Jenner had a hand in forming ten years later. Jenner had felt for some time that new medical ideas should be spread around and discussed with other practitioners, and remembering his mentor, Dr John Hunter's Sunday evening meetings with other likeminded men, decided to form a group of his own. He invited several men to the Ship Inn at Alveston and most of them responded including Jenner's old teacher Daniel Ludlow who came over from Chipping Sodbury, along with his son John who was now established in practice in Corsham. Along with these were Dr John Fewster from Thornbury, Mr Shute from Winterbourne, Mr Bradford from Frenchay, Mr Pountney from Henbury,

Mr Richardson along with Mr Taylor from Wotton-under-Edge, and Mr Davies from Bristol. The men would share ideas and no doubt the ale flowed freely as it was as its title suggests, a group of men who not only talked to each other about medicine, but also enjoyed themselves and certainly each meeting was very much a social event. The man who Jenner attached himself to more than others who made up the group was Dr John Fewster (1738–1824). Fewster had been either a partner or a pupil of Daniel Sutton, the variolator. Although, variolation was a crude and risky way of preventing smallpox it was the only method that was known prior to Jenner using the much less harmful disease of cowpox, and Sutton was superb at the practice. He was so good in fact, that it is worth saying a few words about him at this stage. Sutton was heavily involved in the curing of smallpox by inoculating healthy patients with a very small amount of the disease, hoping that they would recover and be immune from the full-blown disease later on. This was the method by which all medical people treated the disease at that time including Jenner himself. In 1765, Sutton had presented a paper to the Medical Society, although it was never published, entitled 'Cowpox and its ability to Prevent Smallpox'. We do not know why it wasn't published but an educated guess would be that he didn't quite believe that cowpox was the answer given that he chose variolation as the treatment that he would later practice with great skill. Sutton was a superb variolator learning from his father, Robert Sutton, who had modified the technique of inoculation so that it involved a small stab in the skin. This probably seems a little gruesome to us these days but we have to remember that we are in the pre-anaesthetic days where there would be amputations of entire limbs without an anaesthetic so a small cut in the arm would not be considered brutal in any way. Daniel the son, was to attempt experiments in order that knowledge of inoculation would be increased although not for the first time, the medical establishment were against anything that was new, and in any event, Sutton junior still favoured the variolation method although he was open to new ideas, something that cannot always be said of his medical colleagues. In 1796, the year that Jenner tried the first vaccination with smallpox, Sutton senior published his autobiography entitled 'The Inoculator' which he wrote partly to hand on his knowledge to young doctors of the future. In the book, he warns that many of his practices seem like trifles, but:

> Despise not trifles tho they small appear:
> Sands rise to mountains, moments make the year;

and trifles life. Your time to trifles give,
or you may die before you learn to live.

The Suttons didn't try to hide their knowledge and many tried and succeeded with their methods of variolation. The result of this and Jenner's later vaccination methods with cowpox has made the Sutton family and their contribution to medical knowledge all but forgotten. Daniel Sutton was to write sadly:

"Whether from an interested or other sinister motive, I neither know, nor wish to enquire; but I find it has been circulated, That I am not the person who introduced the system of inoculation… In short, That some other person, having assumed my name has proceeded to the exorbitant length of declaring that for many years I had quitted my profession and was long since dead."

His achievements had been all but forgotten, but he did ask for, and was granted a family crest from King George III but it was still a sad end to a great career.

However, returning to Dr John Fewster (1738–1824), he and Jenner were drawn to each other as Fewster too, was of the opinion that cowpox would be a more effective cure for smallpox than the method of variolation whereby a small dose of smallpox was administered to a healthy patient. It seemed that it was Jenner and Fewster who were really the only two who wanted to pursue the idea; in fact, Fewster was linking cowpox as a cure for smallpox as far back as 1768, the same year that Jenner heard of the idea and whilst other members of Jenner's set were against the idea and didn't even want to discuss it, Fewster supported Jenner wholeheartedly. It was no wonder that Fewster and Jenner were drawn to each other over the subject, as Fewster had actually carried out the first vaccination almost by accident. He variolated (deliberately gave them a small dose of smallpox) two brothers with the name of Creed, but to his surprise, only one caught the disease. When he delved further into the brother's medical records, he found that the brother who did not catch smallpox had previously caught cowpox whilst the other had not. This was the first time that Fewster had thought of cowpox being a suitable method of stopping smallpox but he wasn't so obsessed with the idea as Jenner was; in fact he continued to variolate patients as he thought that it was still an effective method of stopping smallpox and when Jenner finally proved that giving a healthy patient cowpox stopped the onset of smallpox, Fewster claimed no credit. Whilst he was always prepared to listen to Jenner's views on the subject, unfortunately, the other members of the club weren't and started to resent Jenner for continually bringing the subject up, and at one point actually threatened to expel him as the continual raising of the subject first irritated and then angered the other members as Jenner had no medical evidence to support the idea. Jenner wasn't actually expelled in the end, but the club itself eventually fizzled out and the meetings stopped. It was to be another ten years before the Medico-Convivial Society was formed which was a slightly more formal affair and was more serious about scientific knowledge than the previous club had been. However, there were still some years to go and more arguments to be had before Jenner was able to try out his theory on cowpox vaccination. We will come to the final part of his achievement and how he went about proving it later on.

One of the many achievements in Jenner's life and career was his part in the launching of the first unmanned hot air balloon from England. Jenner had an inquisitive mind that went beyond the practice of medicine, and in particular, trying to find a cure for smallpox. The idea of the balloon came from the French Montgolfier brothers, Joseph Michel (1740–1810), and Jacques Etienne (1745–99). They were extremely clever men and they found that by studying the movement of clouds, came to the conclusion that a paper bag filled with smoke could possibly fly. They made their balloon out of packing-cloth and paper, carried out tests using this theory and a little while later and after months of painstaking work, launched their balloon on 5th June 1783. A few months later, a French physicist, Jacques Alexandre Cesar Charles (1746–1823) launched a hot air balloon in December, 1783. This balloon was filled with hydrogen and it was made out of varnished silk and after being launched reached a height of three thousand feet and it flew across Paris and managed to stay up for fifteen miles before coming to rest. Charles had discovered what was later called Charles Law which was when the expansion of gas was connected with the rise in temperature and his balloon was the first of its kind to try this theory out.

Edward Jenner was intrigued with what the Montgolfier brothers and Jacques Alexandre Cesar Charles had achieved and started to become very interested with becoming involved in such a project himself. This resulted in him launching his own balloon from Berkeley Castle later that same year, 1783, which he did with the help and full support of the Berkeley family. It was launched from Berkeley Castle and travelled to and landed at Symonds Hall.

When dealing with Jenner's education earlier in the book, we have seen that he had made a lifelong friend in Caleb Hillier Parry (1755–1822) who he had met at Cirencester, but by this time, Parry was a physician practicing in Bath. Jenner invited his old friend along to the launch of his balloon but had also obviously sought his advice on the finer details as he wouldn't have wished for anything to go wrong and was determined to leave nothing to chance.

Edward had received a letter from Parry declining the invitation to the launch citing other commitments, and knowing how fond he was of Jenner, there can be no doubt that his reasons for non-attendance were genuine. However, it is clear from Jenner's PS at the end of his letter of reply that he was keen for his great friend to attend. We do not have a record of Parry's reply to Jenner, but we can quote from Jenner's latest letter. It reads as follows:

My dear Friend,

I am sorry you can't come amongst us; neither Peers nor Plebeians I see can shake your Virtue.

Your directions respecting the Balloon are so clear and so explicit, tis impossible for me to blunder; but to make it quite a certainty, I intend first to fill it and see if it will float in the Castle-Hall, before the public exhibition. Should it prove unwilling to mount and turn shy before a large Assembly, don't you think I may make my escape under cover of three or four dozen Squib and Cracker? I thank you for your kind offer of the tubes and I will send a Man Thursday next to the Crosslands to fetch them. The Mouth of the Balloon is sadly torn; every other part appears sound. Please send to me by return of Mr Marklove half a yard of such silk as you may think most fit for the purpose. I have got some oil ready.

Pray present my respectful Comps to Mrs Parry, and thank her for her very friendly and polite invitation to Bath – I shall certainly come as soon as I possibly can.

Believe me dear doctor ever yours EJ

PS. You shall have the Case in full one of these days.

I shall certainly let you know the day the Balloon is to go off. Perhaps your Patients may suffer you to leave them for a day – Remember the Peer looks a little yellow sometime.

Comps. To Mr Marklove if you please.

The post-office Annual Directory for 1813 (London 1813), p.356 mentions Marklove and Co, Berkeley Banker. It is thought that Jenner was probably referring to his eighteen-month-old son John Marklove whose vaccination on 12th April 1798 is recorded in Jenner's 'Inquiry', p40.

Although Jenner had successfully launched his hot air balloon from Berkeley Castle, he was keen to try another flight from Kingscote especially if the Kingscote family were to be present. It is not hard to understand the reason why. For some time Jenner had wanted to court Catherine Kingscote and this was to be no easy matter. The person Jenner had to impress was Robert Kingscote, the brother of Catherine and so far Jenner had singularly failed to do this. The reasons were almost certainly twofold: firstly, that he was a Physician and Robert obviously thought little of the profession and felt that his sister could do better. The second reason that Robert was unwilling to allow such a courtship to take place was the age difference as Edward was twelve years older than Catherine. The Kingscote family resided in or near the village and parish that held their name and they probably felt that they were a cut above a village physician and so the romance was very much put on hold, although Jenner was not to be put off.

It was known at this time that hedgehogs hibernated during the winter months. Jenner had carried out a lot of experiments on hedgehogs during this period mainly at the behest of his one-time mentor but now his friend, Dr John Hunter. Jenner had noticed that they emerged from their hibernation looking malnourished and underfed which is hardly surprising as they were beneath the ground for so long. However, birds such as sparrows and house-martins disappeared during the winter months and Jenner noticed that they re-appeared looking well fed and healthy. It seems extraordinary to us today, but it was generally assumed that birds did the same as hedgehogs, that is, they hid under the ground, or if not the ground, under the mud. Hunter had taught Jenner well, because he, Jenner, had an enquiring mind, and he heeded Hunter's advice which was that medical people should never just accept what had been handed down from centuries past such as the nonsensical idea of bleeding people for just about any ailment known to man. Instead, he maintained that physicians should experiment and find out for themselves if they had queries about anything. Therefore, Jenner spent some considerable time observing various species of birds and after spending quite some time studying their behaviour patterns came to the correct conclusion that they migrated to places with warmer climates until our own weather improved at which time they returned. This explained just why the birds of whatever species Jenner had studied returned to England looking well fed and healthy.

Jenner produced a paper entitled 'Some Observations on the Migration of Birds' but it was not published until 1824, the year following his death. It was printed in 'Philosophical Transactions' of the Royal Society and Jenner's nephew, George Jenner (1769–1846), sent it with an introductory letter to the then President, Sir Humphrey Davy (1778–1829). For some reason it was not published until 1824, the year after Jenner died. Being President of the Royal Society was a position that carried great prestige and it was only men with a brilliant scientific mind who occupied it. Davy was recognised as a brilliant scientist at an early age and in 1797 at the age of just nineteen years, he was appointed as assistant to Thomas Beddoes (1760–1808) at his Medical Pneumatic Institute which was based in Bristol. Davy is famous for many things and one of the most important was nitrous oxide, otherwise known as laughing gas. Davy saw it as an anaesthetic but his thinking was far ahead of the medical establishment and it was many years before it was used as such. Even then, it was normally only used for recreational purposes by the upper classes.

The first person who actually used it as an anaesthetic was a dentist by the name of Horace Wells (1815–1848) in 1844 when he was carrying out a tooth extraction. Wells was an American dentist and on 11th December of that year, Wells conducted an experiment on himself when he inhaled nitrous oxide and had a John Riggs extract a tooth. Wells felt no pain and was convinced that he had found a substance that would enable surgery to be performed without pain being felt by the patient. He held several demonstrations with mixed results which resulted in a delay of years before it was considered safe to use in surgery. Wells had a sad end to his short life. He suffered unspecified illnesses in his later years and died on 24th January 1844 by committing suicide in a cell of the notorious Tombs prison and is buried at Cedar Hill in Hartford, Connecticut.

Meanwhile, there is another episode in Jenner's life that we must look at. Sometime before his experiments with the balloon flights, he was the victim of unrequited love that hit him very badly. Jenner's depression meant that he was unable to answer Hunter's continual letters to him and one day Hunter thought that he had found the answer, he had heard that his one-time pupil and now friend had recently been married. He wrote to Jenner:

"I was told the other day that you was married, and to a young lady with considerable fortune. I hope it is true, for I do not know anybody more deserving of one. Let me know whether it is so or not. I hope you keep account of all expenses. What is become of your paper on lead in cider?"

However, Hunter had got his facts wrong, not only was Jenner not married, but as we already know, he had had his overtures to a young lady spurned for reasons that we cannot be sure about without knowing the identity of the lady in question, although the reasons already alluded to are probably close to the mark if indeed the lady in question was Catherine Kingscote. Jenner's feelings of depression lasted years, and in 1783, he wrote a sad letter to his old friend, Edward Gardner (1752–1823), the wine merchant from Frampton-upon-Severn, and explained his feelings to him:

"I am jaded almost to death my dear Gardner, by constant fatigue: that of the body I must endure; but how long I shall be able to bear that of the mind, I know not. Still the same dead weight hangs upon my heart. Would to God it would drag it from its unhappy mansion! Then with what pleasure would I see an end of this silly dream of life."

It's an extraordinary letter to have written at his time of life when he already had many achievements under his belt, and this was long before his work with smallpox that would make him famous. However, feelings of a romantic nature can never be explained away by sheer logic. It's a lesson that John Hunter certainly never learnt, as Jenner had also written to his old mentor and friend in London some years earlier. We are not able to trace a copy of Jenner's letter but Hunter's reply, dated 25th September 1778, reads as follows:

Dear Jenner,

I own I was at a loss to account for your silence, and I am sorry at the cause. I can easily conceive how you must feel, for you have two passions to cope with viz that of being disappointed in love, and that of being defeated, but both will wear out, perhaps the first soonest. I own that I was glad, when I heard that you

was moored to a woman of fortune; 'but let her go, never mind her'. I shall
employ you with Hedge Hogs, for I do not know how far I may trust mine.

This is a letter from a man who is clearly still fond of his one-time pupil and now his friend but despite his saying that he understands Jenner's feelings, he seems to misunderstand the depth of those feelings. Either that, or his inability with words to convey his meaning may seem that he is brushing Jenner off with a few lines of sympathy followed by a suggestion that the problem can be cured merely by giving him more work to carry out. However, whatever Hunter thought, one line in this letter has always puzzled historians and it reads – "Let her go, never mind her." Hunter puts it in quotations which could mean that he was quoting someone or it could be that he is merely using the quotations to emphasise the point he is trying to make. We shall probably never know the answer to this. In any event, Hunter was more concerned with wanting to find out more about the fat content of hibernating hedgehogs, and his letter continues:

"I want you to get a Hedge Hog in the beginning of winter and weigh him, put him in your garden and let him have some leaves, hay or straw to cover himself with, which he will do; then weigh him in the spring and see what he has lost. Secondly, I want you to kill one at the beginning of winter to see how fat he is, and another in the spring to see what he has lost of his fat. Thirdly, when the weather is very cold, and about the month of January I could wish you would make a hole in one of their bellies and put the thermometer down into the Pelvis, and see the height of the mercury, then turn it up towards the Diaphragm and observe the heat there, so much at present for Hedge Hogs. I beg pardon, examine the stomach and intestines and see what they contain.

"If Hewson's things go cheap, I will purchase some that I think proper for you. Those you mention I am afraid will be every body's money and go dear. Ever yours,

JOHN HUNTER
London,
Sept 25th 1778."

There is no doubt that Jenner continued to carry out experiments on hedgehogs to Hunter's satisfaction, but whilst the work that Jenner carried out for his friend pleased Hunter, it did little to ease Jenner's pain.

The identity of the woman in question has remained open to conjecture and the mystery has never really been cleared up. Many historians think that it was Catherine herself and this is a distinct possibility. Whilst discussing the launching of the hot air balloon, we have seen that although Jenner wanted to court Catherine Kingscote, the barrier to any such courtship was from Catherine's brother Robert. In 1778, Jenner was twenty-nine whilst Catherine would have been just seventeen years of age. Age and class were huge barriers to be conquered in the 18th century and if Jenner had problems with Robert Kingscote over the affair when the balloon was being launched in 1783, they certainly would have been worse in 1778 when Catherine was five years younger. Even John Baron (1786–1851), Jenner's friend and biographer, is very unclear as to who the lady in question was, and if anyone would know the identity, then it would surely be he. Baron was an English physician who was thirty-seven years younger than Jenner and was in awe of him. He was the first biographer of Jenner and whilst many years younger than him, would have had more first-hand knowledge of the man than biographers who followed on from him possessed. Before we move on, a little knowledge of Baron may be of interest to readers. Dr John Baron (1786–1851) was an English physician who was born in St Andrew's but was sent to Edinburgh to study medicine when he was just fifteen years old. He graduated M.D. at the age of nineteen in 1805 and looked after a patient in Lisbon for two years before returning to England and setting up a medical practice in Gloucester. Quite why he chose Gloucester is unclear but an educated guess could be that he had admired Jenner and his achievements from afar and simply wanted to be nearer to him. He probably met Jenner in 1809 and like Jenner, was very interested in the causes of angina and in fact published two books on the subject. He was given permission to write his hero's life story in 1823, the year that Jenner died, by the late doctor's executors, and the biography of Jenner was finally finished in 1838. To describe Jenner as Baron's hero is not meant unkindly, Baron genuinely admired Jenner and his work very much, but his biography seems to broach no criticism of Jenner whatsoever and Baron sidesteps any questions as to the possibility of vaccination not being seen as a cure for smallpox at a time when there was genuine doubt that it was the right treatment. However, it has to be said that Baron was a very gifted physician and should possibly be given the benefit of the doubt as to his ability to examine the method carefully and come to the conclusion that he did.

Returning to the business of Jenner's unrequited love, he either eventually got over the rejection after many years, or if it was Catherine Kingscote who was the object of his earlier affections, the balloon flight that he arranged with the Kingscote family obviously did his prospects no harm, because he continued to court her and on 6th March 1788, the couple were eventually married at Kingscote parish church and they enjoyed sharing their lives with each other for twenty seven years until Catherine's untimely death on 13th September, 1815 from tuberculosis aged fifty four years. Even in the Georgian period and with their comfortable life style, to die at that age would seem rather young, especially as her husband was a medical man but at the time, tuberculosis, like smallpox was a killer disease and there was no obvious cure. However, the years that they shared were happy and the couple had three children, Edward (b 1789), Catherine (b 1794) and Robert (b1797). If Catherine had been the earlier object of Jenner's affections as many historians believe, then her brother, Robert, need not have had any worries about his sister's choice because the man she married was not only an extraordinarily gifted physician who conquered the world's worst disease, but a very modest man with no pretensions and who clearly loved Catherine deeply.

Edward purchased the Queen Anne/Georgian style house in 1785 for £600, a sizeable sum of money in those days. At least, that was the figure later quoted by Jenner's friend, the Revd Thomas John Fosbroke and he, Jenner, purchased it from a lady by the name of Jane Hicks. Perhaps Edward had Catherine in mind when he bought it, as their marriage was only three years away. They both loved the house and brought their three children up there. Jenner, in fact, lived there for the rest of his life until his death in 1823. The house was called Chantry Cottage although viewed today, it is certainly not a cottage but a beautiful three storey house, which not only still stands today, but houses the Jenner Museum. The house originally belonged to the Chantry Priest of St Andrew's Alter in the parish church and had been built for him by Lady Katharine Berkeley in 1380 and over the years was altered a great deal to reflect the Georgian style that it would have been had it been built at the time that Jenner purchased it. Lady Katherine seems to have been a generous benefactor as she also funded the Grammar School in Wotton-under-Edge in 1384 that the young Edward Jenner had attended as a boy.

Edward and Catherine's children were born and raised in this house which for the most part was a happy household, although Robert, the third child, grew up to have very different characteristics than his conservative God-fearing Christian parents had. However, the first child, Edward, was born on 24th January, 1789, and was a delight to his parents. Edward wrote to his friend and mentor John Hunter to ask him if he would like to be Godfather. The reply he received from Hunter was so typical of the great man in its down to earth approach:

Dear Jenner,

I wish you joy: it never rains but it pours. Rather than the brat should not be a Christian, I will stand Godfather, for I should be unhappy if the poor little thing should go to the devil because I would not stand Godfather. I hope Mrs Jenner is well and that you begin to look grave now that you are a father.

Yours sincerely,
29th January, 1789 John Hunter

Whilst Jenner had only become a father two weeks earlier, he felt quite comfortable sending a letter to his friend, John Clinch (1749–1819), a clergyman-physician, who he had met when they were both schoolboys in Cirencester concerning how he, Clinch, and his wife Hannah should bring up one of their sons. Jenner and Clinch had remained good friends ever since their schooldays even though by now Clinch was living and working in Newfoundland. Jenner wrote to his friend to give him advice as to how to bring up Clinch's own son who was called Edward Jenner Clinch named after Edward Jenner himself, the boy's Godfather. The letter was dated 7th February, 1789. Jenner writes:

"As it is uppermost in my thoughts I must in the first place tell you that I have a son. My dear Catherine has lain in about a fortnight. The child, though small, appears to be remarkably healthy, and I ardently hope that there may as much affection subsist between the young Edward Jenners as between their fathers. There will be no room for more."

Obviously the friendship was not harmed by the letter's following paragraph as eventually, on the advice of his godfather, Edward Jenner Clinch came to England to be educated under the care of Jenner so the affection that Jenner claimed existed between the two fathers was obviously true as Jenner continued in his letter of 7th February:

"I hear by…you and Mrs Clinch keep him under no kind of restraint, but indulge him with a full gratification of all his wants and wishes. Let me entreat you both to take care of what you are about. Remember the path of life is full of thorns, and if you keep him upon velvet until the day arrives he must begin to feel their points, think how much more poignant must be his feelings…"

There must indeed have been a deep affection between the two fathers for John Clinch to have sent his son to Edward to be educated.

Returning to the birth of Edward and Catherine's first child, Edward junior, Edward and Catharine loved the little boy and it is much to their credit that they kept the young Edward at home for he had learning difficulties and in those days, many children with these handicaps were sent away and brought up by different families before returning to their real family two or three years later. It seems cruel to us today, but it was quite normal in the 18th century and Jane Austen's

(1775–1817) parents did it with one of Jane's brothers, George (1766–1838) who stayed with the village nurse. George was seen as backward and prone to having fits. In fact, Jane's father, the Revd George Austen was a vicar and a kindly man who loved his family, and would never countenance anything that he thought would be cruel to any of his children, but it is just the way people thought during those times. Often, the child would be taken back to the original family when he/she was about three years old, and this was often utterly traumatic. The now young child who had never known anything other than the care of the adopting family from birth, was now being taken back to his/her biological parents who were complete strangers to the child. Although it was not meant to be unkind, nevertheless, a child with learning difficulties had the added problems of adjusting to new people, and it must have led to many confused and distressed children. Unluckily for the young George Austen, he was not spared this terrible trauma, and it seems that he was not so lucky as Edward and Catherine Jenner's first-born child, Edward junior who was able to stay with his parents.

Edward and Catherine not only kept their first born at home as he was their son, but they truly loved him. Edward not only had learning difficulties, but he was also ill for a lot of his childhood but a great bond grew between father and son. Edward junior loved nature, as did his father, and the two of them would spend hours together looking at bird's nests whilst father would explain to son how the nests were built. Jenner also showed his son other aspects of wildlife, such as hedgehogs and other forms of anything connected with nature. Edward junior would come alive during his walks with his father – it was clear that young Edward was never going to achieve anything along academic lines, but he was attracted to nature like no other, and this alone gave his life great meaning. Indeed, he was free from the pressures of schooling and had two Christian parents who loved him deeply, so when this happy child who was loved so much became ill with tuberculosis and died at the tragically young age of twenty-one years on 31st January 1810, his parents were distraught. However, we shall look at young Edward's death in a later chapter.

Edward and Catherine's second child was a girl named Catherine after her mother. The exact date that Catherine was born is uncertain but she was christened on 12th August 1794 and so it is almost certain that she was born a week or so before that date. Unlike her two brothers, we don't know much detail about Catherine's character but she seems to have been a normal, well behaved girl who looked after her older brother and played with him in the usual way that siblings played. However, it is fairly certain that she was a clever child as her father used her as his secretary when she was quite young and therefore showed a lot of trust in her intelligence along with her general character. When her mother died in September, 1815, Catherine was just a few weeks past her twenty first birthday and took on the role of being the mother of the house, looking after her father for nearly seven years until she met a gentleman by the name of John Yeend Bedford who courted her and whom she married on 17th August 1822. Her father was happy for her and was generous with the cash gifts that he gave the couple. He gave the couple in excess of £13,000 when she married and this enormous sum was put into trust for her to be held by Colonel Robert Kingscote and the Revd William Richard Bedford. Jenner also gave the couple £1,000 on the wedding day. Even £1,000 was an enormous amount of money in 1822, but Edward – desperately wanted his daughter to be settled and looked after as he knew his health was failing. Her marriage and the money gave him hope that he would be free from any anxiety on that point, especially as no one knew then that Jenner only had just over a year to live. The wedding was a real family affair, as the person who conducted the wedding ceremony was the Revd William Davies, who was Edward's nephew, being the son of Edward's sister Anne (1741–1812) and his brother-in law, the Revd William Davies (1740–1817) and the couple's son had followed his father into the church. The only sadness for Edward on what was a happy occasion was that his new son-in-law had a business in Birmingham and it was there that the couple moved to and lived. During the previous seven years since the death of his wife and Catherine's mother, also named Catherine, his daughter had looked after him, and Jenner felt her absence very deeply and was very lonely during the latter part of his life. Jenner kept on working until the end of his days, but keeping himself busy was no substitute for him losing his first son, Edward with whom he had forged a close bond, the death of his beloved wife, and now his daughter was leaving. They were sad losses to a once happy and fulfilling life, both in career and personal terms.

Edward and Catherine's third born child, a son, Robert Fitzhardinge, gave his parents the initial pleasure that most newly born children give their parents, but sadly he gave his father headaches later on in life. He was born on 4th April 1797, and his names were chosen as the family were close to both the Kingscote and the Berkeley families. The name Robert was chosen after Catherine's brother Robert whilst Fitzhardinge was chosen as it represented the strong link the

Jenner's had with the Berkeley family. Jenner and Catherine were not only their friends but Edward was also their physician.

The birth of Robert came at exactly the right time for Edward as his beloved brother, Stephen, had died a few weeks earlier on the 23rd February 1797 at the age of sixty-four years. After Edward had suffered the trauma of being orphaned at the age of just five years, both parents dying within two months of each other, it was his elder brother Stephen who had brought him up, having to fulfil the roles of brother, guardian, surrogate father and friend. It must be remembered that Stephen himself was only twenty-two years old when after losing both his parents, he had to assume this huge role in bringing up his little brother. Also, Stephen it was who had taken Edward into his house on his return to Berkeley from London after training with Dr John Hunter from 1770 until 1773. He gave Jenner a home for twelve years until Edward had purchased Chantry House in 1785 and Jenner was heartbroken. He had nursed his elder brother for some eight weeks before Stephen finally succumbed. The birth of Robert just a few weeks later gave Edward and Catherine some joy, but Jenner could never have been able to foresee the problems that Robert would cause him right up to the end of his, Jenner's life. Robert was very different from his elder brother Edward. He did not have the same learning difficulties as Edward had but despite the age difference and academic abilities, remarkably they shared the same tutor, John Dawes Worgan. Worgan was extremely clever and was the son of a Bristol watchmaker and was tutoring children whilst hoping to enter the church at a later date. He had lived at a school which was run by the United Brethren in Fulneck near Leeds and had acted as the tutor of the son of Richard Hart Davies who was the Member of Parliament for Clifton before, he, Worgan, was taken on by Jenner to tutor his son Edward in 1806 aged just sixteen years.

Richard Hart (1766–1842) was the MP for Clifton from 1812 until 1831 and prior to that, was MP for Colchester from 1807 until 1812. Before entering Parliament, he had already amassed a fortune as a Bristol Merchant trading from the West Indies. In 1810, it was said that he had amassed £200,000 by 'getting all the Spanish wool in the kingdom' which at that time, was an absolute fortune roughly round the £12 million mark in the prices of 2018. Hart was on friendly terms with Lord Liverpool (1770–1828) who was the Prime Minister from 1812 until 1827. Given that many merchants from Bristol and Liverpool had made their fortunes on the back of the slave trade it was not surprising that the two men got on well. It wasn't until 1833 that this barbaric trade was finally made illegal by Act of Parliament.

Returning to Edward Jenner, whilst both young Edward and his tutor were virtually the same age, and as Worgan was obviously very clever, he would have had to make allowances for the fact that his pupil, young Edward, would test his tutor's patience, but it is almost certain that Jenner would have instructed Worgan to make allowances. It was only a year later that Robert became Worgan's second pupil. This was more difficult as Robert had no learning difficulties but as he was younger than Worgan being only ten years old when taken on by his new young tutor, he was probably easier to teach than his older brother Edward. Sadly, the young John Dawes Worgan did not enjoy good health and in July, 1809, after a short spell tutoring Edward and Robert, became ill and died from consumption at the tragically young age of just seventeen years. Meanwhile, Robert had done quite well at his studies and in 1815 entered Exeter College, Oxford, but found that the classics were not his strong point and was sent to a Mr Joyce from Wiltshire for further tuition.

Edward senior and Robert did not get on at all well. Robert had been better academically than his elder brother Edward, but sadly for his father, did not possess the sweet nature that his elder brother had. Robert's demands for more money from his father was a constant source of stress for Jenner and Robert was always asking for more handouts. Robert returned to Berkeley in May, 1819 at the age of twenty-two years and caused Jenner some immediate hope that he would see more of his son, perhaps leading to a better relationship between the two. However, Jenner was sadly mistaken as Robert was made a JP and Commissioner for Turnpike and it soon became clear that he was far more interested in seeing a lady by the name of Mary Perrington who was the wife of a local tailor. Mary had a daughter called Emily and as Robert was very generous to both mother and daughter in his will, many thought that Emily was Robert's daughter although without the advantage of DNA testing that we have today, it is never going to be proved. There is no record of what Mary's husband made of it, unless of course he didn't live long enough to be involved, but Jenner never did find out whether Emily was his granddaughter. Given his Christian principles and his non-relationship with Robert, it would be unlikely to be happy about the situation and he was long since despairing of his son. Robert ended up as a Colonel in the Gloucester Militia, the militia being a fighting force of non-professional men who tended to be used for defensive purposes and it was felt that they would never stand a chance against professional, well drilled and well-equipped armies. Robert ended his days in 1854 at the age of fifty-seven. Robert never married but had enjoyed a rather colourful life which was never short of women and which was in complete contrast to the hopes and dreams that his father had had for him when he was growing up. There was never a question of Jenner reaching anywhere near the relationship with Robert that he had enjoyed with his first-born son, Edward (1789–1810), the gentle, nature loving boy who died so tragically young.

We have read a short piece that outlines the courtship and marriage in March 1788, of Edward and Catherine and also touched on the birth of their children and the subsequent family life that despite the rather reckless ways of the younger son Robert, was for the most part, very happy. Certainly, Catherine and Edward adored each other. However, we must now go back to the previous year to look at some of the experiments that Jenner was carrying out at the behest of John Hunter, his one-time mentor and now friend and this we do in the next chapter.

-oOOo-

Chapter 6

Observations on the Wolf, Jackal and Dog to Show That They Are Part of the Same Species and Subsequent Letters to Joseph Banks and John Hunter. Work on the Nesting Habits of the Cuckoo and Report to the Royal Society. Election to the Royal Society

On 26th April 1787, Hunter had read a paper to the Royal Society entitled 'Observations tending to show that the Wolf, Jackal, and Dog are all of the same species'. Sir Joseph Banks (1743–1820), the great botanist, like Hunter, had been a good friend of Jenner's since Banks had returned to England having spent three years at sea with Captain Cook between the years 1768 and 1771. Banks too was interested in Hunter's experiments, and on the 5th June, 1787, Jenner wrote the following letter to Banks:

"Sir,

"When I had the honour of waiting on you in London in the Spring, I promised to send you an Account of the Dog and Fox; but the Gentleman from whom I receiv'd it, not sending it so soon as I expected, occasion'd this long delay. His Account is as follows:

"I could not before this day get such intelligence as could be relayed on respecting the Dog-Fox and Terrier Bitch, which I have taken the first opportunity of transmitting to you. The Bitch did not seem very desirous of receiving the Fox at his first approaching her: But after a little amorous dalliance, she came to. They copulated three times in the course of the day, and each time continued together between ten minutes and a quarter of an hour. This happen'd sometime in the month of July. It did not appear in consequence of this union that the Bitch shew'd any signs of pregnancy."

We do not know the name of the gentleman who wrote the above account that Jenner quotes to Banks, but Jenner continued his letter:

"Notwithstanding this Account almost every sportsman asserts that foxes and Dogs will produce an offspring. But I shall use every endeavour to set the matter clear by Experiments with these Animals…"

Jenner carries on with this letter but it is the above that is quoted here that deals with the subject of the family of dogs. The rest of this very long letter deals with some experiments on vegetables and animal manure, but it is the experiments with the dogs and wolves that we must concentrate on here.

In Jenner's time, the medical profession and botanists knew quite a lot about these animals and their relationships with each other, but these days we know more. For instance, we know that the dogs, wolves, foxes, jackals, and dingoes come from the same family and are known collectively as Canidae. An individual member of this family is called a Canid. Canidae are known in just about every continent except Antarctica, the southernmost tip of the world that Captain James Cook was sent to in 1768 to prove or disprove its existence. Antarctica is approximately 5,400,000 square miles which is nearly twice the size of Australia and 98% of it is ice which means that there were certainly no living creatures there. Joseph Banks as mentioned earlier, also went on that first trip of Cook's and it was on the return to England that the two men, Banks and Jenner first met. Cook was actually sent again between the years 1772 and 1775 because Alexander Dalrymple (1737–1808), a Scottish geographer and hydrographer who was respected by the Admiralty, was convinced that the southern landmass existed but that Cook had failed to find it. Dalrymple's persistent arguments on the subject finally convinced the Admiralty and made them uncertain as to whether Cook, on his first voyage, had finally disproved its existence. Neither Banks nor Jenner went on the second trip although Banks wanted to, and wished to take Jenner with him as part of his team. As mentioned earlier, Banks was removed from the trip by the Admiralty as they found that Banks wanted to travel on a much bigger ship than the Whitby Coal Carrier that Cook favoured whilst Jenner, although flattered by the offer, simply wanted to leave London and return to Berkeley where he was born and brought up and set up a practice there.

Another subject that interested Hunter and Jenner was the nesting habits of the cuckoo, although as usual it would appear that it was Jenner who did all the actual work although in fairness to Hunter, it was Jenner who was best placed to carry out this work as he lived in the countryside. For years, probably as far back as when he returned to Berkeley in 1773 from his days with Hunter in London, he had puzzled over what was happening concerning this phenomenon. This is hardly surprising as he had read an article stating that 'this subject had been puzzling philosophers in every age from the days of Aristotle'. Jenner had been puzzled as to what actually happened when the cuckoos built their nests – and that was the problem, they didn't. The cuckoos seemed to have an idea that if they can get another bird to build it for them, they will and that is exactly what Jenner discovered. The year before Jenner married, he was heavily involved in the study of this subject and he came to the correct conclusion that the cuckoo laid its eggs in another bird's nest, often that of the hedge-sparrow or house-martin. After a period of time, Jenner found that the eggs or the chicks of the host parents that had been newly hatched from the eggs had been tipped out, leaving those of the cuckoo unharmed. This meant that any cuckoo chick that was remaining in the nest received not only the food supplied by the adult cuckoo, but also from the foster-parents. At first, Jenner reached the obvious conclusion that it was the foster-parents who threw the eggs out and it was this idea that he put to Joseph Banks in 1787. Banks as well as Hunter was involved as Jenner was hoping to become a member of the Royal Society and saw this report as a possible way in. We have already quoted heavily from the letter to Joseph Banks dated 5th June, 1787 concerning the canidae family, and Jenner ended that letter with the following words about the cuckoo:

"...By a letter from Mr Blagden I have the pleasure of being inform'd my Observations on the Cuckoo are order'd for Publication in the Phil: trans: I shall pursue the Subject during the Summer and hope to have the honour of presenting you with another paper in the Autumn; and also a paper on the exciting cause to emigration in Birds.

"I am Sir with the greatest deference Your most obedient and obliged humble servant

Berkeley 5th June 1787 Edward Jenner"

Rather than leave the name of Mr Blagden in the letter from Jenner to Banks unexplained, we should possibly add a few lines to explain who he was. Sir Charles Brian Blagden, F.R.S., was born in 1748 and lived until 1820. He was a British physician and scientist and served as a medical officer in the army from 1776 until 1780. He was Secretary to the Royal Society from 1784 until 1797 and won the prestigious Copley Medal in 1788 and was knighted in 1792. The Copley Medal is a scientific award given by the Royal Society for outstanding achievements in research in any branch of science. The medal was created following a donation of £100 made by Sir Godfrey Copley, 2nd Baronet, F.R.S., (C1653–1709) who was a wealthy landowner, art collector and public figure.

Returning to Jenner's first report to Joseph Banks concerning the nesting habits of the cuckoo, he, Jenner, was uneasy and felt that after putting some thought into the matter, felt that something wasn't quite right in that report. Jenner had used his nephew Henry (1767–1851) to help him in his research as he, Edward was so busy. Henry was the son of Edward's brother who was also named Henry (1736–98). However, Henry junior had not been as thorough as he should have been concerning how the hosts eggs/chicks were being turfed out of the nests. In fairness to Henry, it would have been an easy mistake to make to think that it was the host-parents, but he got it wrong, it was the cuckoo chicks themselves. Jenner did some further research himself and discovered that it was in fact the cuckoo chicks who were throwing the hosts birds out, and not content with that, if there were two cuckoo chicks left, they would try and push each other out until one of them was successful leaving one exhausted cuckoo chick left in an otherwise empty nest. These findings were extraordinary and many naturalists simply didn't believe Jenner, thinking it was a preposterous notion and it wasn't until 1921 when filming became used that Jenner's ideas were finally proved correct. Jenner had been well taught by Hunter who had always advocated experimenting yourself rather than simply accepting the word of another. With that in mind, Jenner carried out some dissections on the cuckoo chick and saw that there was a small indentation in the back which disappeared after a short period of about twelve days. This certainly added weight to his conclusion that the cuckoo chick was the culprit and he submitted a further paper on the subject, this time to John Hunter himself, entitled 'Observations On The Natural History Of The Cuckoo' and Jenner requested that the paper be sent to the Royal Society.

It is a long letter which shows clearly the huge amount of work that Jenner undertook before he arrived at the correct result. The reader can make his or her mind up whether to read the letter in full – it has been summarised above, but by quoting the letter/report in its entirety, it will give the reader the opportunity to see that Jenner was a patient man, prepared always to take his time in order to arrive at the correct conclusion. His letter to Hunter dated 27th December, 1787, starts thus:

Dear Sir,

Having at your request, some of my leisure hours in attending to the natural history of the Cuckoo, I beg leave to lay before you the result of my observations with a hope that they may tend to illustrate a subject hitherto not sufficiently investigated; and should what is here offered prove, in your opinion, deserving the attention of the Royal Society, you will do me the honour of presenting it to that learned body.

"The first appearance of Cuckoos in Gloucestershire is about the 17th of April. The song of the male, which is well known, soon proclaims its arrival. The song of the female (if the peculiar notes of which it is composed may be so called) is widely different, and has been so little attended to, that I believe few are acquainted with it. I know not how to convey to you a proper idea of it by comparison with the notes of any other bird, but the cry of the Dab-chick bears the nearest resemblance to it.

Unlike the generality of birds do not pair. When a female appears on the wing, she is often attended by two or three males who seem to be earnestly attending for her favours… Like the migrating birds she does not begin to lay till some weeks after her arrival. I could never procure an egg till after the middle of May, although probably an early-coming Cuckoo may produce one sooner.

The Cuckoo makes choice of the nests of a great variety of small birds. I have known its eggs intrusted to the care of the Hedge-sparrow, the Water-wagtail, the Titlark, the Yellow-hammer, the Green Linnet and the Winchat. Among these it generally selects the three former; but shows a much greater partiality to the Hedge-sparrow's than to any of the rest…

The Hedge-sparrow commonly takes up four or five days in laying her eggs. During this time…the Cuckoo contrives to deposit her egg among the rest, leaving the future care of it entirely to the Hedge-sparrow. This intrusion often occasions some discomposure; for the old Hedge-sparrow at intervals, whilst she is sitting, not unfrequently throws out some of her own eggs, so that it more frequently happens that only two or three Hedge-sparrows eggs are hatched with the Cuckoos than otherwise… However, I have never seen an instance when the Hedge-sparrow has thrown out or injured the egg of the Cuckoo.

When the Hedge-sparrow has sat her usual time, and disengaged the young Cuckoo and some of her own offspring from the shell (the young Cuckoo is commonly hatched first), her own young ones, and any of her eggs that remain unhatched, are soon turned out, the young Cuckoo remaining possessor of the nest and sole object of her future care."

Jenner wrote that whilst people had realised that the young Hedge-sparrows had been turfed out, they had been wrong as to how it happened, assuming that the adult Cuckoo was the culprit and he carries on writing to Hunter, pointing out the error and putting forward the correct reason. Jenner then goes on to find out whether the foster parents feed the Cuckoo chicks and tells Hunter of the observations that he has made:

'Example 1: The Titlark is frequently selected by the Cuckoo to take charge of the young one…I…have had one opportunity of seeing the young Cuckoo in the nest of this bird; I saw the old birds feed it repeatedly, and to satisfy myself that they were really Titlarks, shot them both and found them to be so.'

'Example 2: A Cuckoo laid its egg in a Water-wagtail's nest in the thatch of an old cottage. The Wagtail sat her usual time, and then hatched all the eggs but one; which, with all the young ones except the Cuckoo, was turned out of the nest… The Cuckoo was reared by the Wagtails.'

'Example 3: A Hedge-sparrow built her nest in a hawthorn bush in a timber yard; after she had laid two eggs a Cuckoo dropped in a third. The Sparrow continued laying as if nothing had happened, till she had laid five, her usual number, and then sat.'

At this stage, Jenner realised that the foster-parents were definitely looking after the cuckoo's egg(s), but he wasn't sure whether the foster-parents threw their own offspring out. They would have had the strength to have done this certainly, but he felt that it made no sense for them to actually carry it out. Jenner, ever inquisitive, sensed that he was on the verge of finding the answer to a question that had puzzled scientists, naturalists and botanists for many years. Jenner's paper continues:

"June 20th, 1786. On inspecting the nest I found that the bird had hatched this morning, and that everything but the young Cuckoo was thrown out…I…found one egg by the side of the nest entangled with the course woody materials that formed the outside covering…and could see that the Sparrow it contained was yet alive. It was then restored to the nest but in a few minutes was thrown out. The egg being again suspended by the outside of the nest was saved a second time from breaking. To see what would happen if the Cuckoo was removed I took out the Cuckoo and placed the egg…in the nest in its stead. The old birds during this time flew about the spot, showing signs of great anxiety; but when I withdrew they quickly came to the nest again. On looking into it a quarter of an hour afterwards, I found the young one completely hatched, warm and lively. The Hedge-sparrows were suffered to remain undisturbed with their new charge for three hours…when the Cuckoo was again put into the nest. The old Sparrows had been so much disturbed by these intrusions, that for some time they showed an unwillingness to come to it: however, at length they came, and on examining the nest again in a few minutes I found the young Sparrow was tumbled out. It was a second time restored, but again experienced the same fate…"

From these experiments, and supposing from the feeble appearance of the young Cuckoo just disengaged from the shell that it was utterly incapable of displacing either the egg or the young Sparrows I was induced to believe that the old Sparrows were the only agents in this seeming unnatural business…

Jenner had arrived at the wrong conclusion and had sent these findings to Hunter. No mention of his nephew Henry is found here so whether Jenner was at fault or Henry, we do not know. However, the report comes from Jenner who puts his name to it so we must assume that he was happy with the findings. However, having said that, it was not long before Jenner felt that he had made a mistake and he urged Hunter to send the report back to him with all speed in the summer of 1787 – clearly something was troubling him. It was lucky that Hunter, through whatever reason, had failed to send the report to Joseph Banks and this gave Jenner more time to carry out further experiments. He had heard the first Cuckoo by the end of April, but couldn't use them immediately as it was too early for them to lay so he looked again at the behaviour of the Hedge-sparrows. He made the following notes:

"Two Hedge-sparrows about half-fledged were taken from a nest and a Blackbird in about the same state of plumage was placed there in their stead. Two Hedge-sparrows, fellow nestlings of those that were removed, were suffered to remain."

"At the same time I put a young Hedge-sparrow about half fledged into the nest of another Hedge-sparrow, with two young ones newly hatched, having first removed two others to give it room. (April 27th) On examining the nest I found no disturbance had happened in either. The Blackbird, and the large Hedge-sparrow placed among the small ones were both in the nests and taken care of by the Hedge-sparrows."

"(April 28th) The large Hedge-sparrow gone; the two little ones remain. The Blackbird still in the nest, and grown so that it almost filled it up. The Hedge-sparrows sit on its back."

"(April 30th) The Blackbird perched upon the side of the nest; the Hedge-sparrows sit in the bush at a greater distance."

"(May 1st) The Blackbird and Hedge-sparrows flown away. A single swift was seen."

"(May 5th) Heard the grilla talpa (mole cricket) in the evening. Noted the same Cuckoo sung in different keys…"

"(May 10th) Swifts came to the houses."

"(May 12th) Martins came to their old nests."

By this time, spring was coming soon and the Vale of Berkeley was alive to all the various bird songs and Jenner, ever inquisitive, starts to dissect various birds and notes that the cuckoo lays a larger number of eggs than the other species. On the 17th May, he continues to write:

"A Blackbird's egg which had been some time sat upon, was put into a Hedge-sparrow's nest this day with the Hedge-sparrow's eggs consisting of three. The Hedge-sparrow was just beginning to sit."

"The blackbird's egg hatched in the normal way."

"(May 25th) The Hedge-sparrows hatched and smothered by the young Blackbird, which now quite filled the nest."

"The fate of the young Hedge-sparrows was the same as if the cuckoo had entered the nest. However, there was one big difference which was that the young hedge-sparrows had not been thrown out, they had been smothered by the young blackbird. Their fate was the same, but for an entirely different reason."

"(June 1ˢᵗ) A Wryneck's egg was put in a Blackbird's nest with three of her own eggs. It was placed in the centre. The day following it was singled out from the rest and thrown out of the nest. The egg was coloured dark like the Blackbird's. The Blackbird forsook its nest the whole day – the day after it returned again and sat upon its eggs, when the Wryneck's egg was again put in the nest. The Blackbird turned it out a second time, and then finally forsook the nest."

Apart from the fact that the blackbird turfed out the intruder's eggs, it's not clear what information Jenner obtained by carrying out this experiment as it merely muddied the waters and gave Jenner no more information concerning the cuckoo.

"(17ᵗʰ June) Saw a Hedge-sparrow's nest at Mr Bromedge's with two Hedge-sparrows in it just hatched, two eggs not hatched and a Cuckoo just hatched."

"(18ᵗʰ June) In the morning early there were four Hedge-sparrows and the young Cuckoo in it. About noon it contained the Cuckoo and one Hedge-sparrow only, and at night the Cuckoo was left alone in the nest."

This was exciting, as Jenner actually saw what happened as opposed to just seeing the result of the egg laying process. The same day Jenner continues his paper:

"June 18ᵗʰ 1787. The nest was placed so near the extremity of a hedge that I could distinctly see what was going forward in it; and to my astonishment saw the young Cuckoo, though so newly hatched, in the act of turning out the young Hedge-sparrow."

This was incredible – Jenner could hardly believe his eyes, his report continues:

"The mode of accomplishing this was very curious. The little animal, with the assistance of its rump and wings, contrived to get the bird upon its back, and making a logement for the burden by elevating its elbows, clambered backward with it up the side of the nest till it reached the top, where, resting for a moment, it threw off its load with a jerk and quite disengaged it from the nest. It remained in this situation for a short time, feeling about with the extremity of its wings, as if to be convinced whether the business was properly executed, and then dropped into the nest again. With these (the extremities of its wings), I have often seen it examine, as it were, an egg and nestling before it began its operations; and the nice sensibility which these parts appeared to possess seemed sufficiently to compensate the want of sight, which as yet it was destitute of. I afterwards put in an egg, and this by a similar process was conveyed to the side of the nest and thrown out. These experiments I have since repeated several times in different nests, and have always found the young Cuckoo disposed to act in the same manner. In climbing up the nest it sometimes drops it's burden, and thus is foiled of its endeavours: but after a little respite the work is resumed and goes on almost incessantly until it is affected. It is wonderful to see the exertions of the young Cuckoo when it is two or three days old, if a bird be put into the nest with it that is too weighty for it to lift out. In this state it seems ever restless and uneasy. But this disposition for turning out its companions begins to decline from the time it is two or three till it is about twelve days old, when, as far as I have hitherto seen, it ceases. Indeed, the disposition for throwing out the egg appears to cease a few days sooner: for I have frequently seen the young Cuckoo after it had been hatched nine or ten days, remove a nestling that had remained in the nest with it, when it suffered an egg, put there at the same time, to remain unmolested. The singularity of its shape is well adapted to these purposes; for, different from other newly hatched birds, its back, from the scapulae downwards, is very broad, with a considerable depression in the middle. This depression seems formed by nature for the design of giving a more secure logement to the egg of the Hedge-sparrow or its young one, when the young Cuckoo is employed in removing either of them from the nest. When it is about twelve days old this cavity is quite filled up, and then the back assumes the shape of nestling birds in general."

This was yet another extraordinary discovery by Jenner. He has not only seen the young Cuckoo throw the eggs or newly born chicks of the Hedge-sparrow out of the nest with his own eyes, but he now has further ammunition to tell the doubters that this was indeed the case. Once again, his mentor, John Hunter's teachings that physicians should ascertain facts by finding out for themselves rather than meekly accepting what has been written in earlier text books has paid off. Jenner continues:

"Having found that the Hedge-sparrow commonly throws out some of her eggs after her nest has received the Cuckoos, and not knowing how she might treat her young ones if the young Cuckoo was deprived of the power of dispossessing them of the nest, I made the following experiment..."

Jenner continues:

"June 26th, 1787 Cuckoos have appeared to become more and more scarce this last fortnight.' However, he can still find eggs and nestlings and the report goes on."

"June 27th Two Cuckoos which had been laid in one Hedge-sparrow's nest were hatched this morning, and also one of the Hedge-sparrow's. Another Hedge-sparrow's egg remained unhatched."

"June 28th The nest contained the two Cuckoos and the Hedge-sparrow in the morning. The Cuckoos seemed contending for the nest. In the afternoon one of the Cuckoos had turned out the other, and also the Hedge-sparrow."

"July 9th The Hedge-sparrow in Cornock's orchard has hatched her two eggs (she sat on no more of her own) and the Cuckoo's egg this morning. Fastened a piece of lead on the Cuckoo's leg in such a way that he can't throw out his fellow nestlings."

"(July 10th) The Hedge-sparrows are still in the nest. The Cuckoo makes frequent efforts to throw them out."

"(July 11th) The Cuckoo and Hedge-sparrows all in the nest."

"(July 13th) All treated with equal care by the Hedge-sparrow till this day when the nest was plundered."

By this time Jenner had proved that the newly hatched Cuckoo chick had turfed the eggs and/or the newly hatched Hedge-sparrows out of the nest but although having proved his point to his own satisfaction, he continued his report to the Royal Society and expands on his discovery of 28th June:

"This contest was very remarkable. The combatants alternately appeared to have the advantage, as each carried the other several times nearly to the top of the nest, and then sunk down again oppressed by the weight of its burden: till at length, after various efforts, the strongest prevailed, and was afterwards brought up by the Hedge-sparrows."

"A large nestling Martin was put into the nest. The Cuckoo exerted all its powers to turn it out, but to no purpose. The next day however, the Cuckoo effected it. The Martin was replaced... The Martin was thrown out again."

"The smallness of the Cuckoo's egg in proportion to the size of the bird is a circumstance that, hitherto, I believe, has escaped the notice of ornithologists. So great is the disproportion that it is in general smaller than that of the House-sparrow: whereas the difference in size of the birds is nearly as five is to one. I have used the term 'in general' because eggs produced at different times by the same bird vary very much in size. I have found a Cuckoo's egg so light that it weighed only 43 grams, and one so heavy that it weighed 55 grams. The colour of the eggs is extremely variable."

At this stage of his report, Jenner has concerned himself only with facts, but he had an inquisitive mind at the best of times, and continued to look for the reasons for this behaviour. Jenner always loved nature and by this stage, so involved with his project was he that he continued to find a reason for everything so that he could fit them in to a tidy package which he called 'the scheme of nature'. Jenner continues his report:

"The circumstance of the young Cuckoo's being destined by nature to throw out the young Hedge-sparrows, seems to account for the parent Cuckoo's dropping her eggs in the nest of birds so small as those I have particularised… Besides, though many of the larger birds might have fed the nestling Cuckoo very properly…yet they could not have suffered their own young to have been sacrificed…in such great numbers as the smaller ones, which are so much more abundant."

"Here it may be remarked, that though nature permits the young Cuckoo to make this great waste, yet the animals thus destroyed are not thrown away or rendered useless. At the season when this happens, great numbers of tender quadrupeds and reptiles are seeking provision; and if they find the callow nestlings which have fallen victim to the young Cuckoo, they are furnished with food well adapted to their peculiar state."

This obviously seems callous yet we must remember that this was 18th century thinking and whilst Jenner did not like what was happening, he saw it as simply part of nature. Jenner continues with his report:

"To what cause, then, may we attribute the singularities of the Cuckoo? May they not be owing to the following circumstances? The short residence this bird is allowed to make in the country where it is destined to propagate its species, and the call that nature has upon it, during that short residence, to produce numerous progeny? She is reduced (by laying her eggs abroad), to the same state as the bird whose nest we daily rob of an egg, in which case the stimulus for incubation is suspended. Of this we have a familiar example in the common domestic fowl. That the Cuckoo actually lays a great number of eggs dissection seems to prove very decisively. A bird can either retard or bring forward her eggs…"

"The same instinctive impulse which directs the Cuckoo to deposit her eggs in the nests of other birds, directs her young one to throw out the eggs and young of the owner of the nest. The scheme of nature would be incomplete without it: for it would be extremely difficult, if not impossible, for the little birds, destined to find succour for the Cuckoo, to find it also for their own young ones, after a certain period: nor would there be room for the whole to inhabit the nest."

"Thus, Sir, I have, with much pleasure, complied with your request; and here lay before you such observations as I have hitherto been capable of making on the natural history of the Cuckoo; and should they throw some light on a subject that has long laid hid in obscurity, I shall not think my time has been ill employed."

"With a grateful sense of the many obligations I owe to the friendship with which you have so long honoured me,

I remain &c

Edward Jenner

December 27th, 1787"

Despite the amount of effort that Jenner had put into his work on the Cuckoo and the resulting report that would go to the Royal Society, his new found happiness with his beloved wife Catherine and their new born son, also called Edward had caused all the importance of that work to fade into the back of his mind until he received a short note from John Hunter, saying:

"Dear Jenner,

You are to be balloted for next Thursday. I think there can be no fear of success. You shall have a letter from me by the Friday's post.

Yours sincerely,
John Hunter"

Hunter was late in sending the letter, but at last in May, 1788, Jenner hears from him – Hunter writes:

"I have been going to write to you for some time past, but business and a very severe indisposition for three weeks past has prevented me. Your paper has been read (on March 13th), passed the Council, and is in print for I had a proof sheet this day, and I have ordered fifty copies, twenty five for you and twenty five for myself, to give to friends. I spoke to both Sir Joseph Banks and to Dr Blagden about your wish; Sir Joseph has not the least objection and will give us all his assistance, but he thinks the paper had better be first printed and delivered, and let the people rest a little upon it, for he says there are many who can hardly believe it wholly; this will put off the certificate till the beginning of next winter, when we shall hang you up."

Jenner was very excited as he had yearned to be made a Member of the Royal Society but at the same time, he had other things to think about, his marriage to his beloved Catherine being uppermost in his mind. However, his interest in the Royal Society was considerably raised when he received the following letter from John Hunter:

Dear Jenner,

You was this evening voted into the Royal Society. You will have a letter from the Secretary; but as that may not be sent for some days I thought it would not be disagreeable to have the earlier notice.

I am, dear Jenner,

Your most obedient
John Hunter

Jenner was exceedingly happy. He had married Catherine after spending many years courting her, they would soon be able to celebrate the safe arrival of their first born son, and he had become a full member of that august body, the Royal Society, Jenner having been elected on 25th February 1789. He had had to wait nearly a year since the paper had been read to the members on 13th March 1788, but Edward didn't mind. Edward Jenner, F.R.S., husband and father, looked and sounded wonderful – Jenner was never happier than in that moment of time. However, in the not too distant future, his happiness was to be blighted when he would lose the man that was so dear to him, Dr John Hunter.

-oOOo-

Chapter 7

Jenner's Work on Angina Pectoris. His Concerns for the Health of John Hunter. The Death of John Hunter. Jenner Receives Medical Degree. Jenner Ill with Thyphus. The Death of Nephew Stephen Jenner. The Murder of William Reed

In looking at the many dissections of human bodies that both Hunter and Jenner had carried out, Jenner's work on angina takes us back to when Jenner was studying under his mentor. During one dissection in particular which was carried out in 1772, Jenner felt that he had picked up on the hardening of the arteries which could cause angina or even heart attacks on patients, often leading to death.

One of Jenner's friends from school, Caleb Hillier Parry (1755–1822) M.D., F.R.S., like Jenner, a doctor, published a book on the subject in 1799, entitled 'An Inquiry into the symptoms and Causes of the Syncope Anginosa, Commonly called Angina Pectoris'. This book came after a dissection had been carried out on a patient who had died of angina pectoris. Parry gave credit to Jenner for the work that he had carried out on the subject which helped Parry complete the book, although neither man was the first doctor to discover it.

In his book, Parry wrote:

"...it was suggested by Dr Jenner, that the Angina pectoris arose from some morbid change in the structure of the heart, which change was probably ossification, or some similar disease, of the coronary arteries."

Jenner's first contribution to the Medico-Convivial Society, an organisation which we dealt with earlier in this book, was on 29th July, 1789, and was a paper on heart disease which Jenner said followed rheumatism, actually a case of mitral stenosis, hardening and malfunction of one of the heart valves. Only part of the manuscript survives, but in it Jenner continues:

"The Symptoms arising appear to be very different from those which shew themselves in Angina Pectoris."

In his book, Parry was generous in giving credit to Jenner for his great contribution, mainly by his numerous dissections which gave him the knowledge to pass on to Parry details of this subject which allowed Parry to complete his book. Parry published a letter that Jenner had written to him which was in reply to a series of questions that Parry needed answers for. Parry writes in his book this answer from Jenner:

"The first case I ever saw of Angina Pectoris, was that in the year 1772, published by Dr Heberden with Mr John Hunter's dissection. There, I can almost positively say, the coronary arteries of the heart were not examined. Another case of a Mr Carter at Dursley, fell under my care. In that, after having examined the more important parts of the heart, without finding anything by means of which I could account either for his sudden death, or the symptoms preceding it, I was making a transverse section of the heart pretty near its base, when my knife struck against something so hard and gritty, as to notch it. I well remember looking up to the ceiling, which was old and crumbling, conceiving that some plaister (sic) had fallen down. But on a further scrutiny the real cause appeared: the coronaries were become bony canals. Then I began a little to suspect. Soon afterwards Mr Paytherus met with a case. Previously to our examination of the body, I offered him a wager that we should find the coronary arteries ossified. This, however, proved not to be exactly true, but the coats of the arteries were hard, and a sort of cartilaginous canal was formed within the cavity of each artery, and there attached, so however as to be separable as easily as the fingers from a tight glove. We then concluded that merorganization was the cause of the disease."

The Mr Paytherus mentioned a few lines above was Thomas Paytherus (1752–1828), a forward-looking surgeon-apothecary and a great friend and follower of Edward Jenner. Another person mentioned above who Jenner looked up to was William Heberden (1710–1801), sometimes referred to as William Heberden the Elder as he had a son, William Heberden the Younger (1767–1845). William the Younger was a well-known and distinguished physician but was overshadowed by his father although he had a good career and was a physician at St George's Hospital between 1793 and 1803. He also became

Physician in Ordinary to Queen Charlotte in 1806 and King George III in 1809 and was elected to the Royal Society in 1791. It was his father, William Heberden the Elder who named the condition that Parry and Jenner were working on as 'Angina Pectoris'. Heberden named it as such in 1768 when he brought out a publication on the subject. Heberden the Elder was born in London and was sent to St John's College, Cambridge in 1724 and obtained a Fellowship in 1732. In 1739, he took the degree which enabled him to use the letters M.D. after his name and in 1746 became a Fellow of the Royal College of Physicians. He was elected to be a Fellow of that august body, the Royal Society in 1749 and produced a paper on chickenpox in 1767 followed closely by a paper on Angina Pectoris the following year, 1768. He had married Elizabeth Martin in 1752 and they had a son Thomas in 1754, but Elizabeth sadly died in the same year. He married again, this time to Mary Wallaston and the couple had eight children, of which six died. One of the surviving children was the son William who went into medical practice as did his father. The other child was Mary who lived from 1763 until 1832.

Returning to Jenner's letter to Parry, he went on to say, that although he felt that he had discovered something important, he was very concerned that his very good friend and mentor, Dr John Hunter, was showing the very symptoms that Jenner had realised were those of Angina Pectoris. In 1777, Hunter had been unwell, and Jenner had hoped to call on him at Bath where in the September of that year, Hunter had gone for a rest. Jenner felt unable to discuss his findings with Hunter for two reasons, the first being that he did not want to cause his friend any sort of distress, and the other being that he wasn't completely sure that his findings and conclusions from those findings were in fact correct. Jenner went on to tell Parry:

"…my worry about the diagnosis prevented any publication of my ideas on the subject, as it must have brought on an unpleasant conference between Mr Hunter and me. I mentioned both to Mr Cline and Mr Home my notions of the matter at one of Mr Hunter's Sunday night meetings; but they did not seem to think much of them. When, however, Mr Hunter died, Mr Home very candidly wrote to me, immediately after the dissection, to tell me I was right."

Jenner was certainly correct in his findings, but he was totally wrong to think that Hunter was unaware of the symptoms that he had and although hindsight is a wonderful thing, it seems today that it was extraordinary that Jenner thought that Hunter was unaware of the disease especially as he had carried out so many dissections, and not only that, would have been aware of William Herberden's (1710–1801) paper on the subject as far back as 1768. Hunter was only too aware of what he was suffering from but he was a driven man and he nevertheless chose to carry on and work as hard as ever. He knew only too well what the ramifications of the disease would be and he once said in his usual blunt Hunterian way: "My life is in the hands of any fool who chooses to upset me." As it happened, these words were very prophetic, as Hunter, when working at St George's Hospital, collapsed and died after an altercation with one of his medical colleagues there on 16th October 1793.

The circumstances of the death of this great man were as follows. Hunter had started the day having met three of his pupils in the preparations room at the usual time of 7am. He seemed to be very cheerful, no doubt looking forward to seeing his wife Anne, and his children again, twenty-one-year old John and seventeen-year-old Agnes, the three of them having been in Brighton for the previous six weeks. Hunter had helped his students make their preparations with his usual patience and settled down with them, awaiting breakfast at 7am. A student by the name of William Clift, who had signed on with Hunter the previous year, namely, 1792, noted that he had entered the room 'humming a Scotch air' and James Williams, another student, noted that the great man 'was in very good spirits and had eaten as hearty as usual.' At noon, it was time for Hunter to leave the house in Castle Street and go to St George's Hospital where he had a meeting to attend followed by some patients that he had to visit.

Hunter's good mood, however, hid a black cloud that had descended upon him as he knew that he was entering a situation that would doubtless cause him great tension, putting a strain on his now weakened heart. Two young Scottish men had recently written to him asking if they could enrol as his pupils. Hunter was impressed by their enthusiasm but unfortunately they had not served the required apprenticeships and whilst Hunter had written to them explaining the situation, he told them that he would press their case when he was next at the hospital. Accordingly, he had written to the board supporting them being taken on as students and he knew that the subject was due to come up at the meeting of the Board. Among the physicians gathered in the room, there was only one man who he knew that he could rely on for his support, and that was his nephew, Dr Matthew Baillie. Baillie (1761–1823), F.R.S., F.R.S.E., F.R.C.P., F.R.C.S.E., F.R.S.E., had been a pupil of his uncle, John Hunter, and his father-in-law, Dr Thomas Denman, who was a pre-eminent obstetrician, and who had brought out a textbook on childbirth in 1788. On the death of William Hunter, John's elder brother, in 1783, Baillie was bequeathed £5,000 and William's house in Windmill Street. He was also given the medical school nearby and Baillie taught there from the year of William Hunter's death in 1783 until 1803. He then taught anatomy and was appointed Physician at St George's Hospital in 1789. After that he established his own practice in Grosvenor Square and was elected a Fellow of the Royal Society in 1790. He was also appointed Physician-in-Ordinary to King George III. He continued to work and retired in 1820 before dying of tuberculosis in 1823. His sister was Joanna Baillie and who deserves a mention in what was very much a man's world. She lived between the years of 1762 until 1851 and was a well-known poet, following her aunt Anne (Home) Hunter who was John Hunter's wife and who lived from 1742 until 1821 and who was also an accomplished poet and lyricist as we have seen earlier. This was not the last time that Matthew Baillie would support John Hunter and his friend and pupil, Edward Jenner. Many years later, he would be one of the witnesses who spoke up for Jenner at the parliamentary committee that was set up many years later to decide what monetary award Jenner should receive for his tireless work regarding the achievement that he is best known for, and that is his work on the elimination of smallpox. However, that is jumping ahead many years and so we will return to the circumstances that led to Hunter's death.

Despite the quality of people supporting you, it carries little weight if so many others are against you and it wasn't that long in to the meeting when the position of the Scottish students was mentioned and Hunter had hardly begun to speak in their favour when he was contradicted by one of the other physicians present. Had Hunter been of a more placid nature, he may have been able to get through the debate, but the fiery red headed Scottish surgeon couldn't contain his anger and as the meeting descended into an angry debate, Hunter suddenly groaned, collapsed into the arms of one of the surgeons present, and died in the room, surrounded by his fellow medical surgeons whose combined talents sadly were not enough to save the great man. Edward Jenner's great mentor and friend, was dead.

Jenner was absolutely devastated by Hunter's death. Hunter had not merely mentored Jenner, the two men had become good friends, a friendship that had lasted from 1770 when Jenner had first travelled to London to study under Hunter, and ended only at the death of Jenner's teacher in 1793. Naturally, Anne and the children were grief stricken with their beloved husband and father gone, but sadly these feelings were not present with some of his colleagues. Some of them were actually more than happy at his passing, and after a meeting, actually agreed not to send condolences to his widow, which was disgraceful behaviour. Hunter's colleagues didn't have to like the man, but they could have thought of the grief suffered by his widow Anne, and the children. The death of Hunter was not their finest hour. Having said that, not everybody felt the same way as his fellow surgeons. Horace Walpole wrote to a friend of Hunter's: "It is such a blow to his family, as he was in such repute." Joseph Farington who had been a patient of Hunter's towards the end of the doctor's life wrote in his diary: "Much concerned at an acct. in the newspaper of the death of John Hunter, the excellent surgeon, to whom I was greatly obliged in the course of last summer." The press were full of praise for Hunter and his achievements and the European Magazine wrote: "He rose to a rank in his profession scarce ever remembered, that of an acknowledged superiority over the most eminent of his rivals." Perhaps therein lies the clue to the bad feeling toward Hunter from his colleagues, the use of the phrase 'acknowledged superiority' and also the use of the word 'rivals' as opposed to 'colleagues'. Either way, the actions of his fellow physicians in not sending condolences is terribly harsh and does no credit to his fellow physicians at St George's. Another leading paper, 'The Gentleman's Magazine' said, "Hunter was an honour to his profession and to his country." Yet another paper, 'The Sun', said that… Hunter had risen from a humble carpenter to quite simply "the first surgeon in the world." Reverting a moment to Hunter's colleagues at St George's Hospital who had refused to send condolences to Hunter's widow, Anne, they went further and shortly after Hunter's passing, paid a gentleman by the name of Jesse Foot (1744–1826), £400 to write a damning biography of Hunter.

Foot was born in Charlton, Wiltshire and was a physician and biographer. He received his medical education in London and spent three years practicing medicine in the island of Nevis before returning in 1769 to become practitioner of the College of St Petersburg. Eventually he returned to London and was appointed House Surgeon in Middlesex Hospital and when his contract finished, moved to inner London to practice in Salisbury Street in the Strand. After that, he set up another practice in Dean Street, Soho.

Foot was working at the Middlesex Hospital when he was asked to write the biography on Hunter and was only too willing to undertake this project as he had always hated Hunter. Hunter had always tried to pioneer new methods of curing people whilst his colleagues, including Foot, had preferred their usual method of bleeding and purging a patient whatever illness he or she had. Despite his rather reactionary views on medicine, Foot made a very good living out of it and had also written many other biographies. Quite often the reactionary method of bleeding people who were unwell was used and this method of treating often led a patient to their death and even if they survived, it was in spite of the treatment as opposed to because of it. Much of 18th century medicine had been handed down from the Greeks and these methods that had been handed down from generation to generation were meekly accepted by the likes of Foot and he, along with many others in the medical profession were only too happy to accept it all, whilst Hunter was not.

John Hunter has to be recognised as one of the great physicians of his time. Whilst other surgeons and physicians were happy merely to accept without question what their textbooks told them, Hunter refused to comply, and he always encouraged his pupils to question everything and find out the truth for themselves. His favourite pupil, Edward Jenner, accepted his tutor's teaching philosophy and it was a combination of Jenner's diligence and patience along with Hunter's mentoring that enabled Jenner to work out such things as the migrating habits of birds, the nesting habits of the cuckoo along with unquestionably the greatest achievement of Jenner's life, his work on the elimination of smallpox. Hunter left several publications that he had written during his medical career, the following being the most important:

'Blood, Inflammation and Gun-shot Wounds'

'Case Books'

'Essays and Observations on Natural History'

'The Natural History of the Human Teeth'

'A Practical Treatise on the Diseases of the Teeth'

'Observations and Reflections on Geology'

'Observations on the Animal Oeconomy'

'On the Structure of the Placenta'

'A Treatise on the Venereal Disease'

Hunter also left a brilliant legacy in the form of the Hunterian Museum based in London where people are able to visit today. There are no less than eight floors full of cabinets full from floor to ceiling of over 3,000 exhibits. These contain such specimens as a crocodile foetus still attached to its egg by its umbilical cord. It also has a lengthy coil of a man's large intestine. The museum is certainly not for the faint hearted but it is an extraordinary legacy of the man's work and not for nothing is he often referred to as 'The Father of Modern Medicine'.

Before we look at Jenner's work with smallpox however, we must note that on 7th July 1792, Jenner received the degree of Doctor in Medicine which was awarded him by the academic senate of St Andrews University in Scotland. To obtain this degree, it was necessary to purchase a gift to the university along with a letter of recommendation from two recognised doctors, which in Jenner's case were John Hickes, a doctor based in Gloucester and Caleb Hillier Parry, who had a practice in Bath and who was a friend from Jenner's schooldays. The recommendation from the two doctors certified that "candidate for the degree of Doctor in Medicine, is a gentleman of respectable character, that he has received a liberal and classical education, that he has attended a complete course of lectures in the several branches of Medicine, and that from 'personal knowledge', we judge him worthy of the honour of a doctor's degree in Medicine." Both men knew Jenner well and had collaborated in various pieces of work with Jenner over the years. The minute records of the Senatus Academicus for the 8th July read as follows:

"The University agree to confer the Degree of Doctor in Medicine on Mr Edward Jennings (sic), Surgeon, of Berkeley in the County of Gloucester, upon recommendation from J. H. Hickes, M.D. of Gloucester, and C. H. Parry, M.D. of Bath." So there we have it, Jenner had his degree even if the university that awarded it to him couldn't spell his name correctly.

Buying degrees from universities was common practice in Scotland and it arose in order to stop the monopoly of the degree gained from Oxford and Cambridge. A Royal Commission was set up to look at this practice of purchasing degrees and their report of 1830 criticised the system which resulted in the Scottish universities abandoning it but in fact by that time the monopoly that Oxford and Cambridge had enjoyed for so long had been largely broken.

According to Dr John Baron, (1786–1851), Jenner's biographer, Jenner had decided to obtain a degree as he found the continual round of visits of a country doctor rather irksome. Most of his friends and his family were always referring to him as 'Doctor' anyway, and three years earlier he had written as such to his friend from schooldays, the Revd John Clinch in Newfoundland. Jenner writes:

"A man must be guided by his own genius; indeed, without a good portion of this a physician must ever cut a poor figure; and if he should be a man of fine feelings he must often be subject to unpleasant sensations within himself. Something new is forever presenting itself – neither book, lectures, nor the longest experience are sufficient to store his mind with the indescribable something a man of our profession should possess... For it is by appearances...not from a real knowledge of things, that the world...form a judgement. A look of significance, a peculiar habit, and a very scanty acquaintance with the human machine, will make a man pass current for a great physician."

Be that as it may, it would appear that his practice after that changed very little and there is direct evidence to support this view. He kept a visiting book during 1794 detailing fees received and his outgoings along with the type of consultations which more or less stayed constant throughout that year.

At the end of 1794, Jenner became ill and was struck down with what was then known as Typhus but in retrospect, was quite possibly typhoid fever, which was a very serious contagious disease carried in unclean water. The difference between the two diseases was not discovered until a long time after by Sir William Jenner (1815–1898), who despite having the same name as Edward Jenner and despite both being medical men, were not related to each other. Although this book is about Edward Jenner and his work, Sir William's achievements were immense and warrant a few lines here.

Sir William Jenner, 1st Baronet was born on 30th January 1815 in Chatham and was educated at the University College, London. He became a member of the Royal College of Surgeons of England (M.R.C.S.) in 1837 and a Fellow of the Royal College of Physicians (F.R.C.P.) in 1852. He discovered the difference between Typhus and Typhoid by working at the London Fever Hospital and published his book 'On the Identity or Non-Identity of Typhus and Typhus Fever' in 1850. Along with many other honours, he became a Fellow of the Royal Society (F.R.S.) in 1864. Sir William received honorary degrees from the University of Oxford, University of Cambridge, and University of Edinburgh. In 1861 he was appointed Physician Extraordinary to Queen Victoria and the following year, Physician-in-Ordinary to the Queen followed by being appointed Physician-in-Ordinary to the then Prince of Wales who would later rule as King Edward V11 on the death of the Queen in 1901. Jenner married Adela Lucy Leman in 1858 and they had five sons and one daughter. In 1868 he was created a baronet and died in 1898.

Returning to Edward Jenner, around about this time, he involved his family in the work that he carried out. On 27th October 1794, Jenner removed a growth from the face of the Revd William Davies (1740–1817), his brother-in-law as Davies had married Jenner's sister Anne (1741–1812) in 1766. One month later, William again had minor surgery and he recorded in his accounts that he had paid Edward five guineas (£5.25p) and his nephew, Henry Jenner, two guineas (£2.10p) 'For his attendance at the operation'. By now, Henry (1767–1851) had once again become Edward's assistant. This time, Henry was older and wiser and on his uncle's advice had spent some time studying under Dr John Hunter, Edward's mentor and Henry was now able to use the letters M.D. after his name as he had become a fully qualified Doctor of Medicine. Due to some work that he had carried out for Sir Joseph Banks (1743–1820) on botanical specimens, he was made a Fellow of the Linnaean Society, a very prestigious body. Henry seemed to be settling down as apart from his qualifications and having acquired a great deal of knowledge from Hunter, he also married Susanna Pearce (1766–98) in 1792 who was the daughter of a friend of Jenner's and who was also a naturalist.

All looked to be going well for the Jenner family until late in 1795. Edward and Catherine had been away from Berkeley and had returned in the autumn of that year. Jenner's brother Henry (1736–98) and his wife Anne, née Hazeland, who he had married in 1762, had ten children, and the first born of these was Stephen (1764–95) who had a wife, Elizabeth (nee Gale). Stephen was of course, one of the brothers of Jenner's nephew Henry (1767–1851) whose father was Henry (1736–98) who was Edward's brother. Stephen was a Lieutenant in the West Indian Regiment and was on board the transport ship 'Catherine', when along with two other transport ships, 'Venus' and 'Piedmont' were shipwrecked during a terrible storm that had blown up on 18th November, 1795 and were dashed on to Chesil Bank, off the coast of Dorset. Three other merchant ships, 'Thomas', 'Golden Grove' and 'Aeolus' were also wrecked. WF Shrapnell, a surgeon in the South Gloucestershire Militia who at that time were stationed in Weymouth, went down to the wreckage to see if he could find out where the bodies were, and Stephen's in particular so that he could give the Jenner family as much information as possible. However, it was a difficult task to identify any of the bodies because of the battering that they had suffered due to the ferocity of the storm. Three were buried in Wykenham Churchyard with full military honours and it was thought that one of the bodies might have been that of

Stephen. A Mrs Charlotte Smith wrote about the tragedy: "The Chesil Bank was strewn for about two miles with dead bodies of men and animals, with pieces of wreck and piles of plundered goods which groups of people were at work carrying away." She continued, "Lieutenant Jenner was the representative of an ancient and much respected family in Gloucestershire…he possessed all those engaging and manly qualities which belong to the gentleman, the officer, and the friend."

Just who Mrs Charlotte Smith was, we are not quite sure, but she clearly had a great deal of admiration and affection for the Jenner family to have written such a letter.

The loss of men was colossal. Two hundred and thirty-four bodies were found and very few had survived and the scene was one of utter carnage. WF Shrapnel, an army surgeon stationed at Portland wrote Dr Jenner a fairly lengthy letter pointing out, as if it were necessary, the cruelties of both the sea, which men could not control, and the cruelties of the plundering, which men could control. This is the letter he wrote to Jenner:

Nov. 22nd, 1795
My Dear Friend,

Although exhausted with fatigue I cannot avoid telling you that I have every reason to believe my friend Stephen was unfortunately lost in the 'Catherine' Transport. I volunteered the command of a party of forty men of our regiment to bury the dead… I have been three days officiating in the melancholy ceremony. I could not distinguish his features…but I have lodged in coffins two bodies which I thought resembled him. I will faithfully see them interred, with the bodies of fourteen other officers, with all military honours… The labour I and my party have gone through I look back with astonishment… We had every day six miles to walk on a bank of pebbles…and then they (the bodies) lay scattered for two miles further. We have buried about two hundred and thirty.

All this was very bad news for Edward and Catherine but despite their sadness at the dreadful events, Jenner's health improved greatly from the typhoid fever that he had previously suffered from and he started to visit Cheltenham in September, 1795, soon after the terrible accident that had taken his nephew Stephen. Much as they mourned the loss of Stephen, Edward knew that moping all day every day at home would do no good to either himself or Catherine because whilst they loved their house in Berkeley, and Berkeley itself, it had none of the diversions that Cheltenham could provide. Jenner both worked and played in the town and along with Catherine, played a part in the Cheltenham society. Jenner was as said many times before, a country boy at heart, but he and Catherine enjoyed the social events that were held in the town. Another bonus for the Jenners was that King George III was in the town. Jenner wrote to his nephew William:

"I pick up a few Fees – Mrs J has puff'd me too high in her Letter – however, fortune has shewed me the 'Countenance of George the third thirteen times since this day se'enight.' Famous!" Jenner went on to write: "This was owing to a coincidence of Events that cannot come from the nature of things be lasting."

Edward and Catherine eventually left Cheltenham to return to Berkeley, partly because they wished to as although a very sociable man, he and Catherine both loved Berkeley and Chantry Cottage, their beautiful home. But there was also another reason. There was a murder trial that Edward's nephew, Henry (1767–1851) was involved in along with Edward himself, who testified for the prosecution. Jenner found himself involved when the case came to court, whereas Henry was involved earlier in the proceedings. The murder actually took place either late in the evening of 16th April 1794, or the early hours of the following day. In the early hours of 17th April, Henry Jenner was asked to come at once by the landlord of a small cottage on the Bristol Road in Swanley. When Henry arrived, he found a man in his middle years named William Reed who had scalp wounds to his head which were bleeding profusely. Henry cleaned the wound and bound the man's head. He then left but he promised to return the following day.

What had happened to the unfortunate Mr Reed was as follows. He had a wife named Mary who was a great deal younger than her husband and a brother named James Watkins. These three along with a medical student named Robert Edgar were travelling from Poole to Bristol. It transpired that Mary had married William Reed for his money that she would naturally inherit on the husband's death. Soon after the wedding, William Reed had started to feel unwell and so he had made out a will leaving his widow £6,000 which in these days would be worth something in the region of £360,000 in today's value, an astronomical amount for a woman of limited means in the 18th century. It was believed that his wife Mary was slowly poisoning him in order to instigate her husband's death so that she would inherit his fortune. The brother, James, and William Reed's wife Mary decided to join forces and murder William Reed. The idea was for the brother to finish off the murder of Reed and be given £200 for his efforts which seems a strangely small amount given the amount his sister would inherit. The group stopped off at Swanley on the night of the 15th. Mary gave her husband more poison before Edgar then beat her husband very badly with a broomstick. Reed was still clinging on to life and Edgar was going to finish him off the next night but the landlord became very frightened and it was then that he called Henry Jenner in. As said earlier, Henry patched Reed up by cleaning the wound and bandaging the patient's head. After Henry had left the cottage, Mary put her husband to bed again and asked her brother to finish Reed off. William Reed did die, but from the poison rather than the beating. Henry found him on the 18th and gave some of Reed's vomit to a dog which quickly died. It was at this point that Henry asked his Uncle Edward for help. Jenner analysed the contents of Reed's stomach and found both arsenic and mercury. Edward found another dog and gave this dog vomit from Reed just to make doubly sure that Reed had been poisoned and this dog too died. Although by now it was pretty obvious how Reed had died, Jenner, ever the methodical man, called in his great friend, Charles Brandon Trye who by now was a surgeon at the Gloucester Infirmary and he confirmed that it was poison that had killed William Reed. Mary Reed and James Watkins ran from the scene to try and effect an escape. It did neither of them any good. Watkins committed suicide by shooting himself whilst Mary was captured by the Bow Street Runners, the forerunners to the present-day Metropolitan Police Force. She was tried at Gloucester Assizes and found guilty of murder by poisoning and Edward was called by the prosecution to give evidence against her. Although the murder had taken place in April 1794, the trial did not happen for another two years, and was just before Jenner was to embark on a medical journey that was to change the health of people not just in Britain, but of the world. Edward Jenner was at last given the opportunity to seek a cure for the scourge of smallpox.

-oOOo-

Chapter 8

Georgian Kings, the City of Bath and
the Town of Cheltenham

The city of Bath along with the town of Cheltenham has been mentioned in the text a few times, but not enough to make the reader clear as to its importance to the middle and upper classes in the eighteenth century along with Jenner personally. A very close friend of Jenner's, Dr Caleb Hillier Parry (1755–1822) practiced in Bath for many years and most of the famous people of the time would have lived there for part of their lives, and if they didn't live there, like Jenner, they would often travel from their homes to stay there for a holiday. One of the most famous people to have stayed in Bath was Jane Austen (1775–1817) who lived there for a time and while her stay there was not to her liking, the city is often featured in her books. The reason that she lived there at all was due to the fact that her parents, the Revd George Austen (1731–1805) and her mother Cassandra (1739–1827) had decided to retire from the Hampshire village of Steventon and move back to Bath, the city in which they were married in April 1764. Jane's lack of enthusiasm for Bath had nothing to do with the place itself but she was forced to go to the many balls that her parents went to. She felt that as a writer, she had nothing in common with the men who were presented to her as possible future husbands, whilst all she wanted to do was to return to the Hampshire countryside and lead a peaceful life with her much loved sister, Cassandra (1773–1845), which eventually she was able to do. Whilst in Bath, Jane suffered from depression and a complete inability to write, but eventually, she and her sister Cassandra along with her by now widowed mother, also named Cassandra, left Bath and were able to live in the country again. No sooner did she arrive in the cottage that her wealthy brother Edward had provided for them, she started writing again going on to finish the stunning books that sell well even in the present day.

Bath is the largest city in Somerset and apart from London, the country's capital city, the best known of all our cities. It became a spa town with the Latin name of Aquae Sulis (the waters of Sulis) and was built in or around the year 60AD when the Romans built the baths. The abbey was founded in the 7th century but was rebuilt in the 12th and 16th centuries. In the 17th century, it became very fashionable to travel to Bath to take the waters as they were seen as a cure for just about any medical problem. Despite their fine clothes and manners however, it has to be said that the 18th century Georgians would only take a bath about once a year and so a dip into the waters at Bath would probably have made them feel better anyway and give the Bath waters a reputation for curative powers that they almost certainly did not deserve.

Bath as we know it today was largely designed by an architect called John Wood the Elder (1704–1754). It is quite correctly called a Georgian city as the four kings that ruled whilst the houses were being built were all called George and we will look at them in a short while.

We are not sure of the actual date but John the Elder was born in 1754 in Twerton near Bath, that much we do know. The city was crafted from Bath stone and includes the Royal Crescent, Circus, Pump Rooms and Assembly Rooms amongst others. The layout of Bath was designed by John Wood the Elder and these are some of the most famous places in the city. No thanks are due to many people and organisations such as the Corporation, churchmen, money lenders, landowners and moneymen amongst others all of whom put obstacles in his way. However, they underestimated Wood's determination to build the classic city of his dreams. He contacted Robert Gay (1676–1738), the famous surgeon and politician. Gay was the owner of Barton Farm Estate which was situated in the Manor of Walcot just outside the city walls, and it was on these grounds that Wood established the architectural style that became so popular with the architects who followed him. Gay was an MP as well as a surgeon and was MP for Bath from 1720 until 1722, and again from 1727 until 1734. His contribution to the project was not forgotten and there is a street named after him in Bath where Jane Austen lived for a time. John Wood the Elder built many classical pieces, such as the St John's Hospital, Queen Square, Prior Park, and the Royal Mineral Water Hospital, along with too many to mention here, but his final masterpiece has to be the Circus, named because it consists of a circle of thirty houses. Sadly, Wood the Elder did not live to see it completed and in fact only lived long enough to see the first stone laid. Naturally his passing was a very sad event for his family, but future generations can be thankful that his son, John Wood the Younger (1728–81), also became an architect and he finished the mammoth job that his father started. He was born in Bath on 25th February 1728 and was baptised in Bath Abbey. The great pieces that he finished were along with others, the Circus which had been started by his father, the Royal Crescent, Assembly Rooms, and he basically finished creating the Bath that is known and loved today. After the Circus, his next project was to build Gay Street to connect Queen Square and the Circus. During the 1770s, a slightly more severe classical style became popular, and it was Wood the Younger who took this style and virtually made it his own and this is shown by the style of the hot bath, Royal Crescent, and Bath Assembly Rooms. It is a style copied extensively in places such as Bristol, Brighton and London amongst others.

John Wood the Younger left a fine legacy as Bath is visited and loved today by millions, both residents and visitors, be they British people or foreign people on holiday. He has left us fine buildings but many feel that his finest achievement was the Royal Crescent. He died on 16th August 1781 and is buried next to his father in the chancel of St Mary's Church, Swainswick, a village three miles north east of Bath. When the city was finished, many famous people of the day would go there, and along with his many friends and medical colleagues, there would be a certain doctor named Edward Jenner who along with these friends, would dine out together creating a convivial atmosphere. It was one such evening that Jenner showed his colleagues about the myth that if you put your finger just above a flame lit by a candle, that it would be less painful than if you placed your finger much lower, nearer the base of the flame in fact. Remembering his great mentor, John Hunter's advice which was not just to explain certain actions, but to prove or disprove them by demonstration, he decided to show to the assembled friends the truth of what he had been saying which was the opposite of the accepted wisdom of the day. One evening when Jenner was dining with some friends and the wine was flowing nicely, he decided to put his theory to the test and he placed his finger just near enough to the top of the flame that it was barely touching, but had to remove the finger speedily as the pain was hard to bear. He then placed his finger right through the flame whilst virtually touching the base and was able to leave it there for a longer period than the first attempt. A small event, of course, but it lay comfortably beside all of Hunter's teachings which stayed with Jenner throughout the rest of his life. Unlike Bath, Cheltenham is designated a town but the buildings are of the Regency period as are those in

Bath. Cheltenham played an important part in Edward and Catherine's life as they travelled to Cheltenham in 1788, the year of their marriage. However, it was also in 1788 that King George III and Queen Charlotte visited it when the King first experienced early symptoms of his subsequent illness. After the monarch's visit, Cheltenham became a very famous place and like Bath, was the place to be seen if you were either a member of the ruling class or the ever-growing middle classes.

The town itself is situated on the edge of the Cotswolds. Over the years, a gentleman by the name of Captain Henry Skillicorne (1678–1763) has been seen as the first person who first discovered a way of exploiting the visitors who came to the town for their various ailments from the mineral springs. He made the town his home when he moved there in 1738 and immediately made improvements in order to attract more visitors.

Any healing process that worked either in Cheltenham or Bath was probably due to a placebo effect, but if that was the case then the placebo effect was a powerful medicine as a great many people would visit there year after year, convinced that the waters had healing powers. When Edward and Catherine first visited there in 1788, Catherine's delicate health certainly took a turn for the better after she taken the waters. The couple loved their house, 'The Chantry' in Berkeley but Cheltenham obviously had a positive effect on both of them as they purchased a terraced house in the town, 8, St George's Place, and lived there on and off between 1795 and 1820. Edward set up practice there and continued working from there as well as Berkeley for the rest of his working life. In the 1960s, Jenner's house was demolished even after a great deal of local opposition. It is a pity that people who have power in their locality do not think ahead and cannot seem to understand that decisions made during their brief tenure cannot be overturned for future generations. As it happened, the house was re-built but unlike 'The Chantry' which is the same house that Edward and Catherine lived in, the Cheltenham house is just a copy. However, perhaps we should be grateful for that at least.

As Edward Jenner lived through what is known as the Georgian period, it may be a good idea to sketch the background of these times. Many people have a knowledge of the Tudor and Stuart period, but little is known of the Georgian period which is surprising as there were many changes made during this time and it is often referred to as 'The Age of Enlightenment'. It was populated by huge figures such as Samuel Johnson (1709–1784), who was responsible for the famous dictionary which after many years of grafting, was finished in 1755, Admiral Lord Nelson (1758–1805), who gave his life at the all-important Battle of Trafalgar which stemmed the constant threat of invasion from the French during the Napoleonic wars during that period. The first settlement of people at New South Wales which was the birthplace of the huge country that is now Australia, happened in 1788 after a suggestion by Sir Joseph Banks (1743–1820) the great botanist. Banks had visited the place years before with Captain Cook (1728–79) and declared the ground very fertile and ideal for farming and growing vegetables. However, Banks's memory was obviously hazy as it had been nearly twenty years since he had been there with Cook and the ground was anything but fertile. However, the settlers struggled for years and eventually managed to turn things round and a few generations later, the city of Sydney that we know today was built. However, Banks's mistake did not diminish his reputation and after becoming a member of the Royal Society in 1766 became its President in 1779 and he remained in that post until his death in 1820. Cook was the great naval officer who made three great trips around the world, the first trip between 1768 and 1771 was the one that Banks sailed on, the trip that made the reputations of both Cook and Banks himself. The first Governor-General of New South Wales was Admiral Arthur Phillip (1738–1814), the man who started the incredibly difficult task of creating the first settlement there and from that barren land on which he and the first settlers landed on, came the great city of Sydney. It was also this period that started our present system of cabinet government, and with it, the first ever and longest serving Prime Minister in Robert Walpole (1676–1745), but we will look at that on the next page. There are so many more influential people that it is not feasible to list them all here, but the above may hopefully give the reader an idea of the changes that came about during this period.

When we look at the monarchy at that time, it looks to us now as extraordinary that it happened at all. The new Kingdom of Great Britain was formed by the Acts of Union on 1st May 1707 which merged the countries of England and Scotland. Before the Hanoverian Kings ruled, the country was ruled by Queen Anne who was the last of the Stuart line. Queen Anne was born in 1665 and became Queen in 1702 until her death in 1714. The Act of Settlement was passed in 1701 when it was decreed that no Catholic would be able to become a ruling monarch. This left the country with a huge problem as there were no Protestants who were even close to being able to succeed to the throne.

The nearest Protestant was the man who would become George I and he was a very distant member of the Royal Family, and was something like fifty places away to succeed to the throne of Great Britain. He was also German and spoke no English whatsoever, and whilst it may seem ridiculous to many people today that we should have to take someone so obviously completely out of touch with Britain, its people along with its Royal Family, the government saw no other option. The man who spoke no English and had no interest in becoming King was persuaded to become the first of our Hanoverian monarchs ruling from 1714 until his death in 1727. It is strange that George I took the throne but in fact, in many ways it was a good thing as his obvious faults led to the creation of the system of cabinet government that we have today. George I was born in 1660 so he was already well over fifty years old when he came to the throne of a foreign country, and because his interest in being King of Britain was minimal to the point of being non-existent, returned to Hanover as often as he could, often months at a time. In order that he could do this, he left the country in the hands of a selected few members of parliament who would run the country and keep the King informed of events that were taking place in Britain when he made one of his rare visits to this country. A chairman had to be chosen from this group of men and the King asked Sir Robert Walpole (1676–1745) to take charge of affairs and report back to him each time he returned to Britain. Walpole thus became the first Prime Minister although the title at that time was in fact First Lord of the Treasury. Walpole held this post from 1721 until 1742 making him not only the first Prime Minister but also the person who held the post longer than any other, although William Pitt the Younger (1759–1806) ran him a close second in terms of the length of time that he was in post. Pitt held the post twice, from 1783 until 1801, and again from 1804 up to his early death in 1806.

When George I died in 1727, his son, George (1683–1760), took the throne and ruled as George II from 1727 until 1760. George II was born on 30th October, 1683 and came to the throne in 1727 aged forty-three years. He was crowned in Westminster Abbey on 11th October of that year less than three weeks short of his forty fourth birthday. He had married Caroline Brandenburgh-Ansbach (1683–1737) and although the king had had many affairs during their marriage, he adored Caroline and just before she died when he was holding her hand by her bedside, she made him promise to marry again. However, George II refused, telling her that he would continue to have affairs but that he would never remarry and he died on 25th October 1760, a few days short of his 77th birthday having kept his promise. George II had many faults, but lack of courage was not one of them, as he was the last king who would lead his troops from the front when in battle, the last one being the Battle of Dettington on 27th June 1743.

Many people assume that George III was the son of George II, but this is not the case at all. George III's father was in fact Frederick Lewis, Prince of Wales who was born on 1st February 1707 and died on 31st March 1751. He predeceased his father by nine years which is why the monarchy skipped a generation. Whilst no one would wish an early death on anyone, it seems that it may have been a blessing for the country that Frederick did not take the throne and that his son, George, did. It is a trait with Hanoverian monarchs that father hates son and vice versa but it would appear that George II and Prince Frederick turned it into an art form. With Frederick, it was not only his father who didn't like him, but Robert Walpole, the Prime Minister said of him, that he was a 'poor, weak, irresolute, false, lying, dishonest contemptible wretch that nobody loves, that nobody believes, that nobody will trust.' It is not a description that would look good on anyone's CV. Even his mother, Queen Caroline, said of Frederick, that he was, 'an avaricious, sordid monster and that she could not bear the sight of him.' She also said, "My dear first born is the greatest ass and the greatest liar and the greatest canaille and the greatest beast in the whole world and I most heartily wish he were out of it."

We are not quite sure how Frederick died; some say that he was playing tennis and was hit by the tennis ball whilst another view has it that it was a cricket ball. Either way, it caused him to have a painful abscess that burst which caused the Prince of Wales to die at Cliveden House on 31st March 1751 at the age of just forty-four years. It seemed that the Royal family, government and the population at large were able to cope with his loss with great forbearance. In case anyone should doubt this, then we have the words of his father, George II, to prove it. The King's cutting words uttered at the end of the year were – "This has been a fatal year to my family. I have lost my eldest son but I was glad of it." If all of that wasn't enough, Queen Caroline on her deathbed said: "At least I shall have one comfort in having my eyes eternally closed – I shall never see that monster again."

So there we have it. The country was spared probably the worst king in the world, although as the future King George IV had yet to be born, it is a question that will always remain unanswered.

Frederick's son, George, the Prince of Wales was born on 4th June 1738 and after a very strict upbringing took the throne on the death of his grandfather, George II on 25th October 1760. Due to his strict upbringing which amongst other things, meant enduring long periods of study during the day, he was the first of the Georgian Kings to be born in England and unlike his grandfather, and great grandfather, wished very much to be seen as English. He spoke English fluently having been born in the country, and was a very different person to the previous Georgian Kings. George III was expected to marry and produce a son and heir like his predecessors but his choice of a bride was limited. Under the terms of the 1701 Act of Settlement, his bride would have to be a protestant as opposed to her being a catholic and she should not be a commoner. It seems that he fell in love with Lady Sarah Lennox (1745–1826) who was the sister-in-law of Henry Fox (1705–74), the 1st Baron Holland but in the end nothing came of the romance. Shortly afterwards, George settled for an arranged marriage to Sophie Charlotte, Princess of Mecklenburg-Strelitz (1744–1818). Baron Holland was none too pleased with this. He was keen to get involved with the royal circle and he had set his heart on his daughter Sarah Lennox marrying the young king, and failing that would have been quite happy for her to be the monarch's mistress. He wanted high connections and he wanted money and influence, but he was distrusted by the establishment and didn't get his way. Instead, Lord Bute (1713–92) became Prime Minister but was a reluctant holder of the post as he felt that he wasn't up to the job, and as it happened, he was the Prime Minister for only 344 days between 1762 and 1763. Because of the loss of George the third's father and grandfather, Bute was seen as the new King's advisor, and Bute became Prime Minister by chance having met Frederick, the Prince of Wales and became friendly with him. When Frederick died, Baron Holland had wanted to supplant Lord Bute as Prime Minister but he was neither given that post nor did his sister-in-law, Sarah Lennox become the King's wife; she was shifted off to one side to allow the new King to marry Charlotte of Mecklenburg-Strelitz with Henry Fox (Baron Holland) left on the sidelines with some influence now that he was a Baron, but it was not what he wanted.

The marriage between George and Charlotte took place on 8th September 1761 a mere two days after the Princess had arrived in England. Although she spoke virtually no English when she arrived, she picked the language up quickly and their marriage was a long and happy one. Unlike many Monarchs, George III was very frugal and there is a famous cartoon of the Royal couple eating a simple breakfast of boiled eggs, with the Queen being shown as ugly and with half her teeth missing. Cartoonists of the day were very ruthless whether with politicians or royalty.

The King's reign was an eventful one, with probably two main subjects that stick in the mind more than others. On 4th June 1775, the American colonies declared their independence from Britain, the sticking point being that the thirteen colonies on the East coast objected to paying taxes when they had no vote. On 5th March 1770, there had been a big confrontation between the people of Boston and a contingent of British redcoat soldiers which led to the death of five Boston residents. This led to fury being felt by the Bostonians to such a degree that the British government led by Prime Minister Lord North (1732–92) back peddled and reversed all the taxes that had been levied by Charles Townshend (1725–67) except for one, the tax on tea.

These concessions were not enough however, and matters came to a head when on 16th March 1773, three ships entered Boston harbour only to find that there were thousands of locals determined that they should leave without any tax being paid. The Collector of Customs was adamant that the ships would not leave without the tax being collected and there was an inevitable collision course whereby the Bostonians emptied the ships of the tea and threw the cargo into the harbour. This action became known as the Boston Tea Party. Both the King and Prime Minister Lord North were infuriated by this and in March 1774, one year after the confrontation at Boston, the British government passed a series of acts clamping down on the Americans but they misjudged the situation completely and only succeeded in unifying the American people and almost certainly making war inevitable.

This then led to the unification of the colonies into a unified Congress, and whilst they initially tried to stay loyal to the crown, soon realised that the King, along with the British Parliament were completely indifferent to their views and after a Continental Army was formed led by George Washington (1732–99), spasmodic fighting took place at first but the Americans were finally convinced that avoiding total war was impossible. The famous Declaration of Independence was drawn up by Thomas Jefferson (1743–1826) and on 4th July 1776 was adopted by the thirteen colonies. War was now inevitable.

Although at first it appeared that the British could not possibly lose as the trained and armed Redcoat Soldiers were up against no organised resistance or indeed, at the beginning, there wasn't at that time a continental army for them to fight against. However, things were about to change as the French were persuaded to join the American forces, and when the Continental Army was eventually formed it turned the war on its head. The soldiers were issued with uniforms and guns and the picture looked very different now and, in the end, it was a war that Britain could not win. The reason being that the British commanders had to make instant decisions depending on what was going on at the time as there weren't the communications that we have today. The war was being fought 3,000 miles away from the British troops' political masters and in the end, after years of bitter fighting, General Charles Cornwallis (1738–1805) surrendered to the combined American and French armies on 17th October, 1781. Cornwallis was an exceptional soldier who was trusted by both the British King, George III, and Lord North, the Prime Minister. Cornwallis had previously had victories at New York, Brandywine and Camden and it was a bitter pill for him to swallow, for him to capitulate to an army that only a few years previously had not existed.

Both the King, and the Prime Minister, Lord North, were horrified. When told about the surrender, the two men took it in completely different ways.
Lord North opened his arms as if he had taken a musket ball to the chest, and pacing up and down the room in Downing Street, exclaimed wildly: "O God, it is all over!" He repeated this several times and was totally distraught. The King, however, reacted in a very different manner, he seemed to not understand the significance of Cornwallis's surrender and was almost in denial, even thinking that the British troops could fight on. However, they couldn't and the King could do nothing but to accept the situation. Lord North had been Prime Minister since 1770 and had few enemies, indeed, he enjoyed a certain affection from members both sides of the house, but now that the war had been lost, it was clear that his days as Prime Minister were over and he resigned the position in March 1782. There was a period of political instability for the next eighteen months when Britain had three short term Prime Ministers until the brilliant William Pitt the Younger (1759–1806), took the office on 19th December 1783 at the age of just twenty-three years. When he took his seat for the first time opposite Charles James Fox and the Whig opposition, they roared with laughter at one so young taking office, thinking that he would be out of office in six weeks, but as it turned out, he served as Prime Minister from 1783 until 1801 and again from 1804 until 1806 when he died on 23rd January 1806 at the age of just forty six years.

That then covers the first major problem that King George III had to deal with during his reign – the war with America. But there was a second major problem, and that was the King's health. In October 1788, the possibility arose that would test the nerve of the members of parliament, none more so than the Prime Minister, William Pitt the Younger (1759–1806), who despite his age, had already held office for five years. In the summer of 1788, the King was not feeling that well, suffering from a series of bilious attacks coupled with very painful stomach cramps which led to several eminent doctors being called upon to wait upon him, including the famous English physician, Sir George Baker (1722–1809) F.R.S., F.S.A., who was a recognised authority on lead poisoning. Baker had been elected President of the College of Physicians no less than five times but the King had such a low opinion of the medical profession, that he refused to take any notice of any of the doctors who were in attendance, not even the great Sir George Baker. Given the medical treatment that he later had, it is easy to understand why the King was so distrustful of doctors. The team of doctors who had been called in to treat he King weren't actually brought in until October of that year because by then his condition had become worse. Despite being the top physicians of the day, they really hadn't the first clue as to what was wrong with him but in the end, made the collective decision that he was suffering from gout. As it happened, they hadn't much chance of curing the King anyway as he refused to take any of the medicine that they prescribed to him, and the King took the matter into his own hands. He decided to visit the spa town of Cheltenham where he took the waters after which he seemed to improve. As a result of this, he visited several places in the west country including the Abbey Church in Tewksbury, Gloucester Cathedral, and Worcester Cathedral among others.

After visiting these places, he returned to Windsor Castle whereupon he immediately became very ill indeed. However, his illness was never consistent, it came and went back and forth; some days he seemed perfectly normal but the next he was completely out of control. The doctors were at a loss as to how to handle the situation and even in his calmer moments, the King was not sure what was happening to him. During one of these moments he confided in his second and also his favourite son, Frederick, the Duke of York (1764–1827), "I wish to God I may die, for I am going to be mad."

It has to be said that father and his son, George, the Prince of Wales, (1762–1830), were totally different in their personalities and beliefs, and the King's illness was almost advantageous for George, the King's first-born son who would inherit the throne if his father died. Prime Minister William Pitt the Younger and the King wished Pitt to stay in that post. However, should the worst happen and the King died, it was certain that Pitt would be deposed by George, the Prince of Wales and replaced by a Whig government headed by the brilliant but mercurial Charles James Fox (1749–1806). The other danger was that if the king lived but was seen to be unable to discharge his duties, then Prince George would become Regent and rule in his father's place until such time as his father died and he would then take the throne in his place. William Pitt knew only too well the danger signs and kept stalling whilst the opposition were putting pressure on him to produce a Regency Bill for the house to vote on.

As it happened, after about four months, Pitt could stall no longer and on 5th February 1789, the Regency Bill was presented to the House of Commons and then eleven days later to the Lords on 16th February. Then an extraordinary thing happened; with the sort of timing that you wouldn't believe if you read it in a novel, the very next day, on the 17th, the doctors put out a bulletin saying that the King had made a complete recovery and was fully fit to resume his duties. Pitt's Premiership had been saved by just twenty-four hours, whilst during the same period of time, Fox's bid for power had been thwarted. The man mainly credited for having cured the King was Dr Francis Willis (1717–1807), who ran an asylum at Greatford Hall, Lincolnshire for many years and it has to be said that he had a fairly good record in helping people with mental illnesses. He had been called in by the Queen and after appearing before a Commons Committee on 4th December, 1788, he had assured the members that he could cure the King. However, the cure wasn't permanent and in 1811, the King declined to such an extent that his son, George, the Prince of Wales, ruled as the Prince Regent until the King died at Windsor on 29th January 1820, blind and virtually deaf and living in a sad twilight world until he passed away. He lies buried in the chapel at Windsor Castle with Queen Charlotte whose own death preceded that of the King's, she having died on 17th November, 1818 at Kew, Richmond, with her eldest son, the Prince Regent by her side. The King was completely unaware of her death.

It was a very sad ending for a man who had been a popular King, and along with his wife Charlotte, to whom he had always remained completely faithful, he had lived a frugal and sober life. History hasn't always treated him very kindly, referring to him as 'the mad King' and 'the King that lost America' whereas with present day knowledge of medicine it is not thought that he was insane but suffering from a disease called porphyria, an illness that brings on bouts of insanity. It was a lonely and confused end to a man who wanted so much to do his duty and to serve his country as well as he was able.

The public would soon find out that with the coming of George IV, the fourth Georgian Monarch, that they would have a very different King to the one that they had just lost, and a King who had his own unique way of spending the nation's money. Charming on the surface certainly, and a lover of the arts, but a very flawed man for such an onerous task.

George Augustus Frederick was the first child to be born to King George III and Queen Charlotte and he came into the world on 12th August 1762, being born at St James's Palace. He was quickly made the Prince of Wales, and he was the first of fifteen children who were born to his parents.

His brother Frederick (1763–1827), quickly followed and after an initial happy childhood, the two boys, after reaching the ages of eleven and ten years respectively, were soon to be schooled in the classics over long hours and they were subject to a very strict regime. The reason for them being schooled separately from the other children was the fact that they became harder to handle and they were taught by several different tutors, the common thread running between them all being the harsh treatment that they meted out to the boys. The timetable that the royal children were forced to adhere to had them starting lessons at 7am and finishing at 8pm, a very long day for anyone at that age. It was obviously too much for children but it has to be said that the Prince of Wales learned quickly, and was excellent in French, German and Italian.

As said before, it was a constant theme amongst Georgian Kings that they did not get on well with their sons and vice versa, and this was beginning to happen with the young Prince of Wales and his father. George III had been a good father and often played with his children when they were young, but now that the prince was older and beginning to develop his own opinions on subjects, their vastly differing personalities lead to permanent collision courses. These never stopped during their entire lives which was not a surprise given that the King was a sober and frugal man, whilst his son turned into someone who simply never stopped spending. There was a habit amongst the aristocracy of not actually paying their bills on time whilst some never settled their debts at all. If the new King was spending heavily, then it must be hoped that he paid his bills as there were astronomical amounts involved and businesses would have disappeared if the amounts weren't settled.

Stepping back from 1820 when he came to the throne to 1780 when he was still the Prince of Wales, it was when he reached the age of eighteen that he moved away from his parents and lived at Carlton House that he really cut loose and spent most of his time gambling, drinking and womanising. It was no surprise that he became friendly with the famous politician, Charles James Fox (1749–1806), the son of Henry Fox, the 1st Baron Holland, and one of the most famous and brilliant Whig politicians of the time. Despite the fact that Charles James always looked, and almost certainly was, permanently dirty and dishevelled, he was nonetheless a brilliant orator and could hold audiences, including Tory politicians, spellbound with his speeches. He was hated by George III and the effect he was having on his son, especially as he, Fox, supported the Americans during their fight for independence and also the French revolution which led to much blood being spilt. However, against that, in Fox's favour was the fact that he hated slavery and was very supportive of William Wilberforce's (1759–1833) long campaign against this barbaric trade.

In 1783, the Prince reached the age of twenty-one years, and he was given a grant of £60K per annum from Parliament and a further £50K per annum from his father. Given that to reach a figure that these amounts would mean in today's values, it is generally accepted that you would have to multiply the 18th century amount by sixty; however, the Prince was still not satisfied and asked his father for twice his allowance, i.e. £100K. On this, however, the King would not budge and the Prince had no choice but to accept the lower figure. As soon as he knew exactly what he was entitled to, he set about building Carlton House which was built by the great architect, John Nash (1752–1835) who was best known for buildings such as the Brighton Pavilion and Buckingham Palace. Carlton House was undoubtedly beautiful but caused the Prince to be heavily criticised for its grandiose opulence whilst tens of thousands of people in the country were living in grinding poverty. Naturally, the poor felt very aggrieved, but their complaints were backed by many in the Whig party and one such Whig was George Tierney who in 1815 pointed out that whilst the future King's subjects were living in a dreadful hand-to-mouth situation, sometimes not knowing when the next meal was coming from, the bill for the furniture had cost the nation £260,000, along with charges for upholstery which were £49,000 in just one year. On top of that, plates and jewels were in the region of £23,000 every year. These are mindboggling figures bearing in mind that they were early 19th century prices and most of them were not even single payments as the Prince would often change all this on an annual basis.

Soon after he reached the age of twenty-one, the Prince became totally infatuated with a widow some six years older than he named Mrs Maria Fitzherbert (1756–1837) and decided quite quickly that he wanted her as his bride. It was accepted in those days that men such as the Prince of Wales could take as many mistresses as they wanted to, but marriage to Mrs Fitzherbert was out of the question. For the marriage to take place legally, it would have to have the approval of King George III and the Privy Council as required by the Royal Marriages Act of 1772 which was never going to happen. Also, Maria was a catholic and had permission been granted, the Prince would automatically be removed from the succession by a Bill of Rights that had come about in 1689 and also by the Act of Settlement of 1701. However, that did nothing to cool his ardour and he constantly pursued her, even stooping to the extreme act of stabbing himself saying that he would commit suicide if she did not marry him.

After months of rejecting him however, she finally submitted and a totally illegal marriage was conducted between the couple on 15th December 1785 by one of the Prince's Chaplains in Ordinary. It couldn't possibly last because it was only a matter of time before the establishment would find out that their future King had entered into a totally forbidden marriage that would be annulled as soon as was possible, and that indeed happened.

The problem now was to find a suitable bride for the Prince of Wales and after much consideration of the problem the bride that was chosen was Caroline of Brunswick (1768–1821). When they met on 5th April 1795 at St James Palace, the Prince was horrified at this woman who stood before him. He found her deeply unattractive and her lack of personal hygiene offended his rather sensitive sense of smell so badly that he immediately left the room demanding to be brought a brandy as he was not feeling well.

The whole point of an arranged marriage such as this, is for the couple to produce an heir as soon as possible but the Prince went to bed with his new bride but was so revolted by her body odour that he couldn't bring himself to touch her much less be intimate with her. However, the next morning he managed to make love with her and once more the following night, after which there was never any intimacy between them.

The brief union did bring a little baby girl who they christened Charlotte who was born the following year, 1796, but sadly died in 1817 aged just twenty-one years old.

George IV started his rule not as King but as Prince Regent in 1811 due to his father's severe illness and ruled as the King in his own right from 29th January 1820 when his father passed away until his own death on 29th June 1830.

He left a legacy of beautiful architecture and buildings which take their name from his reign as the Prince Regent. However, he was totally irresponsible when it came to money, spending way over his income when the country was full of people who were starving at a time when there was no social security benefit or financial help of any kind for people in their position. His father, George III, was popular, and with Queen Charlotte, lived frugally and would often pass the time of day with local agricultural workers when out riding, hence his nickname of Farmer George. His son, King George IV however, was almost completely unmourned. On his death in 1830, there being no living heir to the throne, it passed to his younger brother, William, the Duke of Clarence (1765–1837) who ruled for seven years as William IV until his death in 1837 which is when the Georgian period ended and the Victorian age commenced.

How interested Edward Jenner was with Royalty we are not quite sure, but as he was born in 1749 and lived until 1823, he lived under three monarchs, George II who was alive between Jenner's birth until he, the King, died in 1760, and George III took the throne until 1820 when he died three years before Jenner, and the last three years of his life, Jenner's monarch was George IV, the appalling spendthrift King.

It is difficult to find anything in writing to allow us to find any way that would enable us to know what Jenner's opinion of the Monarchy was, but it is probably correct to think of him as a person who thought favourably of the institution. Jenner lived in a time where there was no mass communication as there is today, and he was certainly no republican revolutionary – he left the revolutionary side to his approach to medicine.

-oOOo-

Chapter 9

Jenner's Work on Smallpox

Although Jenner had many achievements to his name, the launching of the first hot air balloon in this country, the migration of birds, his work on angina and the nesting habits of the cuckoo to name but a few, it is here that we come to the work that he is most noted for. It is the subject that he first thought about way back in his student days in 1768, even before he met Hunter, let alone study under him. Jenner was subject to the horrors of the then treatment for smallpox when he was a young boy of eight years old studying at the school of Wotton-under-Edge. The treatment that was first introduced to this country by Lady Mary Worsley Montagu (1689–1765) in 1721 left dreadful after effects on Jenner which lasted many years. It consisted of giving a healthy person a small amount of smallpox with the hope that the patient would catch the disease in a mild form, eventually recover and then be immune from the full-blown disease for the rest of his or her life. It was called inoculation or variolation which is discussed in the first chapter, variolation being a derivation of the Latin word Variola which means smallpox. This treatment for smallpox when he was just eight years old left Edward subject to terrible headaches and he became very nervous on hearing sudden noises.

Smallpox had been known about for many centuries. Rhazes, the Persian physician had written about it as far back as the 9th century. His full name was Abu Bakr Muhammad ibn Zakariyya and he was born in Iran in c. 860 AD and died in c. 932AD. He was a clever polymath and amongst other things was a noted physician, alchemist, and philosopher. He followed Hippocrates (460BC–370BC), the great Greek physician who is considered to be the 'Father of Modern Medicine' and who gave his name to the Hippocratic Oath that doctors work to this day. Rhazes also followed Galen (130AD–216AD), the name having been anglicised from the original Aelius Gelenus or Claudius Galenus, the prominent

Greek physician and philosopher who lived through the Antonine Plague and had a special knowledge of the disease which was later thought to be smallpox. Rhazes followed the work of these men but extended the analytical approach of them both. Rhazes's approach to medicine was almost akin to that of John Hunter, Edward Jenner's mentor and friend. Rhazes contributed to various fields of medicine and recorded over 200 manuscripts and is credited with various advances in medicine as well as, and here he seems to remind us of Hunter, observations and discoveries. Nine centuries ahead of Hunter, Rhazes experimented with various medicines for various illnesses, and he eventually became a very successful doctor of hospitals in Bagdad and Ray. He wrote an early book on smallpox and provided a clinical characterisation of the diseases that he wrote about. The early writings of Rhazes about the smallpox included the following:

"Smallpox appears where blood 'boils' and is infected resulting in various vapours being expelled. This juvenile blood (which looks like wet extracts appearing on the skin) is being transformed into richer blood having the colour of mature wine. At this stage, smallpox shows up essentially as 'bubbles found in wine' (as blisters)…this disease can also occur at other times (meaning not only childhood). The best thing to do during this first stage is to keep away from it, otherwise this disease might turn into an epidemic."

This description of the disease and its diagnosis was recorded in the 1911 version of the Encyclopaedia Britannica as follows:

"The most trustworthy statements as to the early existence of the diseases are found in an account by the 9th century Persian physician Rhazes by whom the symptoms were clearly described…"

So there we have proof, if proof were needed, that smallpox was known about for many years before Jenner was even born, but Jenner was determined to do all that he could to find a cure for this wretched illness where others had failed. Variolation was a cure of sorts, but it still meant that the disease could possibly kill the person who was being variolated, and it was to this end that Edward Jenner concentrated his mind to this huge problem that devastated the world. He knew that cowpox was much safer, but his job was to convince the many doubters in the medical profession that it could stop smallpox in its tracks.

After Jenner had finished schooling and had decided on a career in medicine, he remembered his treatment for smallpox a mere ten years before and thought about how to produce a safer, as well as a more effective cure for the disease.

However, he was a long way from doing anything about it as he had years of study before him and after that, many years of arguments with colleagues and friends in the profession before his ideas were accepted.

Jenner had heard many times over the years about the milkmaids who caught cowpox never actually catching smallpox. For many years he had wanted to experiment using this idea but in order to produce large numbers of people that he wished to experiment on, an outbreak of the disease would have to take place. It is ironic that in order to deliver a cure for this dreadful disease there would have to be an epidemic of smallpox for it to happen. However, his chance came in 1796 when smallpox became rife in the county.

In May 1796, a milkmaid by the name of Sarah Nelmes caught the disease of cowpox from a cow named Blossom. We cannot be one hundred percent sure of Sarah's background, but the story goes that she came from a family that were fairly wealthy. She was the daughter of a well to do farmer from Broadstone, a hamlet within the Berkeley parish. The local church at Broadstone has four Nelmes family tombs with armorial bearings which was a sure sign that the family owned a great deal of land, and with it, some not inconsiderable wealth. It may be wondered why a young woman with such a background was undertaking what to her may have been a fairly menial job, but it could well be that her father wanted her to get a hands-on experience of the farming business.

However, getting back to Jenner, he realised that if cowpox was to be an effective preventative medicine to be used for the protection of people catching smallpox, it wasn't nearly enough just to know that someone who had caught cowpox by milking a cow could protect a person from catching the more serious disease. He had to find out whether cowpox could be transferred from one human being to another, and then be effective in preventing smallpox. Jenner's immediate family probably knew of his ideas as Jenner had been thinking about this for nearly thirty years and almost certainly had talked about it many times during that time. Jenner was a sociable person, and we know that he couldn't keep quiet about his ideas either to his immediate family or some of his close medical colleagues, often to the latter's intense irritation. We can be fairly sure that his wife, Catherine, and from her, her brother, Robert Kingscote, knew, along with Jenner's brother Stephen and his sister Mary, who was married to the Revd G. C. Black, and Jenner's other sister Anne, who was married to the Revd William Davies. Apart from immediate family, he would almost certainly have told long-standing medical friends such as Caleb Hillier Parry (1755–1822), and

Charles Brandon Trye (1757–1811) amongst others. Indeed, we have learnt earlier on in the book that he had talked about the subject so much over so many years, that many of his friends had long since tired of it. This, however, was a different scenario as he was now in a position to put his ideas into practice.

The only way to see if his ideas would work would be to inoculate a healthy person with the cowpox, wait a certain amount of time, he felt about two weeks, and then inoculate that same person with smallpox and see if they caught the disease. It sounds dreadful to us today, but it should be remembered that the only cure up until that time was to inoculate a healthy person with a small amount of smallpox, hoping that they would catch a mild form of the disease, if indeed there was such a thing, and then hope that they would then be immune. Bearing these facts in mind, Jenner found no ethical problem on which he was about to embark but it does show us that the Georgian society were not actually big on health and safety.

Jenner had to find a healthy person, hopefully young as they would be less likely to have caught anything that would detract from the experiment. The next stage would be to inoculate them with the cowpox disease and let nature take its course and for that disease to develop. The symptoms were usually inflamed spots or pustules around the area of the joints on the fingers and tended to be circular with the edges around their centres which tended to be a bluish colour. It was important that the patient did not scratch these as they would probably find that other pustules on different parts of the body would appear. Swellings often appeared under the arms and the patient could well have a quickening of the pulse, a fever could develop along with joint pains and a headache and he or she might be sick. Whilst all these symptoms sound very unpleasant, they are as nothing to the symptoms that the patient would experience if he or she caught the full-blown disease of smallpox. Also, and this was the whole point of the exercise, people did not die from catching cowpox, whilst they often suffered a lingering death from the full-blown smallpox.

Jenner did not have to wait long or think too much about the person that he wanted to use for the procedures. His gardener had an eight-year-old son, James Phipps who Jenner knew to be healthy although whether young James succumbed willingly or had any choice in the matter, we do not know. The males in the Phipps' family probably went back several generations as farm labourers and each generation of the Phipps family lived in Berkeley so they almost certainly lived a hand to mouth existence without a particular trade. The parish records clearly show the births, marriages and deaths of all the Phipps.

On the 14th May 1796, Dr Edward Jenner made two incisions, both of which were about half an inch long into young James's arm using a lancet that had been dipped into the pus taken from the pustule on Sarah Nelmes' hand. He then inserted the pus into the boy's arm. After a few days, the cowpox began to take hold of the young James Phipps. Some redness showed up where the small wound caused by the lancet had been inserted, and then four or five days after that, pustules appeared. They had reddish raised edges and a sunken centre rose over them and Jenner was happy that the boy had contracted cowpox. The first part of the experiment had proved successful, that is, that the cowpox could be given from one person to another, in this case, Sarah Nelmes to James Phipps. James had indeed caught cowpox, and thankfully it was a mild form which lasted only a few days.

The second part had to be done, however, and the successful transfer of cowpox from one individual to another was quite useless unless it could be shown that the cowpox stopped the patient from catching smallpox. Jenner was a cautious man and the time from giving James Phipps the cowpox before inoculating him with smallpox would normally have been at the very least two weeks. However, he waited approximately six weeks before Phipps was variolated on 1st July and to his great relief coupled with natural elation, found the young James did not catch the dreaded disease of smallpox. On 19th July, Jenner wrote to his long-standing friend Edward Gardner:

"As I promised to let you know how I proceeded in my Inquiry into the nature of that singular disease the cowpox and being fully satisfied how much you feel interested in its success, you will be gratified in hearing that I have at length accomplish'd what I have been so long waiting for, the passing of the Vaccine Virus from one human being to another by the ordinary mode of Inoculation.

"A boy of the name of Phipps was inoculated in the arm from a Pustule on the hand of a young Woman who was infected by her Masters Cows. Having never seen the disease but in its casual way before, that is, when communicated from the Cow to the hand of the Milker, I was astonish'd at the close resemblance of the Pustules in some of their stages to the variolous Pustules. But now listen to the most delightful part of the Story. The Boy has since been inoculated for the small pox which as I ventured to predict produc'd no effect. I shall now pursue my Experiments with redoubled ardour."

One fact puzzles historians, and that is, that it seems almost certain that Jenner did not perform the variolation himself, but almost certainly left it to his nephew Henry (1767–1851) who had been so careless in earlier years when helping his uncle out concerning the work on the nesting habits of the cuckoo. However, it was almost certainly due to the fact that the Henry that Jenner had used to assist him with the work on the cuckoos was a different man to the one who carried out the variolation. This time Henry was older, hopefully wiser and was qualified to use the letters M.D. after his name and his uncle must have trusted him a great deal to allow him to carry out the procedure.

In the paragraph earlier on in the book we learnt of the name variolation which was used to carry out the treatment for smallpox brought to this country by Lady Mary Montagu, the name being the Latin derivation of variola meaning smallpox. This is where the word vaccination comes in. What Jenner hoped would be the cure for the smallpox was vaccination which was from the Latin word vaccina meaning cowpox. It was Jenner himself who invented the Latin name Variolae Vaccinae meaning smallpox of the cow. Therefore, if you were to vaccinate someone, it would mean that you were giving them cowpox, but if you were to variolate, or inoculate them, it would mean that you were giving them a low dose of smallpox. This was brilliant for Jenner, he felt that he had secured the method of stopping people from catching smallpox, something that he had long dreamed about, but there was still much to be done and many people to convince. At his regular meetings that he had had with other doctors about it in years past, they had all been dismissive of the subject, and they had made it perfectly clear to him that they wished to talk about it no longer. Now, many years later, many of them were not going to eat humble pie very easily, and that was understandable as one swallow does not make a summer, and understandably enough, they would wish to see this process successfully repeated many times before they could have their pre-conceived ideas of negativity changed. Jenner had obtained a positive result in his inoculation of James Phipps, but he had no more cowpox with which to experiment with and although he had hoped to finish his work within the year, it was not until 1798 that he was in a position to continue. On 16th March of that year, Jenner inoculated two children, the first with matter taken from a Thomas Virgoe who had been infected with grease, a disease caught from horses that Jenner thought was a different kind of cowpox. The reason for this thinking was caused by the fact that some time past Jenner had previously sought to help a William Smith, who had been dressing the heel of a horse and who had gone on to milk some cows. One of the cows caught cowpox as did Smith. This could mean that there was a different type of cowpox from the one caught directly from a cow who had not been infected by grease which could have been passed on by someone working with horses. With this in mind Jenner then inoculated a boy called John Baker with the matter taken from Thomas Virgoe but he died fairly shortly afterwards from a fever. The reason for Baker's death is unclear but it is thought that he may have succumbed to a fever caught in the workhouse. He wasn't in fact inoculated with smallpox as it was thought that he was not well enough due to the fever and his death was therefore nothing to do with the vaccination process. Certainly, Jenner's opponents made no capital out of it and there were still many medical men who were unconvinced of Jenner's new method of curing smallpox. Another boy was inoculated from matter taken from a cow with cowpox. This boy was five-year-old William Summers, who did in fact develop cowpox and this cowpox matter was the source by which William Paed could be inoculated along with several other people, one of which was Hannah Excell, a seven-year-old girl who was healthy. Four people were inoculated with pus taken from young Hannah, including Jenner's second son, Robert, who was just eleven months old. Robert seemed to be unaffected at all by this but the other three all developed cowpox and from the matter taken from them, other inoculations followed.

Doctor Jenner about to Vaccinate a Child.

Doctor Jenner was below the middle stature
his hair dark and a little inclining to curl
and it was observed at his death he was not the least
gray. He was rather near sighted but never made
use of Glasses his dress was black, a large collar to
the coat and loose low trowsers the dress of the day

Jenner vaccinated many people with the cowpox taken from the three people that he had infected with cowpox but none succumbed to smallpox. Jenner carried out further work and the more experiments he carried out, the more convinced he became that he had found the answer to the eventual elimination of smallpox. However, before he shared the results of all his work to the rest of the medical profession who had been so negative over so many years, he decided to recruit some supporters. He wrote a short paper on the subject to his great friend Edward Gardner (1752–1823) who he had met all those years ago on Frampton Green, who he knew would support him. He then showed it to Dr Worthington and Henry Hicks from Eastington and these two men suggested presenting the work to a small committee which he then proceeded to do. The committee was made up of the previously mentioned men, along with Mr Thomas Paytherus (1752–1828), who was an entrepreneurial Surgeon/Apothecary with a good reputation, who supported Jenner's work and had worked with him in previous years on angina. Paytherus and Jenner had performed an autopsy on a patient who had suffered from angina and had linked the patient's death to coronary artery ossification. Added to Mr Paytherus was a Mr Thomas Westfaling, who lived and practiced in Cheltenham. Having read the contents of Jenner's report, his companions suggested that he present it to the Royal Society which he did and to his disappointment, they rejected it on the grounds that it was a step too far. In other words, the men of the Royal Society got cold feet and wouldn't back years of work that Jenner had carried out and wanted to play safe as they saw it and stick to the status quo of variolation. Although disappointed, Jenner was heartened by the support of his small group of friends who made up the committee and so it was decided that he should publish it without delay. This he did in June 1798, just two years after his first successful vaccination of James Phipps, and it was entitled 'An Inquiry Into Cause and Effects of the Variolae Vaccinae' and was priced at seven shillings and six pence which in today's currency would amount to about £20.00p.

Jenner published it himself and was given important support by two artists, William Skelton and Edward Pearce. We know that William Skelton (1763–1848) entered the Royal Academy of Schools in 1781 and studied under James Basire (1730–1802) to be an engraver. He was employed on many of the great literary publications of the day and along with Edward Pearce who we cannot find much information on, at the request of Jenner, gave him four hand coloured plates which depicted the cowpox pustule, and there is no doubt that their contribution helped Jenner achieve success with the book.

Jenner had always received enormous support from his great friend and medical colleague, Dr Caleb Hillier Parry (1755–1822) and he dedicated the book to Parry to show his gratitude that he had received from him over the years. Parry had not only given Jenner friendship and support over a long period of time but on a practical level they had also worked together on the subject of angina. The following year, 1799, Parry had published a book entitled 'An Inquiry into the Symptoms and Causes of the Syncope Anginosa, Commonly called Angina Pectoris' and Parry had paid tribute to the help that Jenner had given him on that publication. Jenner was merely returning the compliment to his great friend from their schooldays.

The Inquiry was a small book, but extremely important in its content and it allows the reader to learn the way Jenner's mind worked and his simple straightforward method of looking at the problem of the elimination of smallpox. It was only sixty-four pages long, the print was large and the margins wide, but nevertheless, it was an important book to read given the subject matter.

Edward Jenner was always going to be facing an uphill battle to get his views accepted and discussed properly by many of his medical colleagues. A great many ideas that the 18th century medical people practiced on their patients had been handed down from as far back as Hippocrates (480BC–370BC) as mentioned earlier in this book. Many patients when faced with an illness found that the doctor bled them to reduce, or attempt to reduce a high temperature whatever the illness was. Another procedure that doctors repeatedly tried was applying leeches on a patient's skin. Of course, the law of averages says that some would recover regardless of the treatment and these patients were held up as 'proof' that the treatment was correct. Luckily for Jenner, he had studied under the great Dr John Hunter (1728–93) and Hunter's maxim was always to experiment with new treatments and not simply to confine the treatment to tried and blindly accepted methods that had been handed down.

Jenner starts his book by writing about man's journey from his natural state to the period in which he was now living and describes the so-called civilisation and how in turn the way in which man lives. Jenner writes:

'The deviation of man from the state in which he was originally placed by nature, seems to have proved to him a prolific source of diseases. From the love of splendour, from the indulgence of luxury, and from his fondness for amusement, he has familiarised himself with a great number of animals which may not originally have been intended for his associates.

"The Wolf, disarmed of ferocity, is now pillowed in the lady's lap. The cat, the little Tyger of our island, whose natural home is the forest, is equally domesticated and caressed. The Cow, the Hog, the Sheep and the Horse, are all, for a variety of purposes brought under his care and dominion."

Jenner then goes on to explain the thinking behind the whole idea of eliminating smallpox with cowpox. He continues:

"...what renders the cow-pox virus so extremely singular is that the person who has been thus infected is for ever after secure from the infection of the smallpox; neither exposure to the variolous effluvia, nor the insertion of variolous matter into the skin producing this distemper."

Jenner explains that cows are prone to various sores which when examined by someone with limited medical knowledge are often taken as cowpox which often is not the case. If this happens, then it would mean that if the treatment of this discharge be used to combat smallpox, it would inevitably be unsuccessful, thus leading many people in the early days of Jenner's work on the subject to be convinced that cowpox was not the answer to rid the people of the risk of contracting smallpox. The problem was, of course, that the treatment being used was not cowpox.

Jenner lists a number of cases to prove that what he is saying is true. "Case 1) Joseph Merret, who was an under-gardener to the Earl of Berkeley, who had been a farm servant in 1770 and had dressed a horse with sore heels, milked cows that had developed cow-pox, and himself had caught cow-pox. Jenner had inoculated him in April 1795 but Merret failed to catch smallpox from either inoculation by Jenner, nor did he catch it from anyone else who was unfortunate enough to have the disease." Jenner writes:

"During the whole time that his family had the smallpox, one of whom had it very full, he remained in the house with them, but received no injury from exposure to the contagion."

Jenner anticipated the criticism that might follow that Merret may have previously had smallpox which would make him immune by the following statement that he entered into his report:

"Had these experiments been conducted in a large city, or in a populous neighbourhood, some doubts might have been entertained: but here, where population is thin, and where such an event as a person's having had the smallpox is always faithfully recorded, no risk of inaccuracy in this particular can arise."

Jenner went on to quote another person to show that protection from the smallpox could be for a prolonged time which the first case didn't prove.

"Case 2) Sarah Portlock of this place, was infected with the cow-pox when a servant at a farmer's in the neighbourhood 27 years ago... Note: I have purposely selected several cases in which the disease had appeared at a very distant period previous to the experiments made with the variolous matter to show that the change produced in the constitution is not affected by time."

Sarah did not contract smallpox in the same way that Joseph Merret had failed to, although she had contracted cow-pox many years before. The same thing happened in the next person:

"Case 3) John Phillips, a tradesman of this town, had contracted cow-pox at the age of nine years and when he was 52 was inoculated by Jenner with matter that he described as being matter in its most active state which produced only some minor symptoms that soon disappeared."

Case 4) is much the same again. Mary Barge has since been repeatedly employed as a nurse to smallpox patients without experiencing any ill consequences. This woman had cow-pox when she lived in the service of a farmer in this parish 31 years before.

Case 5) This concerns a lady known only as Mrs H. Jenner goes on to explain what happened with this person. "A respectable Gentlewomen of this town who had the cow-pox when very young. She received the infection in a manner that is not common: it was given by means of her handling some of the same utensils which were in use among the servants of the family, who had the disease from milking the infected cows." She must have caught the disease quite badly as it spread to her nose and for a while she looked rather unsightly. However, Jenner liked her and she regularly attended a retainer who had the disease in so violent a degree that it proved fatal to him. This case is a little unclear. Was Jenner talking about a very serious case of the cowpox when referring to the retainer or smallpox? The answer could be either disease.

Cases 6) and 7) are curious as they turn Jenner's work on its head. Instead of trying to prove that vaccination with cow-pox will stop people catching smallpox, this time Jenner is showing that people who have caught smallpox first are immune from cowpox which on the face of it would appear relatively unimportant. However, he continues:

"It is a fact so well-known among our dairy-farmers that those who have had the smallpox either escape cow-pox or are disposed to have it lightly, so that they are still able to pursue the business of the farm, and when thirty cows at Mr Baker's were infected with the cow-pox by a cow bought at a fair only one of the four servants who did the milking caught the disease, the other three having had smallpox. Mr Andrews, who had also bought a cow, probably at the same fair, was not so lucky, for when cow-pox broke out in his diary all six of the milkers caught it in spite of the fact that five of them had previously had smallpox. However the five had very mild attacks and only the sixth, who had not had smallpox, was seriously incapacitated. The milkers at both farms were inoculated with smallpox in the spring 1797, but none of them developed it. In Case 8), Jenner describes that a lady called Elizabeth Wynne had had cow-pox thirty eight years previously. It was just one small sore but it served as a complete protection when Jenner inoculated her with smallpox in the spring of 1797."

"Case 9) William Smith of Pyrton in this parish had cow-pox four times, and inoculation with smallpox, as might be expected, did not give him the disease." Jenner quotes other case studies before finally getting to the case of Sarah Nelmes and James Phipps in Case 16) and 17). The basic facts of these cases have already been laid out on page 86, but although it's covering the same ground, it is possibly worth quoting again in Jenner's own words as they describe the circumstances in more detail, and are, like the other cases, part of the Inquiry. Jenner writes:

"Case 16) Sarah Nelmes, a dairymaid at a farmer's near this place, was infected with the cow-pox from her master's cows in May, 1796. She received the infection on a part of the hand which had been previously injured by a scratch from a thorn. A large pustulous sore and the usual symptoms accompanying the disease were produced in consequence. The pustule was so expressive of the true character of cow-pox as it commonly appears on the hand that I have given a representation of it in the annexed plate."

"Case 17) James Phipps. The more accurately to observe the progress of the infection, I selected a healthy boy, about eight years old, for the purpose of inoculation for the cow-pox. The matter was taken from the sore on the hand of the dairymaid (Sarah Nelmes)…and it was inserted, on the 14th of May 1796, into the arm of the boy by means of two superficial incisions, barely penetrating the cutis, each about half an inch long."

"On the seventh day he complained of uneasiness in the axilla, and on the ninth he became a little chilly, lost his appetite and had a slight headache. During the whole of this day he was perceptibly indisposed, and spent the night with some degree of restlessness, but on the day following he was perfectly well."

There was no cowpox available until 1798 and in Case 19) a child, William Summers who was five years old, was given cowpox by Jenner and later variolated by Edward's nephew, Henry Jenner whereupon the child showed no sign of smallpox. Jenner took material from Summers' arm and on 28th March, he vaccinated William Paed who developed cowpox, and after a time was variolated but like William Summers, showed no sign of having received smallpox. On 5th April 1798, Jenner took lymph from William Paed in order that he could vaccinate Hannah Excell, who appears in case 21) and she did not develop smallpox. The final case was that of seven-year-old J. Barge who had received matter from a Mary Paed who had been successfully vaccinated at an earlier date. When the young Barge was variolated, he too showed no signs of the smallpox.

The experiments were having a familiar ring to them and Jenner was naturally pleased with his work and the results. He summed up his Inquiry with the following words:

"These experiments afforded me much satisfaction; they proved that the matter, in passing from one human subject to another, through five gradations, lost none of its original properties, J Barge being the fifth who received the infection successively from William Summers, the boy to whom it was communicated from the cow…"

Jenner then writes the paragraph that inspired Louis Pasteur (1822–1875), the famous French biologist, microbiologist and chemist. Pasteur was renowned for his work in the prevention of diseases and he was responsible for the word 'vaccination' being used as a catch-all expression for medicine that would prevent other diseases. He did this quite deliberately as a tribute to Jenner, whose work he greatly admired. The paragraph that inspired Pasteur read as follows:

"May it not be reasonably conjectured that the source of smallpox is morbid matter of a peculiar kind, generated by a disease in the horse, and that accidental circumstances have again and again arisen still working new changes upon it, until it has acquired the contagious and malignant form under which we now commonly see it making its devastations amongst us? And from a consideration of the change which the infectious matter undergoes from producing a disease on the cow, may we not conceive that many contagious diseases now prevalent amongst us, may owe their present appearance not to a simple, but to a compound origin? For example, is it difficult to imagine that the measles, scarlet fever, and the ulcerous sore throat with a spotted skin have all sprung from the same source, assuming some variety in their forms according to the nature of their new combinations?"

Jenner goes on to say that the different outbreaks of smallpox have varied greatly in their severity and type and explains that the increase of the cowpox must be due to the fact that more men along with women have been employed to milk cows. Jenner then finishes his 'Inquiry' by stating what he thought were the advantages of cowpox inoculation (vaccination) against smallpox inoculation.

"Should it be asked whether this investigation be a matter of mere curiosity, or whether it tend to any beneficial purpose, I should answer that notwithstanding the happy effects of inoculation, with all the improvements which the practice has received since its first introduction into this country, it not very unfrequently produces deformity of the skin, and sometimes, under the best management, proves fatal…but as I have never known fatal effects arise from the cow-pox even when impressed in the most unfavourable manner, producing extensive inflammations and suppurations on the hands; and as it clearly appears that this disease leaves the constitution in a state of perfect security from the infection of smallpox may we not infer that a mode of inoculation may be introduced preferable to that at present adopted, especially amongst those families which from previous circumstances, we may judge to be predisposed to have the disease unfavourably?"

Whilst argument can be made as to whether vaccination with cowpox is better than variolation with the smallpox, even under the skilled hands of someone such as Daniel Sutton and his father, Robert Sutton, where variolation was often successful but there was always the chance that someone could die from the smallpox, even if only a small amount had been administered. That is the point, Jenner's mission was to stop smallpox spreading in the first place, not just to cure an individual of it and he knew that the way forward was vaccination with cowpox rather than variolation with smallpox which was just too dangerous. It was a tall order, but after thirty plus years of thinking about it and later on when the time was right, acting upon it, Jenner was confident that he had found the answer as he went on to explain in his publication, 'The Origin of the Vaccine Inoculation' that he published shortly afterwards, in 1801.

In the 1801 paper, Jenner explains it thus:

"In some other points of view the inoculation of this disease appears preferable to the variolous inoculation." He goes on to say that there is no risk of scrofula and whilst there are those who are resistant to the smallpox inoculation, they react favourably to the cow-pox inoculation. He finishes:

"Thus far have I proceeded in an inquiry founded, as it must appear, on the basis of experiment; in which, however, conjecture has been occasionally admitted, in order to present to persons well situated for such discussions, objects for a more minute investigation. In the meantime I shall myself continue to prosecute this inquiry, encouraged by the pleasing hope of its becoming essentially beneficial to mankind."

However, in looking at 'The Origin of the Vaccine Inoculation', we are jumping ahead a while. It's his paper, 'An Inquiry into the Causes and Effects of the Variolae Vaccine' which was published in June, 1798 that we are concentrating on at the moment. Before his very short paper entitled 'The Origin of the Vaccine Inoculation' could be published, there was much work to be done in convincing his medical colleagues as well as the general public, that he had found a different cure for the smallpox that was better and more effective than the variolation techniques that people had been treated with before.

We shall now return to Jenner's 'Inquiry' which has been dealt with in some detail in order to explain to the reader, the lengths to which Jenner went to be sure of his eventual success in finding the way to eliminate small-pox.

As we have seen, its full title was 'An Inquiry into the Causes and Effects of the Variolae Vaccinae, a Disease discovered in some of the Western Counties of England, particularly Gloucestershire, and known by the name of the Cow Pox'. According to the Gloucester Journal, the 'Inquiry' was published by Sampson, Low on Berwick Street in Soho on 17th September and was priced at 7s /6p in pre-decimal currency or 37p in post 1971 decimal currency. That would translate into roughly £20.00p in today's prices. Jenner maybe thought that his work on eliminating smallpox was all but proved and he could return to being a physician quietly practicing his skills in the village of Berkeley which he had always loved since childhood and still loved. There was more work to be done however because not everybody in the medical profession would accept his ideas. He was going to have to convince some of the leading physicians of London along with the men who had stopped him discussing his ideas many years before – would they readily admit that they were wrong?

In the meantime, just as the 'Inquiry' was published, Jenner was approached by an old friend, Henry Cline (1750–1827) and was given some advice as to the direction his future career could go in if he took Cline's advice. Cline was an English surgeon and was President of the Royal College of Surgeons and in 1767, at the age of seventeen years, he was apprenticed to Thomas Smith who was a surgeon at St Thomas's Hospital. On 2nd June, 1774, he obtained a diploma from Surgeon's Hall and in the same year he attended a series of lectures given by John Hunter who of course was the man who had taught Jenner so well between the years 1770 and 1773 and had been such a huge influence on his most famous pupil. On the death of Smith, Henry Cline succeeded him at St Thomas's Hospital as a surgeon and was elected a Fellow of the Royal Society in 1806. In 1815, he became a member of the College of Surgeons and died in 1827.

Cline's reason for approaching Jenner was to tell him that if he moved his practice to London, he would almost certainly receive fees of £10,000 per annum, roughly £600,000 if earned in 2019. In this, Cline was supported by Sir Walter Farquhar (1738–1819) who was a leading physician of the day. Farquhar took a degree at King's College, Aberdeen, but abandoned these medical studies and joined the army as a surgeon. He eventually left the army and opened an apothecary shop in London and eventually became a Baron in 1796. In that same year he became a Fellow of the Royal College of Physicians of Edinburgh and was appointed Physician-in-Ordinary to George, the Prince of Wales (1762–1830). Whilst the latter appointment gave Farquhar great status, it probably gave him little pleasure. The Prince and his father followed the normal pattern of the Hanoverian Kings with the father hating the son and vice versa. Whilst King George III and Queen Charlotte lived their life together very frugally, the Prince of Wales spent money like water in an age when there was a great deal of poverty as the Napoleonic wars had left the country in financial difficulties. Whereas King George III was sober, frugal and completely faithful to his wife, the Prince of Wales had gigantic appetites for both food and drink, and ended his life being grotesquely fat. He also had a huge appetite for sex and it was doubtful whether the thought of being faithful ever entered his mind. He was born on 26th August 1762 and became Prince Regent in 1811 when his father became too ill to carry out his duties. George III remained ill until his death on 29th January 1820 when the Prince succeeded him as King until his own death on 26th June 1830. He died largely unmourned and although he supported the arts and left us with the beautifully designed buildings that bear his name, he is probably the most unlamented monarch that Britain has ever had.

Another person who Farquhar looked after was William Pitt the Younger (1759–1806), who became Prime Minister in 1783 at the extraordinarily young age of 24 holding on to that post until 1801 but returning to it again in 1804 until 1806, when he died at the tragically young age of 46 years having spent twenty years in power. It is probably no surprise that Pitt died so young considering the problems that he faced over his long premiership not least of which were the Napoleonic wars with France which lasted from 1793, ten years after he became Prime Minister, until 1815, when the Duke of Wellington beat the French army at the Battle of Waterloo. He was also involved in the abolition of slavery campaign which was led by his friend William Wilberforce (1759–1833) but by dying in 1806, he missed out in the trading of slaves being made illegal by just one year.

However, despite the encouragement of these influential friends, Cline and Farquhar, to open a medical practice in London, Jenner refused and in so doing, showed himself to be a man of honour. He had not only turned down a magnificent salary by anyone's standards, but he also did not wish to keep the secret of the new way of curing smallpox unlike the father and son team of Robert and Daniel Sutton, who we have read about earlier, and Dr Thomas Dimsdale (1712–1800), who had studied surgery at St Thomas's Hospital and had set up a practice in Hertford after obtaining a medical degree from Aberdeen. After that he started to practise variolation in the same manner as the Suttons. Dimsdale was born into a family of Quakers, his parents being Dr John and Susan Dimsdale. He, like the Suttons, had become something of an expert in variolation and in 1767 wrote a publication called 'The Present Method of Inoculating for the Small-pox' which by 1769 had reached five editions and in that year he was elected as a Fellow of the Royal Society. In 1788 he went by invitation to Russia and inoculated (variolated) the Empress Catherine the Great of Russia. He was handsomely rewarded by her for this and on returning to England became a banker. Quite why he did this we are not quite sure because after his work in Russia, his reputation was high as a surgeon, but maybe he could see the writing was on the wall with Jenner's cow-pox treatment.

Jenner was no doubt grateful that physicians as eminent as Cline and Farquhar were obviously paying him a great compliment but he stuck to his guns in wanting to work from Berkeley and there is part of a letter that was written on 29th September just after the 'Inquiry' was published to an unidentified medical friend whose name we do not know. The letter, although couched in the wordy style that people wrote in during the 18th century, is fairly clear about Jenner's feelings. Jenner writes:

"Shall I, who even in the morning of my days sought the lowly and sequestered paths of life, the valley and not the mountain; shall I now my evening is fast approaching, hold myself up as an object for fortune and for fame? Admitting it as a certainty that I obtain both, what stock should I add to my little fund of happiness?"

"My fortune, with what flows in from my profession, is sufficient to gratify my wishes; indeed so limited is my ambition and that of my nearest connexions, that were I precluded from future practice I should be enabled to obtain all I want. And as for the fame what is it? A gilded butt, for ever pierced with the arrows of malignancy. The name of John Hunter stamps this observation with the signature of truth… On the one hand, unwilling to come to town myself for the sake of practice, and on the other, fearful that the practice I have recommended may fall into the hands of those who are incapable of conducting it, I am thrown into a state that was at first not perceptible as likely to happen to me…"

"How very few are capable of conducting physiological experiments! I am fearful that before we thoroughly understand what is cow-pox matter and what is not, some confusion may arise; for which I shall, unjustly, be made answerable…"

Although the idea that people who had caught cowpox never seemed to catch smallpox had been floating around for years, reading of the entire contents of the 'Inquiry' was much more complicated than that and caused Jenner to make some educated guesses as to how it was to be stored and for how long, etc., many of them were correct.

Jenner's book, 'An Inquiry Into The Causes And Effects Of The Variolae Vaccinae', a shortened title compared to the first one already quoted, was a success, partly because he was helped by two artists, William Skelton and Edward Pearce. At Jenner's request, they produced four hand-coloured plates which depicted the cow-pox pustule. It is difficult to find any information on Edward Pearce, but we know that William Skelton (1763–1848) entered the Royal Academy of schools in 1781 and was a pupil of first James Basire and then later on William Sharp. Skelton was employed on some of the most learned illustrations of the day, notably John and Josiah Boyd's 'Shakespeare' (1803), Thomas Macklin's 'Bible' (1800–16) along with Bowyer's edition of David Hume's 'The History of England'. David Hume (1711–76) was the great Scottish philosopher and historian so that Jenner had chosen well with his artists.

Jenner was more than satisfied that his patient work and the resulting book would satisfy everyone in the medical profession that he had proved upon virtually any doubt, that if the cowpox was stored correctly at the right temperature and in the right conditions, his work in that particular field was complete. Jenner was a modest man but even such a modest man as he could be forgiven for thinking that he could rest assured that the plaudits would soon come his way on the very important new form of cure for smallpox. However, he would soon find out that it would not be as straightforward as he thought.

-oOOo-

Chapter 10

The Fight for Acceptance

If Jenner had thought that he had done all the hard work, then he was sadly mistaken. He had published his book and sat back waiting for the inevitable praise that would surely come his way, but he was taken by surprise as to his dismay, many of the medical profession didn't want to know. On 24th April 1798, Edward and his wife, Catherine, along with their daughter, also named Catherine who was but four years of age, travelled to London. They stopped at Cirencester the first night, and the next night at Benson. On the afternoon of the third day, they reached the home of a friend of Mrs Jenner by the name of Mrs Ladbroke, who lived in Pall Mall. Edward and Catherine stayed in London for three months during which time Jenner attempted to show the vaccination to his medical colleagues and to his utter dismay, failed completely to get their approval. After a while, he realised that he was unable to convince his medical colleagues of it's worth and his biographer, Dr John Baron wrote that during his stay, he was 'unable…to procure one person on whom he could exhibit the disease.'

Jenner realised to his dismay that many medical people, even if they considered themselves friends of Jenner, were not suddenly going to back track after all the years when Jenner had put forward his views on the curative powers of cowpox which they had not only disagreed with, but openly told him to stop talking about it. If the medical people didn't take to the idea, then it is no surprise that he had few patients. However, Jenner felt that his theories had been thoroughly tested and his book showed that it was no longer just an idea, but a fact that had been tried again and again. His main area of proof that his theories were correct would be the pus taken from Hannah Excell which he carried in a quill and which he would use for future demonstrations of cowpox inoculation. Jenner felt that he had proved that the cowpox pus could be transferred from Hannah Excell to another person and then again to another person and so on with its curative powers undimmed. It would not only prevent the person vaccinated with cowpox catching smallpox but in the course of time, smallpox would be completely wiped out which, of course, could never be achieved by the present method of variolation. His great friend and mentor, John Hunter had died in 1793, so a powerful person who without a doubt would have supported him was gone, but there were others who would take his place but apart from the obvious ones mentioned in the previous chapter such as Henry Cline and Walter Farquhar, Jenner to his shock and utter dismay found that he was running into a brick wall with almost everyone.

One of the first names to reach Jenner who expressed disapproval of cowpox vaccination was Dr Jan Ingenhouz, F.R.S., (1730–1799), a well-known physician in his own right and also Physician to the Emperor of Austria and what's more to the point, an experienced variolator. It was always going to be difficult to persuade him of the merits of vaccination over variolation. However, we will learn about him in more detail a little further on in the book.

Jenner wrote another pamphlet entitled 'Further Observations on the Variolae Vaccinae of Cow-Pox' and it was published on 5th April 1799. Rather than be a full report of Jenner's claims, it was but an add on to Jenner's 'Inquiry' explaining yet again the criticism's that had been made which called into question certain aspects of the vaccination process.

This is what Jenner wrote:

"Let me be permitted to observe that Truth in this and every other physiological inquiry that has occupied my attention has ever been the object of my pursuit; and should it appear in the present instance that I have been led into error, fond as I may appear of the offspring of my labours I had rather see it perish at once than exist and do a public injury." These words have been taken from one of his letters to Dr Ingenhouz but with just one or two words being altered.

However, having written that, he still felt that he was right and Ingenhouz was wrong and in the light of that he wrote further:

"Farmers, when they are selling cows often leave them unmilked for a day or two so that their udders may look large, and this brings on inflammation, which however, is not cow-pox, though it may go by that name. The farmer makes no distinction between one pustular condition and another, but the inoculator must." He wrote to Gardner:

"There will be no end to cavil and controversy until it be defined with precision what is and what is not cow-pox." He pointed out that the cow-pox pustule like the smallpox pustule provides effective virus only for a certain period, and that it is possible, although extremely rare, that a person could catch smallpox twice. He then delivers what he believes to be the killer punch:

"Let me suppose for argument's sake, that one person in a hundred after having had the cow-pox should be susceptible of the smallpox, would this invalidate the utility of the practice?"

The answer to this is obviously 'no', and Jenner was not too downcast for long, as people he thought would be on his side were Sir Joseph Banks (1743–1820), the eminent botanist, who was President of the Royal Society and had been a friend of Jenner's since 1771, Mr Thomas Paytherus (1752–1828), who, whilst living in Ross-on-Wye also had an address in Norfolk Street, London, and along with these were the Berkeley family of course, who had known Jenner for years. We can add to these the name of Sir Everard Home (1756–1832), 1st Baronet, who was the brother-in-law of Jenner's great mentor, Sir John Hunter (1728–93). Home was the brother of Hunter's wife Anne Hunter (nee Home), the poet who had written lyrics to none other than music written by the famous Austrian composer, Franz Joseph Haydn (1732–1809). Everard Home was a British surgeon who in 1778 was appointed Assistant surgeon at the naval hospital in Plymouth, and in 1787, was appointed Assistant surgeon and then surgeon to St George's Hospital, London. He was awarded the Copley Medal given by the Royal Society in 1807 and in 1813 was made a Baronet. He was elected a Foreign Honary Member of the American Academy of Arts and Sciences in 1832 and died in London in the same year. He was sometimes accused of copying Hunter's work but if true, it doesn't seem to have harmed his career in any way.

Jenner's positive outlook dropped a little as those he thought were in favour of vaccination, whilst not against, were wary of committing themselves completely. It is difficult to understand why these men felt that they couldn't commit themselves to Jenner's ideas. It isn't that they disbelieved in the theory, it was more the case that they wanted more proof. They all respected him but one thing that could have been against him was that he had no permanent practice in London, but was 'merely a country doctor'. That may have been the reason but if it was, it was a puzzling one given the fact that he had been encouraged to take up a practice in London and was highly thought of in medical circles. Maybe it was simply that the medical people just couldn't admit that there was a better way of curing smallpox by a different method to the one that had been practiced for hundreds of years, i.e., variolation.

Jenner was downcast, but he was not a man to give in easily. He believed in what he was doing and was prepared to be patient for it to be accepted but he knew that he would have to change tactics which is exactly what he did. He decided to return to Berkeley where he was known and respected and start the process locally. His nephew Henry (1767–1851), by now long since medically trained, was already helping him and now he brought in Henry's slightly younger brother George (1769–1846), who although not medically trained, was a clergyman and could talk about his uncle's work from the pulpit. By showing his success with his patients in the Gloucestershire area, Jenner assumed that eventually the word would spread and in time, vaccination rather than variolation would be the method to be used to keep people free from the smallpox.

However, this was all very well, but there was no smallpox breakout in Gloucestershire at the time so Jenner would have to be patient. It was frustrating for Jenner as he knew that people would lose their lives unnecessarily and so he had left his dried pus in a quill with Henry Cline (1750–1827), a surgeon at St Thomas's Hospital. Because Cline had an influence over the cow-pox debate being started, and because he was a friend of Jenner's, it may be a good idea to know a little more about him. Born in 1750, he was an English surgeon and was educated at Merchant Taylor's school. In 1767, he was apprenticed to Mr Thomas Smith, one of the surgeons at St Thomas's hospital, and on 2nd June, 1774, he obtained his diploma from Surgeon's Hall. In that same year he attended a course of lectures from John Hunter, Jenner's mentor and in 1781, he was appointed to lecture on anatomy, the greatest part of which he would have learned from Hunter. In 1784, he succeeded Thomas Smith as one of the surgeons at St Thomas's hospital. In 1796, he moved to Lincoln's Inn Fields where he remained for the rest of his life. He was elected to be a Fellow of the Royal Society in 1806 and in 1815 he became Master of the Royal College of Surgeons and in 1823, was elected President of that body. He died on 2nd January 1827.

That then is a brief summing up of Cline's career but it was a fairly glittering one and one that gave him great leverage in the debate concerning cowpox that followed. Although a friend of Jenner's, Cline had shown little eagerness over the affair and needed to be convinced. However, Cline's lukewarm attitude to

Jenner's method of vaccination was about to change sooner than both he and Jenner thought, and it was almost by accident. Henry Cline did not actually completely disapprove of Jenner's theories on cow-pox inoculation, it was just that the little spark of interest that he did have needed igniting. He did, however, believe firmly in the effectiveness of counter-irritation and it so happened that he had a young boy in his hospital with an inflamed hip-joint. Thinking that he had nothing to lose, he inserted the matter that Jenner had left him into a small wound that he had made in the inflamed area of the hip joint in the hope that the infection would be diverted from that point to another spot. By this time, Jenner had left London and was residing in Cheltenham with the intention of returning to Berkeley at some stage. Cline's experiment was entirely successful and about two weeks after the family had reached Cheltenham, Jenner was astonished to receive the following letter from Henry Cline. Cline was to write:

My dear Sir,

The cow-pox experiment has succeeded admirably. The child sickened on the seventh day, and the fever, which was moderate, subsided on the eleventh. The inflammation arising from the insertion of the virus extended to about four inches in diameter, and then gradually subsided, without having been attended with pain or other inconvenience. There were no eruptions.

Doctor Lister, who was formerly physician to the smallpox hospital, attended the child with me and he is convinced that it is not possible to give him the smallpox. I think the substituting of the cow-pox poison for the smallpox promises to be one of the greatest improvements that has ever been made in medicine, and the more I think on the subject the more I am impressed with its importance,

With great esteem,
I am etc.,
Henry Cline.

Lincoln's inn fields,
August 9th, 1798

The Dr Lister mentioned in the letter was William Lister (1756–1830), a physician, who became very important in Jenner's future concerning the vaccination of the cowpox. Lister was born on 5th April 1756 and studied medicine at Edinburgh University gaining a doctorate in 1781. He worked in a number of hospitals in London and in 1788 was elected a Fellow of the Royal Society of Edinburgh. In 1789, he became Head Physician to the London Smallpox Hospital and then in 1795, he went to St Thomas's Hospital in London. Lister retired in 1817 and was immediately appointed Governor of the hospital, a post that required no work. He died of a heart attack in 1830 at his home in Lincoln's Inn Fields.

Returning to the letter noted on the previous page from Dr Cline, this letter did not come to light until after Jenner's death but the person who found it, possibly his biographer, John Baron, saw that it had a note attached to it which was in Jenner's handwriting. The note read:

"That the matter of the cow-pox, like the smallpox matter, may be preserved without any diminution in its active qualities is evinced by the following experiment: Mr Cline inoculated a child with matter that had been taken from the pustule on the arm of Hannah Excell when in a limpid ichoros state, and dried by exposure to the air after being preserved three months in a quill in a seal."

Henry Cline's sudden support, along with support from Dr Lister, transformed the situation for Jenner. It was soon the main topic of conversation amongst the medical men of London but having said that, it would have been foolish to expect everyone to be converted overnight and there followed much argument about the merits of vaccination with cowpox as opposed to the standard practice of variolation.

Jenner was caught completely off-guard by the ferocity of the debate, however. He was a placid sort of man who did not enjoy confrontation, but if he felt strongly enough about someone or something, could be stubborn and defensive and would not be thrown off course on principle. He was not ready to throw all those years of hard work away simply because there was a chorus of people who were railing against his ideas. Many of the people who were for the new cow-pox vaccination were from high society and their enthusiasm for the subject was inversely proportional to their total lack of knowledge of it. It was a similar situation with the anti-slavery movement that was being led at the same time with William Wilberforce (1759–1833) as its main leader. Josiah Wedgwood (1730–95), whose factories made the famous Wedgwood jasperware that is still popular today, was totally disgusted with the slave trade and created the iconic picture of a slave kneeling down and asking the famous question: 'Am I not a man, am I not a brother?' That argument was hijacked as well with the rich and famous jumping on the bandwagon, women having brooches with that famous picture on it and it became a fashion statement. Still, support was support and was not going to be dismissed by Wilberforce and his people any more than Jenner was going to reject any support from wherever it came from when it came to the variolation versus vaccination debate.

The arguments between the two camps were powerfully put and it is not at all surprising. The first person, and possibly the most famous, to attack Jenner's methods was Dr Jan Ingenhousz (1730–1799), as we have already read about. A Dutch physiologist, who was a biologist as well as a chemist. He is best remembered for showing that light is essential for photosynthesis and therefore in effect, actually discovered photosynthesis. However, in his lifetime, it was his work in the battle against smallpox that he was known, and in 1768, he successfully inoculated or variolated members of the Habsburg family in Vienna against smallpox and he later became the private counsellor and personal physician to the Austrian Empress Maria Theresa. He was nearly twenty years older than Jenner and his successful inoculation was carried out in 1768 which was thirty years before Jenner carried out the first inoculation (vaccination) on the young James Phipps so Jenner was faced with a formidable opponent. Ingenhousz read the 'Inquiry' whilst staying with the Marquis of Lansdowne at Bowood Park which was near Calne in Wiltshire. Bowood Park was in an area whereby it was relatively easy to see what was happening in the local diaries. The first person that Dr Ingenhousz saw in this matter was a farmer, Mr Henry Stiles of Whitley. What Mr Stiles told Dr Ingenhousz must have been music to the physician's ears. Stiles told him that he had in fact caught cowpox thirty years earlier and was later, although we don't know how much later, inoculated with smallpox. However, despite being given cowpox, and then later being inoculated with smallpox, he did in fact catch smallpox. Not only that, but Mr Stiles's father caught smallpox from his son and actually died from the disease. That was all the proof that Ingenhousz needed, as so far as he was concerned, it proved that vaccinating with cowpox didn't work. In October, 1798, he wrote to Jenner a very courteous letter outlining his views which left Jenner with mixed feelings. Ingenhousz's letter was charming to begin with, and Jenner was flattered to be told by this eminent man that 'You enjoy a high and well-deserved reputation as a man of great learning in your profession'. However, Jenner was not so happy with the doctor's conclusion that the tried and tested method of variolation was better than Jenner's cow-pox theory. Jenner was especially irritated by it as he thought that he had already dealt with this problem in the 'Inquiry' which Ingenhousz had read so quickly before writing to Jenner. Jenner wrote back an equally courteous letter but then Ingenhousz wrote back with a letter that was pompous and discourteous that left Jenner confused and angry.

Jenner was nonplussed not knowing what to do other than what he always did in these situations; he wrote to his great friend Edward Gardner:

'I know not what to do with him… This very man Ingenhousz knows no more of the real nature of the cow-pox than Master Selwyn does of Greek, yet he is among the philosophers what Johnson was among the literati, and by the way, not unlike him in figure.' Jenner was of course referring to the great Dr Samuel Johnson (1709–84) who in 1755 published the huge dictionary that all subsequent dictionaries have been based on.

A Dr Paytherus (1752–1828) who we have already met, had been a friend of Jenner's for many years and stepped in and called on Dr Ingenhousz on Jenner's behalf. Paytherus was a distinguished medical man and was very much on Jenner's side. He was born in Fownhope in 1752 and was later apprenticed in Gloucester. He practiced in Gloucester and Ross-on-Wye and with Jenner, carried out an autopsy on a patient with angina and they linked this to the coronary artery ossification, a part of Jenner's work that we have already come across. Paytherus moved to London in 1794 and opened a pharmacy that was very successful but eventually sold his part of the business to his two existing partners. Dr Paytherus also advised Jenner on the publication of his book the 'Inquiry' which dealt with his work on vaccination. After a long career he died in Abergavenny in 1828 where he spent his retirement years with his family.

Returning to his attempt to enable the two eminent men, Dr Jan Ingenhousz (1730–1799), and Edward Jenner (1749–1823) to agree on the best treatment of smallpox, Paytherus's efforts were almost certainly going to be unsuccessful. Ingenhousz was older than Jenner and as he, Ingenhousz, had already had a lifelong career as a successful variolator, he was always going to look down at the much younger man's new ideas on the fight against smallpox. Sadly, Paytherus's endeavours in getting the two men to reach some sort of common ground came to nothing. Ingenhousz and Jenner ended up having a heated argument, and at the end of most heated arguments, nothing was settled or agreed upon. The correspondence between the two medical men began again and it was obvious that any meeting of these two great minds was never going to happen. Because of this, the only thing that Jenner could suggest was that the two men publish their letters so that the public could judge for themselves, but Ingenhousz was having none of it, so they were left with a stalemate, neither man giving way. This was hardly surprising, as Ingenhousz had spent a lifetime working with the variolation theory, whilst although Jenner was the much younger man, was giving nothing away either due to his strong convictions that his new ideas were correct.

At least Jenner had an ally in Dr George Pearson (1751–1828), M.D., F.R.S., probably the first since Henry Cline. Pearson was born in Rotherham whose father John Pearson was an apothecary. Pearson junior studied in Edinburgh and took his M.D. in 1771, after which he moved to London, spent some time in St Thomas's Hospital and on 25th June, 1784, was admitted a Licentiate of the Royal College of Physicians. Nearly three years later, on 23rd February, 1787, he was elected Chief Physician of the Royal College of Surgeons and stayed there a staggering forty years until retiring in 1827. On 23rd June 1791, he had been elected as a Fellow of the Royal Society and after just one year of retirement from the Royal College of Surgeons, he died at his home in Hanover Square on 9th November 1828 after falling down the stairs.

Sometimes Jenner was not always served well with the people who supported him. Dr Pearson had not showed a great deal of interest in cow-pox inoculation (vaccination) until Henry Cline showed his positive interest and then maybe he saw that there was a chance for him to gain some fame on the back of Jenner, along with the chance of making a great deal of money. He had already met Jenner when he, Jenner, had made his annual visit to London and the two men met at Jenner's old hospital, St George's. They had got on reasonably well but there was no great friendship until Pearson became interested in the cow-pox inoculation.

Pearson started work on the project in earnest and spent some considerable time and effort in writing to medical practitioners up and down the country in order to gain as much knowledge as he could about cowpox. He then put together all the information that he had received and put it all down together as a pamphlet and published it as if it had been his own. On 13th November 1798, he wrote to Jenner:

"Unexpectedly my pamphlet made its public appearance a day or two ago."

Even though Jenner was a modest man, it still came as a surprise to some that he was very pleased at what Pearson had done. Pearson was no expert on cowpox inoculation (vaccination) but despite that, Jenner was pleased with the fact that Pearson was keeping the debate open. Seeking no glory for himself, he was happy that Pearson's pamphlet would keep the subject of cowpox inoculation going and would help the pro-vaccination lobby with additional evidence. He wrote:

"Doctor Pearson has established an enquiry into the validity of my principal assertion, the result of which cannot but be highly flattering to my feelings."

However, problems began to emerge between Pearson and Jenner that were never really resolved. Pearson had begun working in earnest on vaccination in 1799, and he helped set up the Original Vaccine Pock Institute and at that time distributed vaccine but unfortunately some of the samples were contaminated with smallpox. Naturally enough, Jenner was annoyed that Pearson's patchy work was overshadowing his own and an unfortunate rift grew between the two men which meant that Pearson retaliated by claiming that Jenner had not discovered vaccination, but that the honour of this claim should belong to a gentleman by the name of Benjamin Jesty, a farmer of substance who we shall look at a little later on.

It was at this time that Dr William Woodville (1752–1805) entered the scene. He was a Quaker and at this time he was the physician in charge of the Smallpox Hospital at Paddington and he was very experienced at smallpox inoculation (variolation). He was born in Cockermouth in Cumberland in 1752 and studied medicine at Edinburgh University graduating M.D. on 12th September, 1775. He moved to London in 1782, was a physician to Middlesex dispensary and admitted a licentiate of the College of Surgeons on 9th August, 1784. On 17th March 1791, he was elected to the Smallpox and Inoculation hospitals at St Pancras, and in 1796, the same year that Jenner had carried out his first vaccination on young James Phipps, Woodville published the first part of a two-part publication of smallpox inoculation (variolation). He died at the smallpox hospital on 26th March 1805.

Despite his background in smallpox inoculation, Woodville was very interested in Jenner's approach to attacking smallpox with the use of cowpox. In fact he became so interested, he set up a series of experiments by carrying out his own cowpox inoculations but with very varied results. This was because although he was open-minded about the new treatment, he seemed to be hopeless at showing that he could provide a scientific approach to the method. If he was to have any success with sufferers of cowpox in the same hospital as smallpox sufferers, then the very least that he should have known was to not mix the two sets of patients up. On Sunday, 20th January 1799, he found out that there was an outbreak of cowpox in a dairy farm in Gray's Inn Lane owned by a Mr Harrison. Woodville then got in touch with a farmer by the name of Mr Tanner, who besides being a farmer, had a great deal of knowledge on veterinary surgery, and they both went to look at the stricken cows. Woodville took matter from a cow and with that matter he vaccinated six in-patients. On 22nd, Woodville went back to the dairy and with pus taken from a cow, he inoculated two more men. By now, practically all London had heard of the outbreak of cowpox and some very distinguished men met Woodville and he called on them all to meet him at Harrison's dairy the following day. These were, Sir Joseph Banks, (1743–1820), the famous botanist, Dr George Pearson (1751–1828), friend and medical ally of Jenner's, Dr Robert Willan, physician to the London Public Dispensary, and a specialist of diseases of the skin, Lord Somerville, President of the Board of Agriculture, Sir William Watson, a prominent variolater along with one or two others.

Woodville produced the 'Inquiry' and the drawings of the hand of Sarah Nelmes was shown to them all. The pustules were then compared and they looked just the same as the drawings done by the Drawing-Master, Mr Cuff. Everybody present came to the conclusion that the cows and the milkers were suffering from the cowpox. Dr Woodville returned to his smallpox hospital and re-commenced his inoculations immediately. Sadly, what he had in enthusiasm was cancelled out by his lack of knowledge. There is a saying 'a little knowledge is a dangerous thing'. Never was a truer statement that resonated with this situation and it could have been written especially for Dr Woodville. Dr Pearson also took some pus away and he too, like Woodville carried out some inoculations with the material. He also went to Woodville's smallpox hospital to study his patients.

Dr Woodville inoculated (vaccinated) a great number of cases and although the numbers vary, it is thought that when he had carried out three hundred, he temporarily stopped and published a pamphlet on the results.

Woodville's findings were very different from Jenner's. Woodville had achieved mixed results because whilst some of the patients had only the inflammation which were carefully described by Jenner in his 'Inquiry', a great many of the other patients had pustules all over the body, and looked very much as if they were suffering from the full-blown smallpox. Dr Jenner was told of these results not by Dr Woodville but by Dr Pearson. Jenner replied:

"Might not the disease have been the confluent smallpox communicated by Dr Woodville, as he is always full of the infection?" Jenner said in his reply to Pearson's letter. Jenner also thought that it was more than likely that the patients were infecting each other as they were not separated regardless of whether they were suffering from cow-pox or smallpox. This must have been very frustrating for Jenner. On 11th March, Jenner's nephew, the Reverend George Jenner (1769–1846) sent a letter to his uncle from London saying:

"Doctor Pearson is going to send a circular letter to the medical gentlemen to let them know that he will supply them with cow-pox matter upon their application to him…"

That was all very well, but how was Jenner to know that Pearson would be sending out the matter which may turn out to be smallpox rather than cowpox? He became very worried and uneasy about the whole process as he did not trust the two doctors, Woodville and Pearson, to have the necessary knowledge to be able to solve this problem. Jenner had no faith in either of them and he thought that the results that they had come up with were undermining Jenner's ideas rather than supporting them. Jenner thought that it would be impossible for him to promote his ideas when Woodville and Pearson were coming up with so many different results. Jenner's problems didn't end there. Dr Pearson was attempting to associate himself with Jenner's work to the extent that after he had successfully given people the idea that he and Jenner were working closely together, he then openly stated to all and sundry that he was the sole inventor of the cowpox vaccination.

For a qualified physician to make such a claim in these circumstances was an extraordinary thing to do and wholly untrue.

Pearson had only had two months experience of working on the idea of cowpox inoculation, but that didn't stop him from giving a public lecture on the matter claiming to be the person who originally thought of the cowpox inoculation (vaccination) which could have been very bad for Jenner's reputation. However, the situation for Jenner was helped by a gentleman who was in the audience named Mr Thomas Tanner, who was a veterinarian. Tanner certainly helped Jenner by telling Dr Pearson 'that he was wrong in some parts of his lecture'.

Jenner was a very modest man, but when it comes to what are in effect scientific discoveries that could possibly change the world view of how best to treat an appalling disease such as smallpox, it would be fair of Jenner to draw the line on that and tell the public the true state of affairs. Jenner then did what he always did when he found himself in some sort of trouble, he consulted his very good friend and confidant, Edward Gardner. Gardner had connections in the literary world and Jenner thought that he could put those connections to good use. He said that:

"Should not some neatly drawn paragraphs appear from time to time in the public prints, by no means reflecting on the conduct of Pearson, but just to keep the idea publicly alive that Pearson was not the author of the discovery – I mean cow-pox inoculation!"

Jenner by now had begun to think that he should publish a follow up pamphlet to the 'Inquiry' coupled with a return journey to London to attempt to discover exactly what was happening, something that he could never do all the while he was in Cheltenham or Berkeley. Jenner did indeed return to London on 21st March 1799, and two days later had an audience with Woodville in Norfolk Street. After the meeting, which seemed to be friendly enough, Jenner wrote:

"Doctor Woodville very ingeniously told me the whole of his proceedings. The inoculated persons were shown to me, and though some were without eruptions and exhibited the appearance of the cow-pox, others were very full of them and I could not discern any difference between them and the perfect smallpox."

This was very alarming for Jenner as Woodville was a respected physician, and if the public, not to mention the medical people that Jenner had to convince about the effectiveness of cow-pox inoculation (vaccination), took these results at face value, far from helping him, would hinder his cause a great deal. Three years later, albeit a bit late in the day, Woodville was to say to a House of Commons Committee:

"I think that if patients under vaccine inoculation are exposed to variolous infection they would frequently be liable to variolous-like eruptions, and should not be considered as fair examples of the vaccine inoculations."

That statement from Woodville was a long time coming but at least it was finally said in front of the Committee, and would have helped Jenner in his seemingly endless quest for his vaccination to be accepted, although there was still much to be done and still more people to persuade and educate on the matter. However, Jenner was frustrated and angered by Woodville's incompetence because he, Woodville, had practised cow-pox inoculation as well as smallpox inoculation not only in the same hospital, but sometimes in the same ward and so he was faced with the result that he was unable to diagnose which disease on each patient had developed due to the infection between patients that was bound to occur. Even allowing for the fact that we are talking about a new type of ground breaking treatment going back to the late 18th century, for a man of Woodville's status, it was taking incompetence to a new level as many lives were involved.

Jenner then produced another paper that he had worked on, and this was basically no more than an appendage to his first book, the 'Inquiry'. This second paper was entitled: 'Further Observations on the Variolae Vaccinae of Cow-pox' and was published on 5th April 1799. Its main purpose was to answer the points that had been questioned by other medics, some who were completely against cow-pox inoculation, and those that wanted to believe in it, but had not yet been entirely convinced. One of the sentences contained within it was the following, that had more or less been lifted from one of his own letters to Dr Ingenhousz but with a few alterations; Jenner wrote: 'Let me be permitted to observe that Truth in this and every other physiological inquiry that has occupied my attention has ever been the object of my pursuit; and should it appear in the present instance that I have been led into error, fond as I may appear of the offspring of my labours I had rather see it perish at once than exist and do a public injury'.

One of the major problems that Jenner encountered was the fact that vaccinations were being made by people who weren't qualified to know what exactly cowpox was. This resulted in people being vaccinated by spurious cowpox which gave the patient no protection against smallpox. This meant that Jenner's whole argument about cowpox being the medicine which would ultimately wipe the disease of smallpox from the face of the world was not so much being undermined, but more than that, being completely destroyed.

Jenner spelt it out when he wrote:

"Farmers, when they are selling cows often leave them unmilked for a day or two so that their udders may look large, and this brings on inflammation, which, however, is not cow-pox, though it may go by that name. The farmer makes no distinction between one pustular condition and another, but the inoculator must."

Jenner turned yet again to his great friend, Edward Gardner, writing to him despairingly, saying that there could never be a cure until people realise precisely the difference between spurious cowpox and the real cow-pox and in the meantime, Jenner will never be able to get his work on the cow-pox accepted and more importantly, many more lives will be lost unnecessarily in the meantime.

In late 1798, an outbreak of cowpox occurred in the Stonehouse area which gave Jenner an opportunity to collect as many examples of cow-pox that he needed in order to once more vaccinate people with the cow-pox, and then, following a wait of probably ten days, the chance to variolate with the smallpox thus allowing Jenner to make further observations as to the effectiveness of his work without Woodhouse and others distorting the results. He sums up his success rate with the following words: 'The aggregate of these observations, though not amounting to positive proof, forms presumptive evidence of so forcible a kind that I imagine it might on any other person have made the same impression it did on me without fixing the imputations of credulity.'

In the summer of 1799, Jenner and his family returned to Cheltenham and he carried on with his practice there. He was kept fairly busy, although he did feel that the need for his services had fallen a little because of the huge arguments that were going on about his new methods for the treatment for smallpox. He became very worried as reports were reaching him that there was further criticism of him back in London, some of which were emanating from Dr Benjamin Moseley, who was physician at Chelsea Hospital and a man credited with having a sense of fun. It is perhaps a description that deserves little credit as the test of a sense of humour is when you can laugh at yourself. There was little evidence of that as he ridiculed the whole idea of cowpox inoculation without virtually any knowledge of it, and as a physician at a London hospital, he should have known better. Jenner had to suffer criticisms from two sides, one being his medical colleagues, and the other being the cartoonists. As they helped sway public opinion it may be a good idea to look at one example of each. The first example is the medical man mentioned above, Dr Benjamin Moseley.

Benjamin Moseley, M.D., (1742–1819) was born in Essex and studied in London, Paris., and Leyden and was appointed surgeon-general in 1768. He performed many operations although it has to be said that many of his patients later died of tetanus. This didn't seem to harm his career however and when he returned to Britain, he gained his M.D. on 25th May, 1784 at St Andrews. He travelled extensively for the next few years and after returning to England once again was admitted as a Licentiate of the College of Physicians on 2nd April 1787. The following year he was appointed Physician to the Royal Hospital at Chelsea and stayed there until his death in 1819. During his career he brought out publications on many different topics, one of which was cowpox where he freely admitted that he was an opponent of vaccination. He wrote that if human beings were inoculated with the diseases of the beasts, would they not succumb to bestial characteristics? His argument was clear nonsense of course but the cartoonists latched on to this idea and as a result they drew pictures of patients growing tails and horns and because of this, it was yet another threat to Jenner's reputation. James Gillray was one of the worst offenders with his cartoons and we will look at him in a few moments. Moseley had a curious belief that a haemorrhage of the lung or lungs was caused by the different phases of the moon. This belief was caused entirely due to the fact that he once saw a captain in the 3rd Regiment of the Guards cough up blood six times at full moon and twice more at the new moon. In later years his reputation became tarnished and his opinions less sought after. Given that he had been a physician with a great career behind him and was now putting his extraordinary ideas to print, it is probably not much of a surprise that he became less revered in later life.

There were many people questioning Jenner's methods. We have looked at one who was a respected medical man, so now we'll look at one of the cartoonists, almost certainly the one who was the most savage, James Gillray (1757–1815).

Gillray was born in Chelsea on 13th August 1757 and was the son of a Lanark trooper. History has often referred to him as 'The father of the political cartoon' and that is probably correct, but it wasn't always that way as he started his career as an engraver and was reasonably successful. However, at some stage he decided to switch to being a cartoonist. His work was known for its savagery and no one escaped his blistering humour. These days, people could be forgiven for thinking that cartoonists would be far more deferential towards royalty in the 18th century than they are today, but the reverse is true. King George III who was on the throne during the greater period in Jenner's life that we are dealing with, certainly came under the barbed wit of the cartoonists as did William Pitt the Younger who was Prime Minister from 1783 until 1801, and again from 1804 until his death in 1806. In Gillray's cartoons about the cowpox, he drew pictures of people with cow's limbs and heads growing out of the people who had been vaccinated and although it was all complete nonsense, it would have alarmed many people and not helped Jenner's cause at all.

Gillray shared a house with his publisher, a one Miss Hannah Humphrey, and many thought that the two were also lovers, but there is no evidence to substantiate this. In 1806, his eyesight started to fail which meant that he was unable to work. He became depressed and as a result drank heavily and during some of his more desperate moments in 1811, attempted to kill himself. One day, he jumped out of the attic floor window of Miss Humphrey's shop but in fact survived. Miss Humphrey, ever loyal to Gillray, nursed him until he finally died on 1st June 1815. The man many people called 'The Father of the political cartoon' was laid to rest in St James's churchyard, Piccadilly.

In November 1799, Jenner left Cheltenham in order to return to his beloved Berkeley but it gave him no release from the depression that he felt from his lack of success in convincing people about his ideas for curing smallpox, because he was not just curing individuals, but he was convinced that he could eliminate the disease completely. This, unlike the inoculation with smallpox which whilst often curing a patient, still left the disease running rampant. What made the problem more complex was the fact that it wasn't simply a contest to see which was more effective, vaccination or variolation, but the fact that many people were believing that they were vaccinating patients, but due to the fact that they were untrained, were actually treating them with smallpox thinking that they were using cowpox, in other words, variolating them rather than vaccinating them, therefore, so far as the public were concerned, vaccination didn't work. However, it was the end of the 18th century and the dawning of the new century, and very gradually, slowly, almost imperceptibly, opinions began to change, although there was still a long road in which Jenner had to travel.

-oOOo-

Chapter 11

The Tide Turns and the World Listens

We have seen the word 'vaccination' used throughout the previous chapters and this was done deliberately so as to make a clear distinction between the treatment of smallpox with cow-pox and the treatment of smallpox with a small dose of smallpox itself, and up until this time the word 'inoculation' was used in both instances. Treatment with cowpox was simply referred to as just that, inoculation with cowpox whilst treatment with smallpox was again, just called inoculation with smallpox although the latter was usually referred to as variolation. Variolation was a derivation of the Latin word 'variola' meaning smallpox and Jenner was anxious to find a word that would make the two treatments distinct from each other. It is said that Jenner himself had used the word 'Vaccinate' but in fact the person who came up with the word 'Vaccination' was a Dr Richard Dunning, who was a surgeon from Plymouth and a friend of Jenner's. It followed naturally from the word 'vaccinate' that the overall procedure would be called vaccination. The word 'Vaccina' translated from Latin into English would simply be cowpox. Jenner, when publishing his first 'Inquiry' in June 1798, came up with the phrase 'Variolae Vaccinae' meaning 'Smallpox of the Cow'.

Jenner was grateful that his friend had thought of the word vaccination and was happy to use it. In fact, it seems so obvious today that one wonders why Jenner himself didn't think of the word. The meaning of the word 'Vaccinate' stayed as it was for over fifty years until Louis Pasteur (1822–95), the famous French biologist, microbiologist and chemist started using it himself. Pasteur was famous for his work on the prevention of diseases and used the word 'vaccinate' as a catch all word when he discovered a method whereby it was possible to inoculate a patient against anthrax. Pasteur, far from wanting to claim the same sort of fame as Jenner had achieved, wanted to use the word as a tribute to the

Gloucestershire doctor and it has been used in the general sense of preventative medicine ever since.

Meanwhile, Jenner was gradually winning his fight for vaccination with cowpox to be accepted as the most effective and safe method of fighting smallpox.

Jenner tells the story of his work with cowpox in his paper 'The Origin of the Vaccine Inoculation' which he published in May, 1801:

"My attention to this singular disease was first excited by observing, that among those whom in the country I was frequently called upon to inoculate, many resisted every effort to give them the smallpox. These patients I found had undergone a disease they called the cow-pox, contracted by milking cows affected with a peculiar eruption on their teats.

"On enquiry it appeared that it had been known among the dairies from time immemorial, and that a vague opinion prevailed that it was a preventive of the smallpox. This opinion I found was comparatively new amongst them, for all the older farmers declared that they had no such ideas in their early days – a circumstance that seemed easily to be accounted for, from my knowing that the common people were very rarely inoculated for the smallpox till that practice was rendered general by the improved method introduced by the Suttons, so that the working people in the dairies were seldom put to the test of the preventive powers of the cowpox…"

Despite the success of the vaccination of cowpox that he gave James Phipps, Jenner realised that because of the improvements that Daniel Sutton who we have read about earlier, had brought to variolation, there was much work to do before he could prove that vaccination not only worked, but was a far better way of ridding the world of smallpox than variolation. Variolation could prevent a larger dose of smallpox later on, but it was a dangerous method even in medical hands and Jenner's long-term aim was to rid mankind of smallpox completely and the risk to a patient in having cowpox was minimal compared to giving them even a small dose of smallpox. Jenner's aim of vaccination as opposed to variolation was a tall order to say the least and he set out to question other doctors on the subject, not all of whom were best pleased. Jenner continues:

"In the course of the investigation of this subject, which like all others of a complex and intricate nature presented many difficulties, I found that some of those 'who seemed to have undergone the cow-pox', nevertheless, on inoculation with the smallpox, felt its influence just the same as if no disease had been communicated by them by the cow. This occurrence led me to enquire among the medical practitioners in the country around me who all agreed in this sentiment, that the Cow Pox was not to be relied upon as a certain preventive of the Smallpox."

This must have been a great disappointment to Jenner, but in his report he continues:

"This for a while damped, but did not extinguish, my ardour; for as I proceeded, I had the satisfaction to learn that the Cow was subject to some varieties of spontaneous eruptions upon her teats; that they were all capable of communicating sores to the hands of the milkers; and that whatever sore was derived from the animal, was called in the dairy the Cow Pox."

Later on in his report, Jenner describes how he found just how he came to vaccinate and then variolate James Phipps:

"...I was struck with the idea that it might be practicable to propagate the disease by inoculation, after the manner of the Small Pox, first from the cow, and finally from one human being to another..."

Jenner then went on to describe his experiment on James Phipps and whilst this was a success, it would be a long time before other medical men would come round to the idea that for so many years they had fought against. Jenner continues in his report:

"The result of these trials gradually led me into a wider field of experiment, which I went over not only with great attention, but with painful solicitude. This became universally known through a Treatise published in June, 1798. The result of my further experience was also brought forward in subsequent publications in the two succeeding years, 1799 and 1800. The distrust and scepticism which naturally arose in the minds of medical men, on my first announcing so unexpected a discovery, has now nearly disappeared."

By the time Jenner wrote this report, 'The Origin of the Vaccine Inoculation' which was published in 1801, he was clearly confident that he had made the breakthrough and the final paragraph he makes the extraordinary claim at the time that the disease of smallpox would completely disappear from the planet. He finishes his report with the following words: "A hundred thousand persons, upon the smallest computation, have been inoculated in these realms. The number who have partaken of its benefits throughout Europe and other parts of the Globe are incalculable: and it now becomes too manifest to admit of controversy, that the annihilation of the Small Pox, the most dreadful scourge of the human species, must be the final result of this practice."

It was an extraordinary claim but one that has been backed up with facts, although it took a long time, and it was not until the latter part of the twentieth century that it was recognised that the disease had been conquered.

By any stretch of the imagination, it was an amazing achievement as he not only had to find the solution to this immense problem, he had another hurdle to jump over; he had to win the hearts and minds of his medical friends and colleagues. This was not an easy task and, in many ways, one could see their point as the original idea had come from a fairly vague folklore emanating from the country, and medically trained men would always need a lot more convincing than a vague idea that has been handed down for at least two centuries. Jenner was convinced however, but in the early days of his great idea, the more Jenner had talked about it, the more irritated they had become, and after initial amusement, told him to stop talking about it at all.

At last Jenner could claim success as to his certainty that the cow-pox vaccination would work more successfully than using that which had been used prior to vaccination, this being variolation. Variolation could possibly be used as a way of attacking the full blown disease of smallpox killing an individual, but in order to rid the world of smallpox altogether, Jenner was at last starting to convince the world that by vaccinating with cow-pox, the patient would not catch the smallpox at all and Jenner's assurance that it would one day wipe the disease out completely that he had prophesied in his 1801 paper, would come to pass. It took a long time, but it happened in 1980, when the World Health Organisation announced that the world was indeed free of small pox, just as Jenner had prophesied in the final paragraph of his 1801 paper, 'The Origin of the Vaccine Inoculation'.

It is strange that this country doctor who was undertaking this work in a quiet village in Gloucestershire, was doing it while the war with France was being waged around him but which he had little contact with, communications being nowhere near as sophisticated as they are today. It is difficult to know how worried Jenner and his family along with their neighbours and friends in the country really were and just how much they knew of what was going on and whether they actually realised just how serious the consequences would be if Britain were defeated.

France was in turmoil during the 1790s and in September, 1792, declared itself to be a republic. The horrifying news that King Louis XVI (1754–93) had been tried for repeated acts of treason during his reign, found guilty and executed by guillotine on 21st January 1793 shocked all of Europe, especially those countries who had a monarch as head of state. As France was now a republic, many people in England were fearful that the same thing could happen over here, especially with George III being in such a vulnerable state with his poor health, and yet in any papers on Jenner, they do not seem to give the proceedings much if any space. However, whilst the British government was wondering how to react, France beat them to it by forming a coalition with Spain and Portugal and declared war on Britain and the Netherlands on 1st February 1793. In due course, Britain was up against a country's forces who were led by a brilliant Corsican general by the name of Napoleon Bonaparte (1765–1821). He dominated European affairs for a decade while leading his French forces against a series of coalitions, and Napoleon's world of foreign battlefields must have been seen as light years away from the tranquil fields of Berkeley. However, nothing could be further from the truth as the war with France gave Jenner a huge problem. He did not seek monetary gain from his work with smallpox as he had always wanted to rid the whole world of the dreaded disease. The only way to achieve that was to share his expertise and knowledge with all nations and of course that included France, at the time, Britain's long-term enemy. France had the information they needed to cure the French troops of smallpox that would naturally make their armies stronger and make them a bigger danger to Britain. We can find little or no knowledge of any discussions about this in the British parliament, with King George III or the Prince Regent and so we can only assume that it was considered a non-controversial idea which may come as a surprise to some readers. However, what we do know is that Napoleon had the utmost respect for Jenner, and whilst the war was being waged, Jenner would sometimes be asked to contact Napoleon Bonaparte to ask him to release a certain prisoner in exchange for another. Here, Bonaparte's high opinion of Jenner helped Britain get important British prisoners of war released. This was because when Jenner did write to Napoleon asking him to release a certain prisoner of war, he was never refused, such was the admiration that Napoleon felt for him. A story about Napoleon that is often told is that on one occasion when presented with a request to release a particular prisoner, Napoleon instantly refused, but when it was pointed out to him by his wife, Josephine, that the request came from Jenner, Napoleon instantly changed his mind, and is supposed to have said, "*Nous ne pouvons nerer rien a Jenner* – We can deny nothing to Jenner."

Many people think that the war with France was effectively finished when the great Lord Nelson (1758–1805) ably assisted by his second-in-command, Admiral Cuthbert Collingwood (1748–1810) beat the combined French and Spanish fleet at the Battle of Trafalgar on 21st October 1805. Nelson certainly achieved victory which meant that the British navy was superior to that of any other country but the actual war with France was not finished for another ten years. The final nail in France's coffin was achieved ten years later at the battle of Waterloo.

The two armies faced each other on 18th June, 1815 for this last great battle in the French wars. The two main protagonists were Napoleon Bonaparte (1765–1821), leading his French troops and the 1st Duke of Wellington (1769–1852), K.G., G.C.B., G.C.H., P.C., F.R.S., born Arthur Wellesley in Dublin on 1st May 1765. Wellington was commissioned as an ensign in the British Army in 1787 and reached the rank of General during the wars with Napoleon, and was promoted to Field Marshall after leading allied forces to victory against the French empire during an earlier battle in 1813.

To describe the battle of Waterloo which raged for hours in detail is not for this book, but in essence, the two armies faced each other and for a long time it was swinging in France's favour. Wellington's British forces were being attacked time and time again by the French but Wellington held firm and beat the French back on each occasion. It was a calculated gamble by Wellington that luckily came off, as he had heard that Prussian forces were coming to shore up the British numbers although he had little or no idea when they would arrive. As luck would have it, they did arrive with the French still attacking the British and their arrival changed the way that the battle was being fought. The Prussians attacked the French on their right flank whilst Wellington cut through the middle of the French, routing them completely. The war with France was effectively won by the British at that point. Napoleon abdicated four days later and the war with France was finally over.

Napoleon was shipped to England with the extraordinary idea in his head that he would live out the rest of his life in comfortable retirement as a member of the aristocracy. It didn't quite work out like that for him as in an era where starving people could be hanged for stealing a sheep, many people thought that he got away with it lightly when he was sentenced to be exiled at the island of

Saint Helena for the rest of his life where he died on 5th May, 1821. We are not completely sure what it was that killed him but the general view is that he died of stomach cancer.

The Duke of Wellington had been in politics and after the war returned to it. He was less successful as a politician than he was a soldier however, although he did become Prime Minister from 1828 until 1830 and again for less than a month in 1834. A Tory to his bones, he opposed the famous Reform Act of 1832 brought in by Earl Grey (1764–1845), the Whig Prime Minister, and then went to sit in the House of Lords, and eventually retired in 1846. He died in Walmer Castle at Deal on 14th September 1852. He was always to describe the Battle of Waterloo as 'the nearest run thing you ever saw in your life.'

Returning to Jenner, when the war with France had started, Jenner was in the throes of trying to get his ideas accepted by the medical profession. They had to be won over from variolation to vaccination and this was always going to take many years. Doctors and surgeons who had held their beliefs all their working lives were not going to be won over easily by a country doctor basing his ideas on an idea that came from milk maids. One of the important rules that practitioners had to learn was that cowpox lymph had to be stored correctly, and for the right period of time. Many people vaccinated patients with cowpox and then after a few days variolated a patient not realising that they were doing this far too soon. Others would store the cowpox for such a long time that it became stale and that too rendered the cowpox useless. The result of this was that smallpox was given to patients by unskilled practitioners which was totally the opposite of what vaccination could achieve when administered properly. The very fact that vaccination by these unskilled people gave the patient smallpox, thus spreading the disease, gave the practice a very bad name and it was to take many years before the vaccination process was refined and used properly. Jenner thought that the smallpox virus should not be administered to the patient for about ten days to two weeks after vaccination had taken place. This was due to the fact that some had been unsuccessful because they had been variolated with smallpox only five days or so after the cowpox had been vaccinated. This was no good at all, and equally, if the virus was administered more than three or four months later it would probably be too stale to be much good. Unskilled people who were operating outside of these parameters were giving Jenner's work and also his reputation an undeserved bad name and were delaying the time that the world would be able to know that the disease of smallpox could be completely eradicated.

For Jenner to get his message across so that it reached other parts of the world, he had to get his name known abroad and to educate the medical profession, probably by letter, as to the correct use of the cowpox vaccination otherwise his ideas would always be in doubt. The first real success abroad was in Geneva where in September, 1799, he received a letter from a gentleman named Dr de Carro. De Carro wrote:

"I am from Geneva. I have studied and taken my degree at Edinburgh, and practice medicine in Vienna since six years…"

He went on to say that he had been very impressed by the 'Inquiry' and his letter continued with the explanation that he had requested and received some vaccine from Dr Pearson. These had been forthcoming and as a result Dr de Carro had been able to carry out several vaccinations, not all of which had been successful although others had been. He fully supported the method of vaccination but his work was severely hampered by the fact that there was no spread of cowpox in Austria at the time of de Carro's letter and so requested that he obtain some vaccine virus from Dr Jenner himself. The effect of this would be twofold; the first being that he knew he would receive the correct virus that would almost certainly mean his treatments would be successful, and the second was the kudos that he would receive from obtaining his material from Dr Jenner personally would be immense.

Other excellent doctors supported Jenner which Dr Baron, Jenner's first biographer lists in great detail. However, Dr de Carro was the best man to be in Jenner's corner because he believed in Jenner's vaccination process as much as Jenner did. He was a Swiss physician who was very supportive of the vaccination process and was responsible for the vaccine virus being sent to Italy, Germany, Poland and Turkey. In 1801, he was responsible for sending the vaccine to Lord Elgin, the British Ambassador at Constantinople. From there it was sent to Bussora (Basra) on the Persian Gulf and from there to Bombay as it was then known. Dr de Carro's vaccinations had an amazing success rate and Mr and Mrs Nesbit, who were the parents of Lady Elgin were deeply worried about their grandchild and managed to persuade Lord Elgin to ask Dr de Carro for some vaccine which he managed to obtain. The boy was successfully vaccinated and as this was the case, other people such as diplomats were vaccinated followed by Turks which led to them favouring vaccination as opposed to the variolation, the latter technique favoured by them a hundred years before that had been brought to England by Lady Mary Montagu.

The Marquis of Wellesley, the Governor-General of India also played his part. Born Richard Wellesley on 20th June 1760, he was created a peer of Great Britain in 1797 and in 1799 became the Marquis of Wellesley in the peerage of Ireland. He was the brother of Arthur Wellesley, the 1st Duke of Wellington, the victorious soldier in the Battle of Waterloo that finally resulted in Napoleon's surrender. In 1794, the Marquis of Wellesley married Hyacinth-Gabrielle Roland, an actress who had already borne him five children, three sons and two daughters. Their first child, Richard, was born in 1787 so quite why it took him all these years to make her his wife is a mystery. However, he must have loved her as being an actress, she was seen by the aristocracy as being of a lower class and was never allowed to enter society as a result, but Wellesley stuck with her until his death on 26th September 1842. During his active life he promoted the distribution of the vaccine and as a result, many thousands of people were vaccinated in India.

We now look at America, a country that up until this time had not had the advantage of being able to practice vaccination. Dr John Coakley Lettsom (1744–1815) was born into a Quaker family on Little Jost Van Dyke in the British Virgin Islands and unlike others who had been born into a certain religion but had not followed it, Lettsom did and was known as a Quaker for his entire life. He was sent to England at the age of six years to be educated and eventually commenced his medical training at St Thomas' Hospital in London. However, he returned to Totola in the Virgin Islands when his father died, and being a Quaker and a very compassionate man, immediately freed the slaves that he had unwillingly inherited. Whilst staying there, he provided care for the local people and as he was the only medical practitioner there, made a considerable amount of money that allowed him to resume his medical studies and he matriculated at Leiden University on 8th June 1769 and he received his medical degree shortly afterwards. He was also a close friend of Benjamin Franklin (1706–90), the brilliant writer, inventor and one of the leading founding fathers of the United States of America.

Thus it was that America became another country where the vaccine virus was taken. Dr Lettsom it was who sent a copy of the 'Inquiry' to Dr Waterhouse (1754–1846), Professor of the Theory and Practice of Physic at Cambridge, Massachusetts who we shall look at in more detail in a moment or two. Dr

Waterhouse replied and asked for vaccine which was sent to him from the Vaccine Institution of Bath, the first of its kind in England. Jenner also sent some vaccine to John Haygarth F.R.S., F.R.S.E., (1740–1827). Haygarth was a British physician who was born to William Haygarth and Magdalen Metcalfe at Garsdale, near Sedburgh, West Riding, Yorkshire. He was originally tutored by John Dawson (1734–1820), who was very famous in his day, being both a mathematician and a surgeon. His pupil, John Haygarth, was a firm believer in Jenner's work and helped him spread the vaccines. In 1778, he had set up the Smallpox Society of Chester and after living in Chester for thirty years, he moved to Bath. He was elected a Fellow of the Royal Society for his work on smallpox. So it was that both Haygarth and Benjamin Waterhouse had ample supplies of the vaccine.

Thus Benjamin Waterhouse (1754–1846) became involved in the vaccination process. He was born into a Quaker family, although he did not take up that religion, on 4th March 1754 in Newport, a colony of Rhode Island and Providence Plantations. At the age of twenty-one years, he left America and travelled to Europe and studied medicine in London. He matriculated on 28th October 1778 at Leiden University as did Dr John Coakley Lettsom (1744–1815) some ten years before. Also like Lettsom, he received his medical degree at the same University in 1780. Leiden University was founded in 1575 by William, Prince of Orange (1533–84), although he was also known as William the Silent or William the Taciturn. Waterhouse returned to the States in 1782 and joined the Faculty of the Medical School of Harvard as one of three Professors. In 1795, he was elected as a Fellow of the American Academy of Arts and Sciences although he resigned his Harvard Professorship in 1814 because he opposed the plan to establish the medical school in Boston. He married Elizabeth Oliver in 1788 and she bore him six children. Sadly, she died in 1815 not long after giving birth to their sixth child. Waterhouse married again in 1819 but there were no children from the second marriage. Waterhouse himself had a long life and died in 1846.

Waterhouse received the vaccine virus directly from Jenner via Haygarth and was responsible for introducing it to America. He commissioned a controlled experiment at the Boston Board of Health whereby twenty-one boys took part. 19 boys were vaccinated whilst two were not. All were exposed to the smallpox virus and the nineteen who were vaccinated survived whilst the two who had not been vaccinated caught the smallpox and died. Looking at this experiment now it seems an extraordinarily cavalier not to say utterly cruel way of treating people of whatever age in this manner, especially children, but it has not been possible to find out the circumstances, for instance, whether large sums of money were handed to the parents who almost certainly were living in poverty. It was the early days of vaccination and there were probably no laws on the statute book to regulate such behaviour.

Waterhouse must have had friends in high places as he sent vaccine to John Adams (1735–1826), the second President of the United States of America, whom Waterhouse had known for some time. Adams was an American Statesman, lawyer, diplomat, and one of the Founding Fathers of the United States and after serving as Vice President under George Washington (1732–99), the first President of the United States and who had held the post between 1789 until 1797, Adams became the second President and held that position between the years 1797 until 1801. Before that, he had been a delegate from Massachusetts to the Continental Congress, a congress made up of delegates from the thirteen colonies which became the governing body of the United States during the revolution. Despite their friendship going back several years, Adams showed little interest and so Waterhouse wrote to Vice-President Thomas Jefferson (1743–1826) who went on to become the third President between the years 1801 to 1809. Jefferson was born on 13th April 1743 in Shadwell, in the colony of Virginia, and like Adams, was an American statesman. He was a great believer in democracy, republicanism, and individual rights. It was Jefferson, amongst others who helped to motivate the American people to break from Britain, taking up arms if necessary. It was no mean feat as the Americans at the time had no army as such, and hardly anything in the way of weapons. Not only that, but the American people were split on the issue, many wanting to stay with Britain, the mother country. With the well drilled British army of redcoats, it didn't seem possible that the people from the colonies could win, but win they did, but only after a great deal of blood had been spilt. The rumblings of the war had started in 1775 and it was not until the British army, led by General Cornwallis surrendered in 1781 at Yorktown that the British defeat was inevitable. One small but nonetheless remarkable co-incidence is that Adams, the second President, and Jefferson, the third President died on the same day, 4th July 1826, exactly fifty years to the day that Jefferson, then aged only thirty three, produced the remarkable Declaration of Independence that was presented to the American people on 4th July 1776.

Returning to Benjamin Waterhouse and his promotion of Jenner's vaccination process, he wrote to Jefferson with a paper entitled 'A Prospect of Exterminating Smallpox'. Jefferson, showed far more interest in Jenner's vaccine than did John Adams. He replied to Waterhouse with a letter dated Christmas Day, 1800 and offered Waterhouse and by definition Jenner his support. Waterhouse introduced Jenner's method of vaccine to the United States and the method and idea caught on in this newly independent country. Unlike Jenner, Waterhouse attempted to keep the method to himself, both for financial reasons but also because he wanted incompetent practitioners kept away from it. The second reason is sound enough, but he could hardly expect physicians from this fledgling but huge country to rely on one man to look after everyone and gradually doctors learned the method and America came yet another country to practice it as a matter of course. However, there was a hiccup after this mass acceptance of Jenner's vaccination and that was due to Jenner's careful explanations of how to go about vaccination being ignored, and shirt sleeves, stiffened with discharge from infected arms, were being sold by quacks with disastrous consequences. However, Waterhouse managed to procure some clean lymph from Jenner and Thomas Jefferson, along with all of his family, relations, and along with them, his neighbours, were all vaccinated with the new vaccine and acceptance of vaccination returned. That this relatively new country of the United States of America being convinced must have been a huge relief to Jenner having had so many setbacks in persuading the world of his methods, which had virtually a 100% success rate when carried out correctly. Convincing America to turn to vaccination in order to conquer smallpox was no mean feat, but there were other countries to convince, the next big one being India, although there were other smaller ones to convince first. Spain was such a one and the practice of vaccination spread from France to the Royal Economical Society of Madrid who took it on board and elected Dr Jenner an honorary member. Jenner's diploma was forwarded to him by the 3rd Lord Holland through his secretary, Mr Allen. The 3rd Lord Holland (1773–1840) was born in Wiltshire and was the grandson of the rather notorious 1st Baron Holland (1705–1774) who held high office in politics but managed to come out of it all with a great deal more riches than when he entered as plain Henry Fox. He married Caroline Lennox (1723–74), the eldest of the famous Lennox sisters and two years later Caroline gave birth to Stephen Fox (1745–74) who was the 1st Baron's first-born son and the 3rd Baron's father. The 1st Baron and his wife, Lady Caroline had a second child who went on to become the famous Whig politician, Charles James Fox (1749–1806) and who was therefore the 3rd Baron's uncle. Returning to Mr Allen, the 3rd Baron's secretary, and the letter that he sent Jenner along with the diploma, this is what the 3rd Baron wrote:

"There is no country likely to receive more benefit from your labours than Spain; for on the one hand the mortality among children from smallpox, and its consequences, has always been very great; and on the other hand the inoculation for the cowpox has been received with the same enthusiasm here as in the rest of Europe: though I am sorry to add that the inoculation of the spurious sort has proved fatal to many children at Seville, who have fallen victims to the smallpox after they had been pronounced secure from that disease…as one of the many proofs of the estimation in which the cow-pox and its discoverer are held in Spain, I have enclosed a small engraving…to be prefixed to a dissertation…to be published by the Royal Society of Medicine (of Madrid)."

Meanwhile, the spread of vaccination was by now travelling the world. A naval expedition was fitted out due to the fact that Spain had now taken vaccination on board. The expedition sailed from Corunna with over twenty children on board which was to make sure that the strain of the lymph was continued. It sailed to Porto Rico, and from there it split into two and the two smaller fleets sailed in two different directions, one for South America, and the other for Havana. Having spread the gospel of vaccination to various Spanish colonies, they then decided to sail to China where they proposed to teach this huge number of people the process of vaccination. In this they were supported by Sir John Barrow, F.R.S., F.R.G.S., (1764–1848), a statesman and writer who had held the post of Second Secretary to the Admiralty from 1804 until 1844, serving under all the Prime Ministers of that time apart from 1806–7 when there was a Whig administration headed by Lord Grenville (1759–1834). Grenville held the post for one year only before falling out with King George III over the question of Catholic emancipation. The King had always held the firm belief that Ireland should stay Protestant and he would never budge on this issue.

Returning to the spread of the lymph, Dr de Carro of Vienna, had received what he needed from Jenner, and had been busy spreading the practice of vaccination through Austria, Hungary, Poland and part of Germany. The technique was practiced amongst Europeans in Constantinople, followed by Mohammedans, whilst Lord and Lady Elgin promoted the practice through the islands of the Archipelago. Turkey and Greece were too more countries that started practicing it and in Salonika 1130 people were vaccinated.

Jenner wanted the lymph to be sent to India, like China, a huge country and the Indian people were equally desperate to receive it. The Governor of Bombay as it was then called, asked Lord Elgin for material and consequently Elgin sent a quill containing the precious lymph in 1801. It was becoming really sought after. Elgin later wrote to the Honourable Arthur Paget:

"I have so many applications for vaccine virus from Bussora, the East Indies, and Ceylon, that I beg that you will immediately apply to Dr De Carro and request him to send some by every courier."

At this stage, demand seemed to exceed stock which was available but good fortune appeared from round the corner. A Dr Sacco of Milan found that there was an outbreak of cowpox in Lombardy, and he claimed that he had successfully vaccinated 8000 people and was in a position to send Dr de Carro lymph for India. Hindu and Mohammeden physicians were taught vaccination with the Hindu physicians picking it up more readily due to the importance of the cow in their religion. It was obviously successful as Ceylon gratefully sent Jenner a figure of £3,000, whilst Bombay sent £2,000 and Madras £1,383.

The vaccination was now totally accepted by all these various places even if doctors in Jenner's homeland didn't. Jenner was at Cheltenham whilst all this was going on, and he gave free vaccination to the poor, and amongst these were great numbers of children. The people of one parish, who had long held back asking for help, suddenly appeared with great numbers of children which initially was a mystery for Jenner, but on enquiring as to the reason why, it was discovered that the parish authorities had requested the vaccination on the grounds that "the cost of the coffins for the children who were cut off by smallpox proved burdensome to the parish." A sad reason why Jenner's work should be recognised by a particular parish, but a gratifying one for Jenner all the same.

Vaccination was carried on in great numbers on the continent. At Brunn a temple was dedicated to Dr Jenner. He also received a letter from the Dowager-Empress of Russia who wrote a gracious letter to him on the service he had rendered to humanity and enclosed with the letter was a valuable diamond ring. Its monetary value at the time was £1,500 which in today's terms would be something approaching £90,000, an extraordinary sum. In his book 'The reminiscences of a Literary Life' published in 1836, the Rev TF Dibdin wrote:

"…We could never prevail upon its owner to wear it except on the birthday of one of his children." Jenner was also elected an honorary member of the Royal Society of Gottingjen and his name by now was revered around Europe. There was a Dr Davids of Rotterdam who had earlier received lymph from Jenner and he wrote:

"The name of Jenner is adored…vaccination was introduced just at the moment the smallpox made ravages through the whole country, but, thank God, not one is infected after the vaccine."

Dr de Carro who had done so much to help Jenner get vaccination known and accepted around Europe, wrote to Mr Ring:

"After three years of success I need not tell you what I think of vaccination… Remember me to Dr Jenner. No medical man ever excited my admiration and veneration so much. He is not only great by the magnitude of his discovery, but he is also great by the manner in which he conducted his researches; by the perfection that he gave to them before he published his work, and by the extreme modesty with which he speaks of himself. His fame increases daily."

We have learned of only a few countries that have accepted the vaccine virus but in fact it was spreading round the world and Jenner's assertion that the smallpox would be completely wiped out which he had forecast in his 'The Origin of the Vaccine Inoculation' which had been printed in 1801 was looking to be a very sound statement indeed. Not only that, but a very brave one considering the amount of dissent that the whole idea of cowpox vaccination having such an effect had been voiced, and sadly, many of those voices being qualified and experienced physicians from Jenner's own country. However, despite his huge success with the vaccination and the inevitable fame that went with it, Jenner was running into financial problems due to the fact that he had not tried to keep his ideas secret, but in fact had freely shared his methods meaning he received little financial benefit from his unselfishness. Many people thought that something had to be done for the man who had saved so many lives and the problem had to be addressed.

It took a little while, but over the next few years, the problem would be looked at sympathetically with the hope that it would be rectified.

Something did happen that cheered Jenner greatly, because at the end of 1799, he learned that he was to be granted an audience with King George III. He wrote to his great friend Edward Gardner:

"Great news from St James's. The King has sent me a very civil message, so you will produce a page to wait upon his majesty and express the obligation." Early in March when it had all been arranged, he wrote to WF Shrapnell: "What will you give for a sight of me all in velvet, girt with a sword too? What a queer creature is a human being!" We can be sure that Shrapnell was not fooled by the letter for a minute. Jenner was poking fun at the upcoming proceedings, but in truth he loved it, and the audience took place on 7th March 1800. And why shouldn't he love it? It was not only the work that he had done on the elimination of smallpox that had brought this audience about, but the opposition to it received by so many of his contemporaries that year in year out he had been forced to reply to. Jenner was presented to the king by his friend, the 5th Earl of Berkeley, and the sovereign gave his permission that the second edition of the 'Inquiry' should be dedicated to him. The word 'permission' in this context meant that it was a Royal Command. The first edition was dedicated to Jenner's friend Caleb Hillier Parry but we can assume that he raised no objection.

That day in March was much more than a mere audience with the King, a treasured day to be remembered but not much more. It was anything but. The approval of the King meant that Jenner's work received nationwide approval which the anti-vaccinators couldn't compete with. Later that year, Jenner received a letter from a doctor in Hadleigh in Suffolk, which read as follows:

"I am happy to inform you, that in spite of ignorant prejudice, and wilful misrepresentation, this wonderful discovery is spreading far and wide in this county. The first people we vaccinated in Hadleigh were pelted, and drove into their houses, if they appeared out. We have now persuaded our apothecary to vaccinate the whole town (700 or 800 persons)...a physician at Ipswich has taken it up in a very liberal manner."

Jenner based himself in London for the early part of 1800 taking advantage of his audience with the King, and spent that time promoting the theory and practice of vaccination which at the same time would have the effect of ramming home the faults of variolation. Jenner felt, and he was surely right in this assumption, that the two cures could not live with each other. All the while variolation was practiced, the smallpox would always exist. It had to be vaccination or it was nothing, and Jenner was determined that in the long run, vaccination would win the day.

-oOOo-

Chapter 12
Dr Jenner's Finances – What Can Be Done to Help?

At the beginning of the 19th century, his finances, or lack of them were beginning to worry Dr Jenner, and many learned people in the medical profession felt strongly that he should be recompensed for the incredible achievements in the treatment of smallpox that he had brought about. Dr Samuel Johnson (1709–84) never needed to work again after spending years producing his extraordinary dictionary and after the countless lives that Jenner had saved, there was a feeling amongst many that the same type of reward should be given to him. Johnson's dictionary affected people's lives as most of the dictionaries printed since then have been based on his remarkable book that he produced in 1755. Jenner's work was different, but whilst taking nothing away from the extraordinary piece of work that Johnson produced, Jenner's work saved millions of lives and it is now recognised that the terrible scourge of smallpox has been wiped away from our lives.

Jenner had been desperate to find a way of eliminating smallpox for years, and for his ideas to work, it was essential for him to let his techniques be known throughout the world. However, this meant that he had forfeited any monetary gains that he would have made by keeping his ideas a secret, but now the reality was beginning to dawn on him. Unfortunately, Jenner still had his critics from the medical world so it was not going to be easy as would seem to get an award through for him. Some of them were powerful voices too, and one of them was Dr Thomas Beddoes (1760–1808) of Bristol, an eminent medical practitioner at that time. Beddoes was a physician and writer and who was considered to be a brilliant man who between 1798 and 1801 worked at his Medical Pneumatic Institute in Clifton and had taken on Humphrey (later to be knighted) Davy (1778–1829) where they both discovered the beneficial effects of laughing gas as an anaesthetic. On 25th February 1798, Beddoes told a German Medical Writer that: "The facts which I have collected are not favourable to his (Jenner's) opinion that cowpox gives complete immunity from the natural infection of smallpox." Strong words from a formidable person but there was more.

Another was Dr Benjamin Moseley who had been Physician to the Royal Medical Hospital in London for thirty years. He enjoyed a high reputation and as mentioned earlier in the book, had written a number of important journals on the subject of tropical diseases over the years. This was as a result of him having practiced medicine in Jamaica over a number of years and he was totally opposed to human beings being vaccinated with any matter emanating from animals. James Gillray (1757–1815), the famous cartoonist latched on to this and produced his extraordinary, some would say horrifying, cartoon previously mentioned on page 138 showing a crowd of people who had been vaccinated with cowpox with parts of cows growing out of their bodies. Obviously, medical men would not be swayed by this cartoon produced as it was by a man who was later to be certified as insane, but it did not help the population as a whole having confidence in the vaccination process.

However, Jenner was not going to take this criticism lying down, he believed in the theory and the practice of the vaccination process, and he had come back with three papers in three years showing the great successes that he had had. He felt that any failures were probably due to the incorrect way that many vaccinations had been carried out. His papers included the correct method of how long to store the vaccine matter and went on to carefully explain how to carry out vaccinations themselves. Despite opposition from people such as mentioned above, many senior men in the medical world came out and showed clearly that they were on Jenner's side. One such was Dr John Coakley Lettsome (1744–1815). Lettsome had become a physician as well as a philanthropist and he was a powerful man to have on Jenner's side.

Another powerful man, despite not having had medical training, was the 5th Earl of Berkeley (1745–1810), who along with some grateful residents of the county along with some of Jenner's friends, got together and wrote a testimonial stating their appreciation of his work in the elimination of smallpox. It was printed in the Gloucester Journal of 21st December 1801. This stated:

"Many of the Noblemen and most respectful gentlemen of the County of Gloucester having expressed a wish that some public Acknowledgement should be made to Dr JENNER for his singularly happy and ingenious discovery of

VACCINE INOCULATION: We, the undersigned, desirous of promoting so laudable and so patriotic a design, have commenced a Subscription for carrying the same into Effect… We trust it will only be the Prelude to a Remuneration in some degree adequate to his deserts, and to which he has the best-founded claim on the gratitude of the British Nation."

Jenner was not quite going broke, but he certainly made little or no money from his incredible achievement mainly due to the fact that his generous mind stopped him keeping his findings secret. To put this matter right, Jenner would have to face a Parliamentary Committee which we have already alluded to in a previous chapter. This had to be the case due to the fact that his long-term aim was to eradicate the disease from the whole world, and this meant sharing his knowledge with just about everyone. However, this produced not just a strain on his finances, but also on his nerves as many learned medical men said that his methods were not infallible. Unfortunately, too many of them had not learned the simple truth that a little knowledge is a dangerous thing and were vaccinating people carelessly. It was not just a question of giving a healthy patient a swab of cowpox in the hope of a cure, because the cowpox would not work if smallpox was variolated in to the patient after too short a time, such as five days which was much too soon for the vaccine to work. The very minimum time would have been ten days and even then, it would be better to leave it a few more days after that. Also, it had to be stored correctly and then the final test was not to keep it too long as stale cowpox was just as ineffective as cowpox that had been vaccinated too early.

Jenner had little to do with politics or politicians, not because he didn't like them, but he hadn't felt it necessary to have much contact with them in order to do his job. However, things were now going to change as in order to obtain some monetary reward for the work that he had carried out and was still to carry out on smallpox, he was going to have to face a Parliamentary Committee in order for this to happen. If Jenner was to receive a Treasury grant, he was told that he had to arrange for a petition to be drawn up and presented to the House by one of its leading members. Jenner by now hated being in London as he would much preferred to have been able to retreat back to his beloved Berkeley but it could not be so until at least the grant could be sorted out. Jenner had gone to London on 19th December 1801, and on 12th January 1802, had an audience with the Prime Minister, Henry Addington (1757–1844), and he also saw William Pitt (1759–1806), who had resigned as Prime Minister on 5th February 1801 due to the Irish problem although having been in the top job since December 1783, was still considered to be a very senior member of the House of Commons. As it happened, Pitt returned to the job of Prime Minister on the 10th May 1804 as Addington's government was thought to be very ineffective. Jenner also met with William Wilberforce (1759–1833), a leading member of the anti-slavery movement.

The time leading up to the hearing was a nightmare for Jenner. Endless meetings, letters and interviews were lined up and Jenner had his own speech to prepare. It must have seemed that he would have to go through all the arguments again as to why the vaccination process was successful before he could be presented to the House of Commons Committee in order that that august body would be able to judge the payment that could be made to him. All that he wanted was to get the proceedings over with and get out of London and go back to his tranquil and peaceful Berkeley and resume his normal practice as soon as was possible. Whether that would ever be a realistic ambition he was not yet sure. At first he had the ordeal of a long and protracted Committee in order to convince the members of the House of the worth of the vaccination process.

After what seemed like an eternity, the petition was drawn up and presented to the House of Commons on 17th March 1802. It held its first meeting on 22nd March which was chaired by Admiral Berkeley, the 5th Earl of Berkeley's brother. Edward's nephew, the Revd George Charles Jenner (1769–1846) attended the proceedings in order to take notes which he did and published them under the title 'The Evidence at Large as Laid Before the Committee of the House of Commons Respecting Dr Jenner's Discovery of Vaccination'.

The inquiry started off on the right foot, three main questions to be answered one way or another. The three questions were:

1) Were the effects of vaccination entirely beneficial?
2) Was Dr Jenner the discoverer of vaccination?
3) What pecuniary advantage or increase in practice had he reaped from it?

Admiral Berkeley started the proceedings with a speech that was entirely on Jenner's side and finished with a plea that Jenner should receive an award of £10,000. It was a strange way of starting the meeting as the Admiral actually thought that the sum should be higher, rather in the region of £20,000 but for some reason he started with the lower figure. One can only guess why he pitched the sum at a low amount. Doubtless he was aware of the fact that the country was at war with France and many of the population were starving, there being no benefit payments that we enjoy today if out of work. The other reason could be that he pitched it at a fairly low level in the hope that someone else would substantially increase the suggested amount once the committee members had got into their stride. However, as what happens in all such meetings, the discussions were a lengthy affair and there would be plenty of time for the final figure to be raised. Jenner then had his say which he had already prepared and was reading from a paper. After that, it was opened to the floor and there were many speeches and one can only guess at the amount of hours that took place where certain points were repeated many times by different members, not all of whom had Jenner's respect. This went on and on and after several days of this Jenner was getting tetchy and complained bitterly to his long-time friend from their schooldays together in Cirencester, Henry Hicks:

"Having been put in possession of the laws of vaccination by so great a number of the first medical men of the world…they should not have listened to every blockhead who chose to send up a supposed case of its imperfection; but this is the plan pursued, and if they do not give up they may sit to the end of their lives."

Although the expression had yet to be invented, Jenner was obviously one of those who subscribed to the view that 'a camel is a horse designed by a meeting'.

Despite having Henry Hicks to unburden himself on, the normally placid Jenner was growing increasingly irritable. He had already had his say and the people who had spoken against him were unable to substantiate their arguments in any coherent way, in fact it seemed that Jenner's speech early in the proceedings had bypassed them completely as they ploughed on through their already prepared speeches ignoring the facts that Jenner had already laid out before them.

Not even Hicks could console him. Hicks had come a long way since he and Jenner were friends at school. He had lived in Easington since childhood and rose to become the Lord of the Manor there and was the owner of a considerable amount of land, along with some properties and mills. Hicks had a great deal of confidence in his friend and allowed him to vaccinate two of his children along with sixteen servants from the Churchend mill. The inoculations took place on 27th November 1798. Jenner was later to write:

"Having been requested by my friend, Mr Henry Hicks of Easington in this county, to inoculate two of his children and at the same time some of his servants and the people employed in his manufactory, matter was taken from the arm of this boy (a farm boy in Stonehouse) for the purpose. The numbers inoculated were eighteen. They all took this infection and either on the fifth or sixth day a vesicle was perceptible on the punctured part. Some of them began to feel a little unwell on the eighth day, but the greater number on the ninth. Their illness, as in the former cases described was of short duration, and not sufficient to interrupt, but at very short intervals, the children from their amusements, or the servants and manufacturers from following their ordinary business.

"Three of the children whose employment in the manufactory was in some degree laborious had an inflammation on their arms beyond the common boundary about the eleventh or twelfth day, when the feverish symptoms which before were nearly gone off again, returned, accompanied with increase of axillary tumour. In the cases (clearly perceiving that the symptoms were governed by the state of the arms), I applied on the inoculated pustules, and renewed the application three or four times within an hour, a pledget of lint, previously soaked in aqua lythargyri acetati and covered the hot efflorescence surrounding them with cloths dipped in cold water. The next day I found this simple mode of treatment had succeeded perfectly."

Having Henry Hicks as a friend that he could trust completely was of great comfort to Jenner and the latter had written a personal dedication to Hicks inside the cover of one of his books, 'An Inquiry into the Causes and Effects of the Variolae Vaccinae, a Disease discovered in Some of the Western Counties'.

Going back to the hearing, of the laymen present, one of the first to speak on Jenner's behalf was another great friend, Edward Gardner, who Jenner had known for many years and confided in him on all his personal and professional matters. Gardner was not a doctor, but as he was a faithful friend to Jenner over many years, he was able to get across to the committee members of Jenner's initial enthusiasm and why they should support a qualified doctor who had been tutored by the great John Hunter. Jenner also had William Cuff, a master of drawing and who could show the difference between cowpox and smallpox pustules, the difference being very hard to detect. Gardner also explained that the difficulty of seeing the difference was experienced by Mr Savis, a vaccinator who practiced in Bath. The Duke of Clarence (1765–1837), George the IV's brother, who ruled as William IV from 1830 until his own death in 1837 which ended the Georgian era and led to the Victorian era, also gave his support to Jenner. Clarence said that his coach driver would not accept being vaccinated which resulted in him catching smallpox and nearly lost his life in the process. Clarence also told the committee that his servants at Bushey Palace, regardless of their health and whether they had ever been infected with the smallpox or not, all slept in the kitchen with the food that was being cooked there, and before vaccination came in, deaths from smallpox amongst the soldiers of the regiments of light dragoons, along with their wives who billeted in the stables, were very high, but after vaccination had been introduced, the deaths had virtually ceased.

The evidence given by Admiral Berkeley, Edward Gardner and the Duke of Clarence was very helpful to Jenner in as much as they were all supportive of him, and their views were noted by the committee even though they were not medical people. However, what Jenner needed more than anything else was medical heavyweights, and fortunately for him, there was no shortage of them.

The first was Sir Walter Farquhar, who was the surgeon-in-ordinary to the Prince of Wales. Farquhar was in no doubt when asked about the effectiveness of vaccination and he told the committee that it was the greatest discovery made for many years. Sometime previously, Farquhar had told Jenner that had he practiced medicine in London, he could expect to earn around £10,000 per annum which translated into a figure in 2019, would be roughly £600,000. To earn in excess of half a million pounds per annum would turn the heads of most doctors at the time, but it didn't register with Jenner at all. He was determined to give all of his time and skills to eliminate smallpox, but if he stayed in London and took Farquhar's advice, the disease would spread and Jenner's work would ultimately fail. This is precisely what he had told the Prime Minister, Henry Addington (1757–1844) when the two men had met on 12th January 1802 as mentioned earlier.

Dr Henry Cline (1750–1827) was a surgeon in St Thomas's hospital, and had been left some dry pus in a quill by Jenner some time before on one of Jenner's visits to London. After some initial doubts, Cline was a convert, and the reason was this. When Jenner had left Cline with some dried cowpox on that earlier visit, he had little hope that Cline would be interested and given Cline's manner on receiving the cow-pox pus, Jenner was correct in his assumption. However, Cline like Jenner, had once been a pupil of Dr John Hunter, and he was not averse to trying something new. He was now a surgeon at St Thomas's Hospital and had a boy in his charge with an inflamed hip joint. He had run out of ideas as to how to treat the boy and as a last resort, inserted some of the pus that Jenner had left into the young patient's hip hoping that the inflammation would be diverted into a different spot. Much to his amazement, this treatment worked, and Cline wrote a letter to Jenner a short while after he, Jenner, had arrived back in Cheltenham. The letter read as follows:

My dear Sir,

The cow-pox experiment has succeeded admirably. The child sickened on the seventh day, and the fever, which was moderate, subsided on the eleventh. The inflammation arising from the insertion of the virus extended to about four inches in diameter, and then gradually subsided, without having been attended with pain or other inconvenience. There were no eruptions.

Dr Lister, who was formerly physician to the smallpox hospital, attended the child with me and he is convinced that it is not possible to give him the smallpox. I think the substituting of the cow-pox poison for the smallpox promises to be one of the greatest improvements that has ever been made in medicine, and the more I think on the subject the more I am impressed with its importance.

With great esteem,
I am etc.

Henry Cline
Lincoln's Inn Fields,
August 9th, 1798.

Henry Cline was unenthusiastic when Jenner had left the quills containing the cow pox, but after his successful treatment of the young patient with the inflamed hip, had completely changed his mind and was now in Jenner's corner. He told the committee that: "It is the greatest discovery ever made in the practice of Physic for the preservation of human life; as the smallpox has been more destructive than any other disease." Another witness was Dr Blane, F.R.S., who was the assistant surgeon to the regiment who were based in Hounslow, where it was claimed that two of his soldiers had died after vaccination. Blane dismissed this as no help whatsoever because he said that the lancets with which it was claimed that the soldiers had been vaccinated with, had supposedly been full of the cowpox pustule, but he told the committee that they had been mixed up with lancets that were full of smallpox making any findings completely useless. Blane went on to say that his view was, that if vaccination was made compulsory, an average of ninety-three lives would be saved per year in the United Kingdom alone. His statement was based on the statistics that had been put together by Dr Heberden. Dr Blane was right to use Heberden's statistics as the latter was a very well-respected physician.

Dr William Heberden (1710–1801) was born in London on 13th August 1710 and became a famous physician. When he was young he attended Saint Saviour's school and in 1724 at the age of just 14 years, was sent to St John's College, Cambridge and obtained a Fellowship in 1730 before becoming an M.A. in 1732 and in 1739, took the degree of M.D. In 1746, he became a member of the Royal College of Physicians whereupon he stayed in Cambridge for another ten years practicing medicine before moving to London and was elected as a Fellow of the Royal Society in 1749. It was in London that he continued his medical practice for another thirty years.

Heberden was a classical scholar and was a highly respected physician. He published several papers in the Philosophical Transactions of the Royal Society and two of these which were considered the best were papers on chickenpox which was published in 1767 and angina pectoris the following year, and these papers helped confirm his high standing as a physician. These were obviously subjects, dear to Jenner's heart so it is understandable why Heberden's findings were used to support Jenner's case. In his private life Heberden married Elizabeth Martin in 1752 but she died in 1754 having given birth to their only child. He then married again, this time to a lady named Mary Wollaston and the couple produced eight children, one of them, William Heberden the Younger (1767–1845) followed his father into medicine, and whilst becoming a successful and respected physician, never quite became so well known as his father.

There were dissidents of course, most of whom supported the treatment that came before Jenner's vaccination, and this was variolation which we have already learned was so risky as it involved giving a healthy person a small dose of the actual smallpox itself. If the patient recovered, then it worked but it was very risky and would sometimes lead to the death of a previously healthy person. It also did little to actually eliminate the spread of smallpox.

One of these dissidents was a Dr Benjamin Moseley (1746–1819) who was totally unconvinced about the value of vaccination. We have no research material suggesting that he had put much work in to the subject which drew him to that conclusion, but he was a respected physician whose views the committee listened to. He was born in 1746 on the north Essex coast. His father, Edward, was thought to have made his living as a sheep farmer supplying wool to the rest of the world. Benjamin Moseley trained as a doctor in London, Leiden and Paris and in 1767 settled in Kingston, Jamaica where he earned his living as a surgeon apothecary and on 9th January 1768 married Martha Clare. There is an entry in the parish register for St Osyth recording the fact that after an outbreak of smallpox, 86 people died. We can only take an educated guess as to whether he looked into a cure for smallpox at that time, but he certainly favoured the variolation as carried out by the Suttons than the vaccination method which Jenner had introduced. To be fair to Moseley, his pro-variolation views were formed thirty years before Jenner vaccinated the young James Phipps, and perhaps he felt no need to change the method of treatment which may have felt to him was a satisfactory way of treating the disease. Of vaccination, he was supposed to have said: "There is no reasoning with minds in a state of inflammation, showing a rather arrogant attitude to those who felt passionately about this new method of treatment for smallpox." Moseley was a friend of Lord Nelson (1758–1805) and he spent thirty years of his career as Physician to the Royal Medical Hospital, Chelsea, and so that many people would be swayed by his opinions. Moseley's views on vaccination were fixed and in 1799 he published a pamphlet entitled 'A Treatise on Sugar with Miscellaneous Medical Observations'. Included in the latter part of this pamphlet were written some very negative views on what he termed 'Cowmania' which were written to negate the work of Jenner.

Mr John Birch (1744–1815), surgeon to St Thomas's Hospital was also unhelpful to Jenner's cause. He had previously attended an anniversary dinner at Guy's Hospital in which he found to his consternation that the sole purpose was to canvas names in order to support Jenner's petition to Parliament. Birch refused point blank to sign it so there was to be no help for Jenner from that quarter. He said of the cowpox vaccination that it was 'a subject he had not much attended to, as he did not like it.' In other words, he had carried out little or no study of the question and wasn't very interested in doing so, therefore he would simply carry on with the beneficial, as he saw it, treatment of smallpox with variolation.

The reason that Birch had carried out little work on studying the vaccination process was due to the fact that he had merely declared his complete confidence with the method of variolation that Baron Thomas Dimsdale F.R.S. (1712–1800) favoured. After being a believer of variolation for so many years, he was certainly not going to bother himself with carrying out any work that would challenge his own beliefs that were wedded so closely to those of Baron Dimsdale.

Dimsdale certainly had enjoyed a varied and successful career. He was born on 29th May 1712 to his Quaker father John and his wife Susan. He was not only an English doctor but in his long life he had also been a banker and a politician who sat in the House of Commons for ten years from 1780 until 1790. He was also created Baron Dimsdale of the Russian Empire by Catherine the Great (1729–96) who was Empress of Russia from 1762. A formidable and learned woman, she corresponded throughout her life with Voltaire (1694–78), the French writer and historian. Known for her ambitious but totally impractical ideas, she once even came up with the idea of expelling the British from India. It eventually happened of course, but at that time one can imagine that the response would have been something like, "Good luck with that one." She was obviously ahead of her time by roughly two hundred years. Returning to Dimsdale, he was initially trained in medicine by his father and then moved on to St Thomas's Hospital in London. He became interested in the treatment of smallpox and favoured the method of variolation whereby a healthy person was inoculated with a small amount of smallpox in the hope that they would completely recover and thereby be immune from the full-blown disease. As we have already seen, in many cases it did work but it was risky and even if that patient did make a full recovery it wouldn't necessarily stop the disease from spreading. However, Jenner's method would stop the disease as he predicted in his 1801 pamphlet 'The Origin of the Vaccine Inoculation', in fact making the then extraordinarily brave claim that the disease would be wiped out entirely. Jenner was right although it would take time and he knew that he wouldn't live to see it.

However, returning to John Birch, he simply would not budge and followed the example of Baron Dimsdale who in 1767 had published 'The Present Method of Inoculating for the Smallpox' and in that same year was elected a Fellow of the Royal Society. Birch said that he had seen patients at St Thomas's who he felt had been vaccinated with the cowpox but nevertheless had caught smallpox. This was reason enough for him to dismiss Jenner's methods but this statement was quite useless in evaluating Jenner's claims as Birch had not seen the patients vaccinated, and for all he knew, they could have been given smallpox rather than cowpox. Birch was questioned further about so-called vaccinations that had been unsuccessful but gave vague replies and fortunately the committee did not pay much heed to his views.

The evidence supplied by the next witness, Dr Saunders, was very helpful to Jenner's cause, not simply because he was in favour of vaccination but his evidence was clear and concise and he answered all of the questions put to him showing that he had a great deal more knowledge and interest than the languid Dr Birch possessed. Sir William Saunders was born in 1743 although we do not know the exact date. He was a Scottish physician and was the first President of the Royal Medical Chirurgical Society. He was born in Banff, Scotland, the son of a doctor, James Saunders, and he graduated as M.D. at the University of Edinburgh, the alma mater of so many leading physicians at that time, in 1765. A few years later, he moved to London where he became a physician at Guy's Hospital in 1770, and along with the normal work that he undertook with patients, he also lectured on a regular basis on various medical matters. In 1790, Saunders was elected a Fellow of the Royal College of Physicians and it was to this august body that he delivered the Goulstonian lecture of 1792 on diseases of the liver. The following year, 1793, saw him elected as a Fellow of the Royal Society, the society that all men of medicine and science wanted to be part of. He was a founding member of the Royal Medical and Chirugical Society and in 1805 was elected their first President. In 1807, he gained yet another accolade when he was appointed Physician Extraordinary to the Prince of Wales, later to become the Prince Regent, and who eventually reigned as King George IV from 1820 until 1830. Saunders retired in 1814 after a lengthy and distinguished career and died in Enfield, London in 1817. To have such a man as a supporting witness was obviously going to carry great weight to Jenner's cause.

Here are just two examples of the questions that he was asked and the answers that he gave:

Question: Do you conceive the new system of inoculation introduced by Dr Jenner to be perfectly safe, and an efficacious preventive of smallpox?

Dr Saunders: Yes I do, provided the vaccine virus be properly introduced into the system and goes through its complete progress.

Question: What is your general opinion of the vaccine inoculation?

Dr Saunders: That it is one of the most important discoveries ever made for the benefit of the human race, and that if the practice continue and prevail it bids fair ultimately to extirpate the poison of the natural smallpox.

There we have it, two totally unequivocal answers given by Dr Saunders that were completely different from those given by Dr Birch, both in tone and content and Saunders makes exactly the same claim as Dr Jenner makes, that is, the total eradication of the disease of smallpox.

The answers that Dr Saunders gave not only cheered Jenner, but also Admiral Berkeley, the Chairman of this committee. As chairman, Berkeley would have been expected to be neutral on this case, but he was not. How could he be? He was a friend of Jenner's who looked after the family's health. He must have been as pleased as Jenner was that not only had they just interviewed a witness who had given the committee clear answers, they were also the answers that Jenner along with Admiral Berkeley wanted to hear.

The next witness was Dr Joseph Marshall who described a trial that had taken place at the Foundling Hospital at Naples although he was not there himself to witness it. A large number of children had been vaccinated and had been exposed to smallpox both by variolation and also sleeping with people who had been infected with the disease. None of these children who had been vaccinated caught smallpox, and whilst it seemed to be a fairly rough and ready way of experimenting as to the worth of the powers of the cowpox, it certainly worked in Jenner's favour so far as the committee were concerned. Dr Marshall was eventually appointed to be Physician Extraordinary to King George III who had reigned from 1760 until 1820 when he died, although his son, the Prince of Wales, due to the illness that his father suffered in the latter stages of his life, effectively ruled as Prince Regent from 1811 until 1820 and then from 1820 until 1830 as George IV until his own death.

There followed a witness by the name of Dr Thomas Dale although it is not clear how much weight his answers carried with the committee. He had to admit that he had no experience of vaccination but had been assured that it worked by another doctor who was 'highly deserving of credit' It is not clear as to whether he named this person, but if he did not, although the Statement supported Jenner, it probably carried little weight with the committee.

We then come to the next witness who was Dr John Coakley Lettsom (1744–1815) who we have already seen was a close friend of the brilliant Benjamin Franklin (1706–90) who was involved in the fight for American independence while Dr Lettsom helped get the vaccination process known in that new country. He was a powerful witness for Dr Jenner to have on his side. The committee asked him if he thought that inoculation with the smallpox, in other words, variolation, had lessened the deaths caused by the smallpox. Lettsom's answer was very brief and very much to the point. He simply answered 'No'. However, he then added 'I think it has increased the number of deaths by extending the disease'. Not only was Lettsom's answer straight to the point and was more effective because of it, he brought written proof in the form of bills of mortality which clearly showed that just as the popularity of smallpox inoculation (variolation) had increased, so had the number of deaths by smallpox increased by the same proportion. After he had mustered his papers, he said: 'no less than 36,000 of our fellow-subjects are annually sacrificed by the smallpox, but out of 60,000 vaccinated only three have died, and they not of the smallpox.' If accurate, and we have no reason to suppose that they are not, this was devastating evidence which was very much in Jenner's favour.

Dr Matthew Baillie (1761–1823), a nephew of John Hunter, also came down heavily on Jenner's side. Amongst his evidence he made a definitive statement: 'I believe the benefits to be so great that in my opinion it is the most important discovery that has ever been made in medicine'. Whilst we have seen only the main statement that he made here, we have looked at Matthew Baillie's career earlier in the book when Jenner was a student of John Hunter's. However, a small reminder of Baillie's brilliant career will show the reader just what a powerful witness in Jenner's favour that Baillie was. Matthew Baillie was born in Shotts Manse, Lanarkshire on 27th October 1761, the son of Professor Revd James Baillie and Dorothea Hunter. Matthew's sister was Joanna Baillie (1762–1851), the well-known poet who followed her aunt Anne Hunter (nee Home) into writing poetry and who lived between 1742 and 1821.

Matthew Baillie (1761–1823) was taught both by Dr Thomas Denman (1733–1815) an eminent obstetrician who practiced in London at the end of the 18th century and early part of the 19th century, and also with his famous uncle, the physician, Dr John Hunter (1728–93) who taught Edward Jenner between 1770 and 1773. Matthew Baillie was educated in the grammar school in Hamilton which changed its name to the Hamilton Academy in 1848 before Baillie moved in order to attend the University of Glasgow. After leaving Glasgow he attended the University of Oxford where he received his M.D. in 1789. Given his background, his views had to be taken seriously which indeed they were. Baillie's early tutor, Thomas Denman, M.D. (1733–1815), had come to London in 1753, at the age of twenty years, and studied medicine at St George's Hospital. By 1791, after a brilliant career, he amassed a fortune and purchased a house in Feltham, Middlesex. He intended to retire there, but in fact he semi-retired because although he had given up any ideas of setting up his practice again, he continued with consultations only. He died on 26th November, 1815 at his town house in London and was buried at St James' Church in Piccadilly, London.

The 6th Baronet, Dr Sir Richard Croft (1762–1816), was an English physician to the Royal Family. After Dr Baillie had given his evidence, Dr Croft added amongst other favourable opinions: 'Should vaccine inoculation be generally introduced I think it may be productive of greater blessings to mankind than any other discovery that has ever been made in medicine'. He later cleared up uses of the cowpox vaccination that had seemingly failed and this was often happening when the person carrying out the vaccination had not been properly trained.

Another witness, Dr James Lind, F.R.S., F.R.S.E., F.R.C.P.E., (1736–1812), an eminent physician, suggested to the committee that a marine who had been vaccinated and was thought to have caught smallpox had in fact caught chickenpox as the diseases were similar but that chickenpox was far less life threatening. This Dr James Lind is often confused with the Dr James Lind (1716–94) who had carried out work on the curing of scurvy that affected 18th century sailors. As both men shared the same name and were in the same profession, it is very possible that the two men were cousins but we have no direct evidence of this.

Dr Francis Knight was another physician who was on the side of Jenner. Knight had vaccinated the Duke of Clarence's mistress, Mrs Jordan, along with two of the many children that they had had together. Mrs Jordan and the children recovered and so the vaccination was a success. Knight then took matter from one of the Duke's and Mrs Jordan's children and vaccinated a ten-year-old girl who lived in a village where there was an outbreak of smallpox. It appeared that she contracted smallpox but this was most unlikely as she suffered no ill effects.

Dr Knight was totally supportive of vaccination being the answer to the cure of smallpox. He said: "To the want of knowledge which the eye of experience gives I attribute the whole of the discredit that has occasionally been thrown on the cowpox."

Dr John Ring was another witness who was asked by the committee:

"What, in your opinion, will be the consequence of vaccine inoculation?"

Dr Ring replied that it would be the 'annihilation of the smallpox'.

John Ring was a surgeon at St Thomas's Hospital, London and he had been tutored by both William Hunter (1718–83) and his ultimately more famous brother John Hunter (1728–1793), the latter being Edward Jenner's mentor. Ring was also a poet and classicist and a medical journalist. We do not know when he and Jenner first met but we do know that at some stage after Dr Benjamin Moseley's (1746–1819) comments on the so-called 'Cowmania' that Jenner's supporters were supposed to be suffering from, Jenner wrote to Ring in 1799 to thank him for his support in attacking Moseley's views. At that stage Ring was an ardent supporter of Jenner's vaccination but he overdid it. From 1799 he wrote thousands of words in defence of the vaccination that his friend Jenner had to endure, and this went on for fifteen years. Everything he wrote was totally uncritical of vaccination and there is a fine line between friendship and hero worship and Jenner felt that Dr Ring had crossed that line. People with genuine doubts about vaccination were attacked in print by Ring, and Jenner, although not wishing to be unkind, decided that Ring's support for him was making him a liability and he started to put some distance between himself and Ring. In 1811, Jenner wrote to his friend and future biographer, John Baron, that 'poor John Ring's derangements' were due to 'mental irritation of the most painful kind'.

Jenner was aware of the fact that Dr Ring had vaccinated more people than anyone else in the country, and James Moore who was then Assistant Director of the National Vaccine Establishment wrote that Ring had 'vaccinated vast numbers of the poor' and 'distributed to the friends and enemies of the Vaccine both lymph and sarcasms with equal liberality'.

Jenner was later to write to Ring but received no reply so that he then wrote to Moore to ask why Ring had stopped answering his letters for at least a year. We do not know what Moore's reply was but it does seem quite extraordinary given Jenner's written criticisms of Ring for Jenner to ask such a question. This was the second important person that Jenner seemed to upset as we have seen on page 130 when he fell out with Dr George Pearson (1751–1828). However, it was a slightly different reason as it appeared to Jenner that Pearson was claiming more credit for the Vaccine discovery that he should have done.

Now before we look at the final decision of the committee concerning whether Jenner was entitled to compensation and if so, by what amount, we should mention the fact that there were people who claimed that they had in fact discovered the vaccine before Jenner did, and probably the most important one was a farmer by the name of Benjamin Jesty who farmed near Yetminster in

Dorset. Jesty, like so many others, had heard that dairymaids who had caught cowpox never caught the much more dangerous smallpox. Both Jesty in his youth and later two of his servants, Ann Notley and Mary Read had caught cowpox, the servants later nursing relatives who had caught smallpox but they had remained free of the disease. In 1774, there was an outbreak of smallpox in the area and Jesty had a wife and two children who had never caught either cowpox or smallpox. Although it was to be over twenty years before Jenner was able to perform the first vaccination, Jesty took a huge risk and without any prior training, took his wife and two children to the area where the cows were grazing and after first scratching their arms with a needle, rubbed in matter from the pustules on the infected cow's udder. By doing this, he had in fact vaccinated his family. He was either a very brave man or a foolish one because he possessed no medical qualifications at all.

Thankfully, all three survived but not without drama that caused Jesty to cease both promoting the idea or ever carrying the as yet untried treatment ever again. Both the children were fine and recovered well, but unfortunately Mrs Jesty didn't and became very ill to the point where it was thought that her life was in danger. Jesty called in a Mr Read, who was a surgeon from Carne, and Jesty explained to him what he had done. We do not know exactly what Mr Read's attitude was on hearing of this or whether he ever treated Mrs Jesty, but the villagers got to hear of it and all the while she was ill, Jesty was treated like a leper. When stories that alarm people spread, they tend to get exaggerated along the way, and all the while Mrs Jesty was ill, her husband was pelted with stones and mud and shunned by everyone in the village. He was even likened to that of a murderer, but Jesty was a courageous man and carried on with his work as a farmer while all this furore was going on. Thankfully, in time his wife recovered, and the hysteria faded away and village life settled down but although deeply relieved, Jesty never tried the cowpox vaccination again.

The story of Benjamin Jesty was laid before the House of Commons Committee and Dr George Pearson (1751–1828), who had earlier tried to give the impression that it was in fact he, and not Jenner who had first come up with the idea, was now trying to find people who had come up with the cowpox vaccine idea before Jenner, and therefore before him, Dr Pearson. In her excellent book 'Doctor Jenner of Berkeley', Dorothy Fisk explains that Pearson had tried to prove to the committee that there were several people who had come up with the idea before Jenner, but if that was the case, it would have meant that they would have beaten Pearson himself to finding the cowpox vaccine. Perhaps he was trying to find possible claimants who were not strong candidates, and that he, Pearson, was the rightful person to claim the credit. If this was the case, it was muddle headed and did him no good at all. Pearson was aware of the story of Benjamin Jesty, but he was not aware of all the facts and so could make little capital out of the story to the committee.

Out of all the people whose names were put forward as being worthy of recognition, Benjamin Jesty had by far the strongest claim. The Vaccine-Pock Institution of which Dr Pearson was part, brought him to London in 1805 for the first and only time in his life, and presented him with a testimonial along with gold mounted lancets which was felt he thoroughly deserved. One doctor by the name of Bell went further and said that if Jesty had taken his findings outside the confines of his immediate family, and publicised them more, then he would have warranted further recognition. This is arguable as Jesty did not have the medical knowledge that Jenner had and whilst the risk he took with his family was brave, it was no more than simply putting into practice that which dairymaids had known for decades, whilst Jenner studied the cowpox, and refined the procedure by showing others how it should be stored, how long it should be before patients were variolated after vaccination and what length of time it took before the stored cowpox was of no benefit for use.

However, returning to some of the witnesses who were brought before the committee, Dr Pearson produced others who felt that they had a prior claim and one of these was a surgeon from Axminster, Mr Nicholas Bragge who wrote to Sir William Elford, who as it happened was a member of the Committee, and in the letter he claimed that he, Bragge, had carried out experiments more than thirty years before claiming that the cowpox vaccine worked. Whilst Sir William supported Bragge's claim, the written proof that he made this claim many years previously was lost, and therefore Bragge's case fell apart.

Another gentleman by the name of the Revd Herman Drew of Abbots, Dorset, produced a claimant and told the committee that: 'Above twenty years ago a woman inoculated her child with matter taken from the cow with the point of a large needle' and Mr Bragge, the Axminster surgeon had written: "It is now I believe twenty years ago that Mrs Rendall, the wife of a farmer of Whitchurch near Lyme, inoculated herself and three or four children and the children of others." It is possible that these two samples are but one and the same, but be that as it may, it was all too vague for the committee to give too much credence to the examples and they were largely ignored. It was no wonder though, that Jenner felt a great deal of irritation at having to listen to all this.

But on and on it went with the committee listening to spurious claims that were unproven by any documentation. Encouraged by Dr Pearson, a Mr Thomas Nash appeared before the committee and told them that he thought that he had been inoculated with the cowpox by his father who was a surgeon. The word 'thought' is important, he didn't actually know for sure. Nash's mother had some papers in her possession which seemed to confirm this and she passed them on to her brother, Dr Battiscombe. Battiscombe hadn't bothered to open them by 1795 and he gave them to his nephew, Thomas, and Thomas then gave them to Robert Keate who told Dr Pearson. According to the papers, Thomas Nash's father had inoculated about sixty people with cowpox of which forty had been protected. However, Nash's earlier opinion that he had been inoculated by his father with the cowpox was put into doubt by a Mr Pew, who had practiced at Shaftesbury. Pew said that Nash senior had not vaccinated his son but had in fact variolated him. One more example presented by Dr Pearson was that of Mr Peter Platt, a German tutor from Schonwaide, Holstein, who it was claimed, vaccinated his three children. No more is really known about this man as to when his vaccinations were carried out and whether or not they were successful so it was all rather unsatisfactory and did little to help the committee come to an informed decision as to Jenner's award.

The time had come to conclude the inquiry, weigh the evidence for and against Jenner and come to a decision as to whether he was entitled to an award, and if so, by how much. Admiral Berkeley had wanted an award of £20,000 to be made although he accepted the fact that British citizens were suffering financially because of the war with France and Spain and that an amount of £10,000 would in all probability be more acceptable.

However, before the committee could come to a decision about this, they would want to decide the following:
a) Was vaccination with cowpox preferable to the previous treatment of variolation?

b) If so, was Jenner the first to discover it?

With regard to question b), the waters were a bit muddied as to what constituted a 'yes' or 'no' answer. One thought could be that Benjamin Jesty had been the first as to all intents and purposes, he had vaccinated his wife and children in 1774, over twenty years before Jenner had carried out the vaccination on James Phipps in 1796. However, we could go back even further as there were rumours amongst dairymaids that if someone had caught cowpox, they would never catch smallpox and it was rumours such as these that had convinced Benjamin Jesty that it would be well worth the risk of vaccinating his family.

However, if Jenner was to be judged on that alone, it would be most unfair. The dairymaids were doing no more than repeating a rumour, whilst Jesty although taking that rumour a stage further, simply took some cowpox pus and rubbed into a small wound on each member of his family.

Jenner took it several stages further than Jesty. He took the idea and spent many years refining it, and had been the first to define what was true cowpox. He had also spent a great deal of time discovering how long the person inoculating the patient should wait after vaccinating them before variolating them. For some time, some untutored people had performed a vaccination and waited as little as five days before variolating them. This meant that the cowpox failed to act as a deterrent against smallpox with the result that Jenner had been heavily criticised and it had taken that much longer before the vaccination became the recognised treatment against smallpox. Another task Jenner carried out was teaching people the correct way of storing cowpox, and how long it could be stored for as this too had been a problem. Some people had vaccinated patients with cow pox that had been stored for months rendering it useless. Jenner may not have been the very first to discover that cowpox was a good antidote for catching smallpox, but without the extra work carried out by him it would not have worked as well as it did.

The other reason as to whether the committee should decide as to whether they were going to award Jenner a sum of money was the fact that he had made a point of making the technique of vaccination public, thus losing a great fortune in the process. Jenner was exhausted too. He had not only made available to all the technique and methods of vaccination, but he had spent many years attempting to persuade all of his medical colleagues to change their way of thinking concerning the treatment of smallpox. People who had previously spent many years treating the disease with one method, in this case variolation, were not too easily persuaded that another method was better. The fact that top medical men were being asked to use a method that had originally started because of rumours spread by dairymaids was another stumbling block, but Jenner, taking that rumour, and with careful study, making it more scientific had always been sure that vaccination was the way ahead.

Jenner had one more trick up his sleeve. On 28th April 1802, he wrote to his friend Henry Hicks and told him that he had vaccinated the brother of the famous Whig politician Charles James Fox, (1749–1806). The brother in question was less well known than Charles James but nonetheless had a distinguished army career reaching the rank of General. General Henry Edward Fox (1755–1811) served as Governor of Minorca and also Governor of Gibraltar. The brothers in turn were the sons of Lord Holland, a controversial figure who had held high office but had made a great deal of money in the process. As previously mentioned, Lord Holland (1705–1774), had been an able politician and was married to Lady Caroline Holland (1723–1774), previously Caroline Lennox, one of the famous Lennox sisters. During his political career, amongst other posts, Lord Holland had served as Secretary of War, Southern Secretary and Paymaster of the Forces. It was this latter position that was the most controversial and no one knows quite how he did it, but he managed to make a great deal of money during this period. Tipped for the job as Prime Minister, he failed to make it, but his political career was nonetheless colourful.

Returning to the work of the Committee, the members finally finished listening to the many witnesses and they wrote their report that was presented to the House of Commons. The Commons held their debate on the matter on 2nd June 1802 and the first person to speak was Admiral Berkeley. The Admiral had always thought that Jenner should receive £20,000 but had originally suggested half that figure as he thought that it would be easier to get the award accepted. In the elaborate language so prevalent in the 18th century, he addressed the House with the following words:

"We descended to sift information from every anonymous letter. We raked the very kennels for information against the practice… It is proved that in these United Kingdom's alone 45,000 persons die annually from the smallpox…not a second is struck by the hand of time but a victim is sacrificed at the altar of that most terrible of all disorders… Suppose it was proposed in this house to reward any man who saved the life of a fellow creature with ten shillings I should be laughed at for the smallness of the sum, but small as it is I should contented with it, for if the statement of 40,000 deaths is true, and this discovery prevents it, Dr Jenner would be entitled to £20,000 per annum."

Admiral Berkeley actually said earlier in his statement that 45,000 lives could be saved but be that as it may, even to use the smaller figure of 40,000, he had argued brilliantly that £20,000 per annum would be a just reward for Jenner.

We must assume that he had little confidence that the sum would go through and played safe in keeping the figure at £10,000.

It was certainly agreed that Jenner should receive an award, and there were several members present who wanted to award £20,000 and the debate ran until it was time to make a final decision. The vote was taken and the original motion that Admiral Berkeley had proposed, that is, that Jenner receive £10,000 was carried by the House. One respected biographer of Jenner had the votes running at 59 to 56 but in the notes of William Davies (1740–1817) Jenner's brother-in-law, he noted in his household accounts a quite different vote:

"June 2 1802 Dr Jenner had a Reward from Parliament by a unanimous Vote for the most important Discovery that perhaps was ever made of preventing the Ravages of the small Pox by introducing Vaccine Inoculation. Ten thousand pounds." If we are to believe the first stated result, then it was a close-run thing and maybe if Admiral Berkeley had shown more determination, it is possible that Jenner would have received the larger sum. Although smaller than many medical people had wished, the sum of £10,000 was adequate for the time being, and some years later, 1807 to be exact, he would be awarded a further £20,000 that would keep him very comfortably off until the day that he died, so after many years he received the award that many felt he deserved.

It had been felt for some time that the original £10,000 that Jenner had been awarded was too low. Indeed, some members of the original committee thought it too low at the time as Jenner had already eaten into some of his own money before he had received it and it was felt by many that he had been poorly treated. The position he was in was looked at again and this time more sympathetically. There was a small group who wanted the second award to remain at £10,000 but the majority favoured £20,000. The clinching argument had already been put forward by Admiral Berkeley five years earlier at the original hearing, but put again was the statement that he had made concerning a payment of ten shillings per life saved. Many people would feel this a small amount but had 40,000 lives per year been saved, then a payment of £20,000 would hardly seem excessive. The Chancellor of the Exchequer at the time was Spencer Perceval (1762–1812), a cautious man and one who was careful with the nation's finances. Perceval had no objections so Jenner received the further £20,000 and at last, all his financial worries would now be over for the rest of his life. A sad postscript to this is the fact that Perceval would go on to be Prime Minister of a Tory government in 1809 but was shot dead three years later in the lobby of the House of Commons by John Bellingham, a bankrupt Liverpool broker. At that time, and one hopes for all time, Perceval was the only Prime Minister to be assassinated holding that office.

-oOOo-

Chapter 13

Portraits and Fame, Formation of the Royal Jennerian Society, and Jenner's Relationship with Napoleon Bonaparte

As a young doctor, Edward Jenner did not like the idea of fame and his achievements over the years had not changed him. Ideally, he would have gone back to Berkeley, the place he loved more than anywhere else with Catherine, his beloved wife who he adored so much, and to live in 'The Chantry' where he could resume living with his family in the house that he and Catherine both loved.

However, he had spent years fighting many of the members of the medical profession to get his method of defeating smallpox accepted, and to expect a quiet life now would be no more than a dream. In an age where there was no photography, he would be required to have his portrait painted, and some of the artists who painted him were famous themselves and so Jenner had little choice other than to sit and suffer the inevitable. As the portrait painters themselves were well known and extremely gifted it is only fair that a few words on some of them should be written here.

It was almost certain that the first portrait of him was painted by James Northcote (1746–1831) as it was completed in 1803 and hangs in the National Portrait Gallery in London. Northcote was born on 22nd October, 1746 at Plymouth to a father named Samuel Northcote who was a watchmaker. Regrettably, we do not know the name of Samuel's wife and therefore James's mother. Although Samuel was a watchmaker by trade, he was a good amateur artist and drew and painted in his spare time. He was so good in fact, that his son was apprenticed to his father for several years until 1769 when James set up as a portrait painter and was fairly successful. However, he decided that he still had much to learn and four years later he travelled to London and became a pupil of the famous English painter, Sir Joshua Reynolds (1723–1792), R.A., F.R.S., F.R.S.A. Northcote was lucky finding such a great teacher in Reynolds because he, Reynolds, specialised in producing portraits and became the 1st President of the Royal Academy of Arts.

Northcote spent two years with Reynolds before setting up once more as a portrait painter before travelling to Italy to study. He was elected an associate member of the Royal Academy in 1786 and was made a full member the following year.

Northcote was also an author and besides other works he wrote 'A Life of Reynolds', the first series coming out in 1813 whilst the second came out posthumously twenty years later in 1833, two years after his death.

The background of Northcote's picture of Jenner was not finished until after Jenner's death in 1823. In this painting, we see that Jenner is seated, his right arm is resting on the 'Inquiry' which is open at a page of drawings showing the progress of the vesicle. He is dressed in knee breeches along with a full coat trimmed with a fur collar and a waistcoat. We can obtain a further description of the portrait from Northcote himself, who wrote: 'On a table in the picture I have introduced the bones and joints of a cow's hoof and in a glass case, the cow's hoof injected, all of which is to show what were his peculiar studies'.

However, good though it is considered to be and Northcote was certainly a highly thought of portrait painter, Jenner preferred the painting by Sir Thomas Lawrence P.R.A., F.R.S., (1769–1830), and it's not difficult to see why. Lawrence's portrait takes about ten years off Jenner and sees him looking very relaxed, in fact the face looks very different from that which Northcote painted although it is difficult for us in this day and age to know who got the best likeness as it would seem that every portrait taken of Jenner is different.

Lawrence, was born on 13th April 1769 and ended up as a leading portrait painter and was the 4th President of the Royal Academy. He was a child prodigy and at the age of ten years, moved with his family to Bath and found that his talents were so great he was supporting his family with the money that he was earning from creating pastel portraits. Despite his youthful success, he was modest and became very popular with Bath residents. They must have been sad then, when in 1787, at the age of eighteen, he moved to London and soon built up a reputation as a very good portrait painter. So good was he in fact, that he was given his first Royal Commission in 1790 at the age of twenty-one to paint

Queen Charlotte (1744–1818), wife of King George III along with their daughter, Princess Amelia (1780–1810). However, although Queen Charlotte didn't care for the picture too much and she never wanted it to be displayed, at one stage in the life of the portrait it was exhibited in the Royal Academy and won fulsome praise. Lawrence became an associate member of the Royal Academy in 1791 and a full member in 1794 and later on he became the President of this august body in 1820. In 1810 he acquired the patronage of the Prince of Wales who in 1811 ruled the country as the Prince Regent when his father, George III became too ill to handle the duties of the monarch. When George III died in 1820, the Prince Regent ruled in his own right as King George IV from 1820 until his own death in 1830.

Thomas Lawrence never married although he had several relationships with various women. He died in London on 7th January 1830, the same year as George IV and although his reputation as a portrait painter never diminished, the wealth that he had created during his career which should have been immense, disappeared and in fact he died almost penniless. The reason or reasons are not clear as he led a rather conventional life, never gambling nor spending huge amounts of money as George IV did, but the best guess that people have come up with is that he was probably overgenerous to his friends and either gave them money, or lent them money which they did not return. It is also possible that he was owed a considerable amount of money from members of the aristocracy who engaged his services but never got round to paying him, a not uncommon trait in people who moved in these circles.

John Raphael Smith (1751–1812) was another artist who painted Jenner. He was born in 1751 and baptised in St Alkmund's Church on 25th May, 1751. Although we don't know his exact date of birth due to the high infant mortality rate that was common in those days, it is almost certain that he was born only a day or two before his baptism. His elder brother, Thomas Corregio Smith (1743–1811) was also a painter although he never achieved the popularity that his younger brother did. John moved to London in 1767 to set up a printmaking business and from there he produced miniatures. He met a lady named Ann Darlow when he was young and they were married on 20th May, 1768, a few days before his seventeenth birthday at the Chapel of Savoy. Smith had a very successful career and at one time did a mezzotint of Sir Joseph Banks (1743–1820) from a very famous portrait by Benjamin West. Smith produced a mezzotint of Edward Jenner in 1800.

So there we have just three examples of top portrait painters who Jenner sat for. He didn't enjoy any of it very much but learnt to live with it as he had wanted to rid the world of the dreadful disease of smallpox and he did it, although it didn't finally happen until the World Health Organisation (WHO) announced that smallpox had finally been conquered in 1980. It wasn't Jenner's fault that it wasn't finally dismissed until after his death, the main thing is that he did it. All the years of fighting for his beliefs paid off and the portraits of Jenner proved that he was the man who achieved it, although being the modest man that he was, he claimed no great talent, telling people that he had simply been the instrument of God's will.

We have looked at how Jenner's two awards, £10,000 in 1802, followed by a further £20,000 in 1807 were made, but now as we touch on the formation of the Royal Jennerian Society, we must back track a little to the 3rd December, 1802, when a gentleman by the name of Benjamin Travers, who it is thought was the brother of a London sugar merchant, arranged a meeting at Joseph's factory in Queen Street, off Cheapside. The reason for this meeting was to get a group of distinguished medical practitioners together in order that they would meet on a regular basis 'for the purpose of considering the propriety of establishing an Institution for promoting universal Vaccination with a view to the extinction of the Small Pox'. Given his staunch support of the vaccination process, it was hoped that Dr John Coakley Lettsom (1744–1815) who had helped get the process known in the United States of America would be able to attend, but unfortunately it was not to be. However, many did, including Dr William Hawes (1736–1808), an English physician who was one of the founders of the Royal Humane Society and a campaigner for the possibility of resuscitating people who appeared to be dead by drowning. He was also a friend of John Coakley Lettsom. Lettsom was also a friend of Joseph Leaper and John Addington, both of whom were surgeons and had been prominent supporters of the vaccination method. Because of the absence of both Lettsom and Jenner himself who was in Berkeley, the meeting was postponed for another day. Addington wrote to Jenner telling him what had taken place and Jenner replied on 10th December, 1802 from Berkeley. In his reply, Jenner pointed out that he hadn't been back at Berkeley for very long after a very lengthy absence. Jenner said that he approved of the institution as he understood its aims and objectives to be but still wished to remain at 'The Chantry' in Berkeley and suggested to Addington that John

Coakley Lettsom be his representative in future meetings, certainly for the foreseeable future anyway.

The next meeting was held a few days later, on the 16th December and it was acknowledged that Jenner would not be attending and agreed that Lettsom would be his representative. Benjamin Travers again took the chair, and the original members were joined by amongst others, Dr Lettsom, Dr William Bradley, who was the editor of the 'Medical and Physical Journal' and John Ring (1752–1821), a surgeon who one would think would be particularly useful to have on this committee. However, although Ring was a staunch supporter of vaccination, Jenner had long since felt that due to Ring's zeal added to a point-blank refusal to discuss any other treatment beyond vaccination, and he was almost becoming a liability to Jenner. However, when training, he had attended lectures by John Hunter (1728–1793) and his elder brother, William Hunter (1718–1783), and so his knowledge had to be respected. John Hunter was of course, Edward Jenner's mentor in the 1770s. Along with the above named were nine other medical men and city businessmen. Others also wrote in support of the plan and one of these was William Wilberforce (1759–1833), the great campaigner for the ending of the barbaric use of slavery on which so much of Britain's wealth was created. In 1802, when the beginning of the institution was set up, Wilberforce was exhausted after many years campaigning and by 1802, the slavery issue was still not resolved, and so it was understandable that he was unable to commit to the meetings in person. It was agreed that Dr Lettsom chair the meetings and that he and Jenner would work together with the intention of forming a committee which would result in an address being given to the public. Despite the fact that Dr Jenner could not commit to attending meetings on a regular basis, the committee was promoting his ideas and so it was suggested that it be called the Jennerian Society and with the business concluded for that particular meeting, it was agreed that they would end business for the day and meet again one week later.

The next meeting was held two days before Christmas and attention was drawn to the fact that 40,000 people died from smallpox each year, and this despite the fact that variolation had been thought of as the cure for this dreadful disease. The people who were against vaccination, and some of these were senior medical people, could not get it into their heads that variolation was extremely dangerous and could lead to the death of a previously healthy person, and whilst it may stop that person catching the full blown disease of smallpox, it was still impossible under that method to kill off smallpox completely which of course was Jenner's intent. However, the people who were at the meetings of the Jennerian Society were broadly in agreement of Jenner's vaccination being the best cure. The address was agreed and the meeting was adjourned for another week.

It was about this time that a medical practitioner by the name of James Parkinson F.G.S., (1755–1824) entered Jenner's life. He was an English surgeon, apothecary, geologist, and palaeontologist and if that wasn't enough, he was also a political activist, his views being decidedly left of centre. Within his medical career, he was best known for his publication 'An Essay on the Shaking Palsy' which came out in 1817. He was the first man to describe the disease which was later named after his death as Parkinson's Disease by a doctor called Jean-Martin Chariot (1825–93) who was known as the father of neurology. In later years, he was also called 'The Napoleon of the Neurosis'. Whether that was considered a compliment or not could be open to conjecture.

Besides medicine, Parkinson was also deeply interested in politics and was a constant critic of William Pitt the Younger (1759–1806), who had become Prime Minister at the age of twenty four and apart from a three year break, continued in that role from 1783 until his death in 1806 at the age of forty six years, a time when nowadays most Prime Ministers begin that role. It is almost certain that Parkinson supported the French revolution and he also supported universal suffrage and from the latter viewpoint, he was ahead of his time. Reverting back to the medical side of his life, like many people, he practiced variolation as a cure for smallpox, but hated the fact that many people carried the procedure out when they simply weren't qualified to do so. He was skilled at the treatment but when he came to learn of Jenner's newly found method of vaccination, he quickly changed his views as to the way that the disease was treated and became a supporter of Jenner, and became a member of the Jennerian society. Over the years, Parkinson and Jenner became friends and worked together well. So well in fact that in 1808, Parkinson gave Jenner a present of his dissecting microscope. Jenner was pleased and proud to receive this and wrote inside the lid of its box: 'This microscope belonged to and was used by James Parkinson, Surgeon, Hoxton, Author of 'Organic Remains.''. It was at this time that Parkinson had recently published the second volume of a publication that described new work on fossils, and it was this work that Jenner refers to in his inscription. Both Jenner and Parkinson had a shared interest in fossils so that was another reason why the two men became firm friends.

Reverting back a few years to Jenner, he and Catherine decided that they would leave Berkeley for London, which they did on 1st February 1803, for what they thought would be a long stay. There was no question that they would ever leave 'The Chantry' as their home in Berkeley was always going to be there for them to spend the rest of their days, but Edward and Catherine had taken a house at number 10, Hertford Street as temporary accommodation when needed in London. The house had recently been vacated by Richard Brinsley Sheridan for a while so that Edward and Catharine could use it while Jenner was needed at any particular meeting of the Jennerian Society, very shortly to be named the Royal Jennerian Society. Sheridan (1751–1816) was from Irish descent and was a satirist, playwright and poet and for a long time owned the Theatre Royal in Drury Lane, London. He wrote several plays that were to become famous such as School for Scandal and The Rivals, amongst others. He was a Whig MP for thirty two years from 1780 until 1812 and was a supporter of Charles James Fox (1749–1806), the famous Whig MP who was sympathetic to the American colonists who were fighting for their independence from 1775 until 1783. Jenner took over the chair for the next meeting which was held the day after he arrived in London, and it was then that it was to be called the Royal Jennerian Society due to the fact that King George III (1738–1820) agreed to be Patron, as well as Queen Charlotte (1744–1818), along with four of their offspring, the Prince of Wales (1762–1830), and three of his brothers, the Dukes of York (1763–1827), Clarence (1765–1837), and Cumberland (1771–1851). King George III and Queen Charlotte were ruling the country at the time and were succeeded by the Prince of Wales who ruled as King George IV from 1820 until his own death in 1830, although he effectively ruled from 1811 as the Prince Regent due to the severe illness that his father suffered from during the last nine years of his life. The Duke of Clarence was the last of the Hanoverian kings, ruling as William IV from 1830 until 1837 when the young Princess Victoria inherited the throne. It was quite an impressive array of support from the present and future monarchs for the modest country doctor from Berkeley.

Premises were found in Salisbury Square and shortly after that, the Medical Council needed to address the problem of having a resident vaccinator and a Dr William Domeier (1763–1815) was recommended by the Royal Family who would also ask him to act as secretary to the medical men. Dr Domeier was born in Hanover and was educated at the University of Gottingdon where he graduated as a Doctor of Medicine in 1784 at the very young age of twenty-one years.

Eventually he settled in London and was admitted as a Licentiate of the College of Physicians on 22nd December 1809. He was also appointed as one of the Physicians to Augustus, Duke of Sussex (1773–1843), another of King George III and Queen Charlotte's sons. Everybody seemed to be in favour of Domeier except for the Duke of Clarence who disliked Domeier intensely. Clarence must have had a dislike of Germans generally as opposed to Domeier in particular but he didn't attempt to pull rank amongst the Committee as he was fair in his solution, suggesting that the Medical Council were the best people to make the decision. Despite Dr Domeier's qualities the Council overlooked him in favour of Dr John Walker (1759–1830) which pleased the Duke greatly although not, we can assume, his German born mother, Queen Charlotte. Although this was a popular decision amongst most of the men present, it caused a tension to develop in the group as Walker had returned from the Mediterranean an even greater believer in the process of vaccination to such an extent that he considered himself an expert which did not go down well with Jenner who would not entertain the notion that anybody knew more about the treatment than he.

Jenner certainly did not admire Dr Walker in any way shape or form and was unhappy at his appointment as secretary to the medical men. John Walker was born in Cockermouth in Cumberland in 1759 and he was the son of a smith and ironmonger. He was educated in the local grammar school and on leaving became a blacksmith. Walker was very interested in Quaker ideals and with that in mind set up a school in Dublin and one of the rules that he brought to that school was that the children must be treated kindly by those that taught them. It seems that Walker was an unsettled man with itchy feet because he then moved to London where he became a medical student at Guy's Hospital and from there studied at the University of Leyden and in 1799 graduated as an M.D. Soon after graduating, he lived in Stonehouse, Gloucestershire, where he met and befriended Edward Jenner and as a result became very interested in the process of vaccination. At that point, the friendship between the two men was strong, it was later on that it disintegrated.

A Dr Marshall had previously invited Walker to Naples to help him introduce the practice of vaccination to the population there and on his return to England, Walker was convinced that he was an expert on the process. When the Jennerian Society was formed, it was clear that Walker's methods of vaccination were different from Edward Jenner's and he, Walker, resigned in August, 1806 after a huge row which unfortunately entered the public domain. It was not good for the public to see that there was internal dissention amongst the vaccinators that would give Jenner yet another hurdle to jump over before he could hope to get vaccination accepted by the public. The result of this falling out was that when the London Vaccination Institution was formed on 25th August, 1806, the Jennerian Society virtually disintegrated and in 1813 was swallowed up by the Vaccination Institution which became one body. Edward Jenner was elected President and John Walker became the Director. Time would tell whether the new body with these two men at the helm would work, and indeed whether they could work together at all given their differences. Walker felt that he knew more about vaccination than just about anyone else. Unfortunately he included Jenner as someone whose knowledge was inferior to his own. Jenner however, felt that he had no need to alter any of the ways in which he practiced vaccination – he felt that he had enjoyed spectacular success himself and was adamant that he wouldn't change any of his methods. One of Domeier's friends put his case for him: 'Dr Jenner and you, I find, hold different opinions on some little points in vaccination, and your enemies wished to avail themselves of the circumstance to your hurt, but they have been defeated. Is the man who launches the vessel the only one who can navigate her?' This is where Walker and Jenner could not be reconciled as Jenner thought that he was indeed the navigator as well as the man who had launched her.

Walker's attitude that he knew more about vaccination than Jenner had made a quarrel between Walker and Jenner inevitable and it simmered for a time. The animosity between the two men was the main reason that the Royal Jennerian Society was ultimately destroyed and now the new arrangement would test whether the two men could work together. In 1816 there had been an article on the history of the Society which made the claim 'The idea of the formation of a vaccine institution in London…originated with Dr Walker'. This could have been written by Walker or certainly he would have been aware of the statement before it was published and it went to great lengths to describe the work that he had carried out in Malta and Paris without mentioning Dr Marshall at all. This must have been especially galling for Dr Marshall as it was he who had been responsible for Walker going to Naples, and certainly there was little doubt that Dr Marshall was the senior of the two men. It seems that Dr Walker was not the easiest of men to get along with although it has to be said that his attitude to children put him way ahead of his time on that score, although that was of no help for him to work alongside people like Edward Jenner in the field of vaccination. Out of all the men who could have claimed to have thought of the original idea however, it was far more likely to be Dr Pearson (1751–1828), although we have seen earlier in the book that Dr Pearson, although originally a friend of Dr Jenner's because of his interest in Jenner's work on vaccination, had spoiled his friendship with Jenner because of his, Pearson's, shoddy work and the fact that it had undermined Jenner's case for vaccination. It was this sort of work carried out by people who made mistakes time after time that upset Jenner over the years, because he needed near 100% positive results in order to be in a position to take the medical world with him in changing the treatment for smallpox from variolation to vaccination. We have already read of Dr Pearson in the previous chapter when a House of Commons Committee had been set up to discuss awarding Jenner a grant for the loss of income he suffered whilst working on the cowpox vaccination as the means of eventually killing off the disease of smallpox. As part of the Inquiry was to decide whether Jenner had been the first man to conclude that cowpox was the correct remedy for curing smallpox, Pearson had gone out of his way to produce names who had thought of the idea before Jenner, and Pearson's work in producing names did nothing to help Jenner. However, what Pearson failed to recognise was the fact that it was Jenner who took the idea of cowpox as a way to stem the tide of smallpox, and unlike others, refined it and put forward detailed instructions as to how long the cowpox matter should be stored until it was too late to vaccinate people. That was the crucial thing that Jenner had had to calculate, how long it would take for stored cowpox to be kept before it ceased to be effective. Benjamin Jesty, the farmer who had farmed in Dorset was someone who had deserved some recognition but lack of time and medical qualifications meant that he hadn't been able to carry out anything like the work that Jenner had done with cowpox. Also, to take the original Inquiry committee terms of reference which included who the first person was in discovering cowpox to its logical conclusion, then they may as well have included any number of dairymaids who thought that there was a connection between the mild disease of cowpox and the reduction in smallpox. It sounds ridiculous and it is ridiculous but the truth is that Edward Jenner turned the mere rumour that cowpox could be a preventative measure into a scientific reality.

Moving back a few years, Britain had been at war with France ever since France had carried out a shocking deed in beheading their King, Louis XV1 on 21st January 1793 quickly followed by Marie Antoinette. European countries whose head of state was a monarch were panicking that the same thing could happen to them and their fears were compounded when France declared war on Britain on 1st February 1793. France was later lead by a brilliant young Corsican general by the name of Napoleon Bonaparte (1769–1821) who had appointed himself Emperor of France. However, it looked as if Napoleon was beaten as after the Treaty of Fontainebleau on the 11th April, 1814, Napoleon was exiled to the Mediterranean island of Elba where he was allowed his own staff and a limited number of troops. Some would say that he got away with it lightly given the number of people that were killed in battle needlessly but it was not enough for Napoleon. He arranged an escape plan and left Elba on 26th February, 1815 on the 26 gun Inconstant, along with other ships called Saint Esprit, Etoile, and Caroline, along with three smaller vessels. Napoleon raised another army and the war with France recommenced and although there were many battles over the years, it was not until the Battle of Waterloo when the British and Prussian troops lead by the Duke of Wellington (1769–1852) on 18th June, 1815, defeated the French that the war was finally over. Wellington later admitted that the battle of Waterloo was a close-run fight and one that we might well have lost if the Prussian army had not become involved in the latter stages. The reader may think at this stage why it was felt necessary to mention the war with France in a book concerning the elimination of smallpox, but it is included here in order to put Jenner's theory as to how the disease would be finally eradicated from the world into some sort of context. Jenner knew that he could make himself rich by keeping the idea of vaccination to himself, but by doing that, he would stand no chance of smallpox ceasing to be a threat to the world so the only hope of vaccination being effective world-wide, was to share his knowledge to every country, regardless of whether we were at war with them or not. It was a calculated risk by Jenner as vaccination was used on the very same French troops who were fighting us.

Whilst the war between Britain and France was raging, it was not uncommon for the two nations to exchange prisoners, and on more than one occasion, Jenner wrote to Napoleon requesting the release of certain prisoners and his letters were always met with a favourable response. In the eighteenth century English was written and spoken in a rather elegant manner, but people would never use one word if twenty would do and Jenner was no exception. In February 1805, he wrote the following letter to Napoleon:

Having by the blessings of Providence, made a discovery of which all nations acknowledge the beneficial effects, I presume upon that plea alone, with great deference, to request a favour from your Imperial Majesty, who early appreciated the importance of vaccination, and encouraged its propagation, and who is universally admitted to be a patron of the arts.

My humble request is that your Imperial Majesty will graciously permit two of my friends, both men of science and literature, to return to England; one, Mr William Thomas Williams, residing at Nancy; the other Dr Wickham, at present in Geneva. Should your Imperial Majesty be pleased to listen to the prayer of my petition, you will impress my mind with sentiments never to be effaced.

I have the honour to be, with most profound deference and respect, Your Imperial Majesty's most obedient and humble servant.

Edward Jenner

(Berkeley February 1805)

Considering that Britain was at war with France, many readers will doubtless feel that Jenner has gone way over the top with his courtesy, but it has to be taken in the context of the times when that style of addressing people was considered quite normal and the letter certainly did the trick. Indeed, Napoleon had a deep respect for Jenner and in fact never refused any other request of this nature from the English doctor from Berkeley. When one such letter was received by Napoleon from Jenner, the French Emperor was heard to say: "We can deny nothing to the name of Jenner."

So Jenner had established some sort of relationship based on mutual respect with the French Emperor, Napoleon Bonaparte. It was a strange relationship given that Britain was at war with France and Jenner had taken a massive gamble in allowing the very people who were intent on invading us information that would enable the French troops to be increased in number and therefore more likely to succeed. It was also strange that two such different men could forge this relationship with each other. Napoleon, the brilliant young general who seemed comfortable with the fact that his battles were costing thousands of unnecessary lives in atrocious conditions, whilst Jenner was the kindly peace loving doctor from rural Gloucestershire whose raison d'etre was to save lives and who never cared if he had to stay in the tranquillity of Berkeley permanently. It was certainly a world apart from the mud, bullets and mass killing that was going to happen at Waterloo. However, if smallpox was to be eliminated from the world, the brave country doctor from Berkeley in Gloucestershire felt he had no other option than to make that decision. Only time would tell whether he would be proven right and as it happens, Jenner was proven right, but to quote the Duke of Wellington after the battle of Waterloo: "That it was the nearest run thing you ever saw in your life."

-oOOo-

Chapter 14

Further Requests from Jenner for the Release of French Prisoners. Further Financial Awards. The Deaths of Edward, Edward and Catherine's Beloved Son, and John Worgan. Various Acts of Parliament Concerning Vaccination

Napoleon was not the only person that Jenner had influence with. There were the Peploe family who were on their way to Spa (Belgium) to take the waters when to their horror found that their journey was stopped in Paris and they were not allowed to proceed any further. They represented no threat whatsoever and so the family contacted Jenner to see if he could be of any help. Jenner wrote to the General Andreossi to this effect and whilst he received no reply to his letter, it was felt that his intervention had solved the problem as the family were allowed to continue their journey. Later on that year (1803), Jenner was once again called upon to help a British family, this time help was sought from the Marquis of Hertford (1743–1822), a British Peer and politician. To give him his full name and title, he was Francis Ingram-Seymour-Conway, 2nd Marquis of Hertford. He was a Member of the Irish House of Commons from 1761 until 1776 and became a Member of the British Parliament in 1766 and served under Lord North (Prime Minister 1770–82) from 1774 as a Lord of the Treasury and in 1780 he was sworn in as a member of the British Privy Council. In 1804 he was made Master of the Horse by William Pitt the Younger (Prime Minister 1783–1801, then again 1804–1806). He also served as Lord Chamberlain of the Household under Spencer Perceval (Prime Minister 1809–1812) and on Perceval's death, continued to carry out those same duties under Lord Liverpool (Prime Minister (1812–27) from 1812 until 1821 before his death the following year. To be precise, Hertford died on 17th June, 1822 in London aged 79 years. For somebody of this stature to write to Jenner showed that the latter's fame had certainly become worldwide and therefore so had his vaccination treatment. Hertford was asking Jenner for help because his son was being held prisoner in the fortress of Verdun. Jenner wrote to the National Institute of Paris on behalf of Hertford's son, Lord Yarmouth (1777–1842). Again, we will give his son his full title which was Francis Ingram-Seymour-Conway, 3rd Marquis of Hertford, K.G., G.C.H., P.C. The 3rd Marquis became a Member of Parliament in 1797 and continued to serve there until 1822. He was the Member for Orford from 1797 until 1802, and then represented Lisburn from 1802 until 1812, Antrim from 1812 until 1818, and finally Camelford from 1820 until 1822. In March 1812, he became a member of the Privy Council and appointed Vice Chamberlain of the Household by Spencer Perceval (Prime Minister 1809–12), the only Prime Minister to be assassinated whilst holding that office. He stayed in that post when Lord Liverpool took over as Prime Minister after Perceval's death in 1812 but only stayed a few months before leaving that position in July of the same year. He was then appointed Lord Warden of the Stannaries which was largely a ceremonial position and held it until he died on 1st March 1842.

Benjamin Disraeli was supposed to have modelled the character of the Marquis of Monmouth in his novel 'Coningsby' and the character of Lord Steyne in William Makepeace Thackeray's 1847–8 serial 'Vanity Fair'. Hertford was a fairly dissolute character and was said to have lived with a number of prostitutes in his final years but not before he had married Maria Emilia Fagnani on 18th May, 1798, a marriage that produced three children. The Marchioness died in March 1856 aged 84 years.

Returning to Jenner's intervention, Hertford's release didn't happen overnight, in fact, he wasn't released for another three years but he didn't seem to mind too much and was probably given an easy time of it by his captors. In any event, he was an avid art collector and when released by Napoleon founded the Wallace Collection which is housed in Hertford House, Manchester Square, London to this day and is now open to the public.

This then is a snapshot of the fame that Jenner had acquired in his work over the years in his quest to wipe smallpox from the entire world. However, whilst his methods were making a name for himself, it didn't pay the bills and Jenner was back home in the village of Berkeley that he loved so much. He had been awarded £10,000 from the Committee of the House of Commons in 1802 and whilst transferred to its worth today would be well in excess of half a million pounds, given the amount of money that Jenner had had to pay out, it was simply not enough. This meant that a suggestion was made for a second grant to be made. Jenner was in a difficult position because as incredible as it may seem, he had yet to receive the £10,000 that he had been awarded in 1802, and had still not received any of it nearly two years later. He was in a position where he was actually losing money and it must have been a worrying and distressing time for both himself and Catherine. According to his biographer, John Baron, he told an 'intimate friend' that 'The Treasury still withholds the payment of what was voted to me two years ago'. We do not know the name of Jenner's confidante but later that year, he eventually received the money, although £1,000 was deducted for taxation. William Pitt the Younger had returned to number 10, Downing Street as Prime Minister in May, 1804, having been away from the job since 1801. As Pitt had been out of office when the first payment had been authorised but not yet received, it is quite possible that he, Pitt, had hastened up the delayed payment on his return to the premiership. Jenner was hardly a wealthy man and there was no question that the matter had to be looked upon again. However, before that could happen, he had to deal with yet another attack on his vaccination methods and one of them came in the form of a pamphlet entitled 'An Examination of That Part of the Evidence Relative to Cow-Pox, which was Delivered to the Committee of the House of Commons, by Two of the Surgeons of St Thomas's Hospital'. It was an anonymous paper but was almost certainly the work of a gentleman by the name of W. R. Rogers who was intent on proving that the process of vaccination had too many flaws in it to be considered a safe and reliable method of stopping the spread of smallpox, and the logic of this paper was of course to deprive Jenner of any more grants.

However, if that was the intention, it didn't work. The battle for the acceptance of vaccination over variolation had been fought and to all intents and purposes had been won. In 1807, the College of Physicians had interviewed Jenner and he had clearly won them over. They had listened to and we can quote from their findings; 'the irresistible weight of evidence, along with the number, the respectability, the disinterestedness, and the extreme experience of its advocates' which was set against 'the feeble and imperfect testimonies of its few opposers'. The College was completely satisfied with the skill and diligence of Dr Jenner and the battles that he had had to fight over the years. The College was very optimistic and said that 'the public may reasonably look forward with some degree of hope to the time when all opposition shall cease'. Because of the difficulties caused by Napoleon Bonaparte in terms of any foreign trade, some of the Committee thought that the sum awarded should be the same as was awarded five years earlier, in other words £10,000. However, in terms of macro-economic spread over the whole nation, an extra £10,000 on top of that making the total sum of this second award £20,000 would be more appropriate and this was duly awarded. However, it didn't stop there and further awards were now coming in from other quarters. In the previous year, Jenner had received an instalment of £2,000 from the Government of Bengal and within the next few years he was given extra amounts from various parts of India that altogether amounted to £7,382. Jenner was now in a position to live out the rest of his days with no financial worries and had clearly won the long battle with Parliament's acceptance of cowpox vaccination. At this stage and with all the financial awards, Jenner had just one regret, and that was the fact that with all the success that the cowpox vaccination had, there was one more thing that Jenner would like, and that was that the smallpox inoculation be abolished by law. However, with that hope in his head, he would have to be patient and it was surely only a matter of time before that would come to pass. As it was, with his financial situation settled, Jenner could look out for a well-earned retirement, but unfortunately, things don't always turn out as planned and in the way that we hope.

The winter of 1808/9 was a very severe one and the weather was freezing. Edward Junior felt unwell in November, 1809, and nothing else seemed to matter for Jenner at that moment in time. Edward was the first-born child of Edward and Catherine and was deeply loved by both parents and Jenner had loved taking his son around exploring the countryside when he was a young boy. Both father and son loved nature and, in a time, when people with learning difficulties were often looked down upon, young Edward's sweet natured simplified look on life endeared him even more to his parents. He was born on 24th January 1789 and he was not yet twenty-one but his father suspected tuberculosis, at that time, a certain killer.

Meanwhile, Jenner had gone back to study geology, an interest he held in the earlier parts of his life and by 1809, he had acquired a great deal of knowledge on the subject, knowledge that matched many of his contemporaries. On the 2nd November of that year he recorded in his notebook: 'Rec'd the books of the Geological Society of London and a letter acquainting me that I was an Honorary Member'.

In normal circumstances such a letter would have given him untold pleasure as it would have given his retirement a structure and also put him in touch with other likeminded men. However, it came at the wrong time because all Jenner could think about was the failing health of his beloved son. He wrote the following to a friend: "My poor dear Edward is much as you left him as I am commonly either sitting with him or the sound of his hollow Cough, I am at times most miserably depress'd." Jenner received support from his nephew, the Revd William Davies, the son of Edward's sister, Anne Jenner (1741–1812) who married the Revd William Davies Snr (1740–1817) in 1810, and who saw his uncle every day and dined with him for several days up to the day the young Edward died which was on 31st January 1810. He had died of tuberculosis, pulmonary consumption which is all that we know.

Jenner was friendly with a lawyer named Charles Murray who was the Secretary to the National Vaccine Establishment and who he had met through his wife Catherine. On 3rd February, Edward and Catherine's daughter, also called Catherine, wrote to Murray as she was very concerned about the level of grief and depression that her father was experiencing over the death of her brother the previous month. However, we do not know of any reply that Murray sent to Catherine although he surely had, and in any event, it was unlikely that Jenner would have gained much comfort from it whatever it would have said. Young Edward was buried in Berkeley church on 7th February 1810 and today lies in the family tomb in the church along with his grandparents, Stephen and Sarah who both died in 1754, and his parents, Catherine who died in 1815 and Dr Edward who passed away in 1823. However, that is jumping ahead.

As mentioned earlier, the winter of 1808 and 1809 was exceptionally cold and it was completely impossible to keep The Chantry warm. The weather was so cold that nobody, not even the Royal Family, escaped it. The King and Queen lived very frugally and if it was impossible to keep The Chantry warm, one wonders how bad it must have been at Windsor Castle where King George III and Queen Charlotte lived. In fact it was absolutely freezing. The courtiers would run through the corridors and arrive from one freezing room to another to carry out the royal couple's bidding and they, the courtiers, must have suffered from bad health due to working in such conditions. The King, who was soon to fall into his final illness within just two years, carried on with his daily pursuit of riding. His equerries had no choice but to ride with the King as it was part of their job, but they must have had frozen joints and limbs that would have caused them to suffer from extreme rheumatism at a later date. It is a wonder that the King and Queen survived it that winter as it was quite possible that many of their subjects didn't.

Returning to the Jenner household, the grief-stricken Edward Jenner wrote to his friend Henry Hicks on the 10th February 1810, three days after Edward Junior was buried:

"I had no conception till it happened that the gash would have been so deep; but God's will be done."

It would be plainly obvious that young Edward's mother would have felt grief stricken at the death of their son, but she was a very deeply committed Christian and would have gained comfort from her religious beliefs. Edward senior, despite the fact that he too was a Christian, probably found the tragedy harder to cope with as his Christian views were not quite as strong as Catherine's. Either way, it was very hard to bear for both of them.

It wasn't only Edward Junior who died in what was to be a very sad household at that time. John Dawes Worgan, the brilliant young man who had tutored Edward also died. In 1806, Worgan was asked by Jenner if he, Worgan, would tutor Edward and Catherine's first-born son, Edward Junior. Worgan was the son of a watchmaker based in Bristol. He was a very clever young man and had mentioned to the Jenners that sometime in the future, he would like to enter the church. Whether he had talked about this to Catherine and had been swept along by her strong religious beliefs, we do not know. However, it would be strange if having told her of his interest that he would not be influenced by her and that is certainly how he saw his future. Worgan also saw himself as a poet but was sensible enough to know that it was very difficult to make a living in the field of the arts and so it was to the church that he felt that he would enter in the future. After a year tutoring the young Edward, Worgan was then asked if he would also tutor Robert, Edward's younger brother and whilst he did this for a few months, he became ill and developed tuberculosis. Before his illness, Worgan was a very hard-working young man and he read Demosthenes, 384–322 BC, a Greek Statesman, and orator of ancient Athens. Demosthenes had delivered his first speech when he was just twenty years of age and also became a speech writer and lawyer. He died on 12th October, 322 BC and his bust is in the Louvre, Paris. Worgan also read the tragedies of Sophocles, and Plato. Sophocles 497/6–406/5 BC was one of just three Greek Tragedians whose plays have survived over the years. Having said that, he wrote over 120 plays although only seven have survived in their complete form. These are Ajax, Antigone, The Women of Trachis, Oedipus Rex, Electra, Philoctetes and Colonus. In his time Sophocles was a most celebrated playwright and he won many of the competitions that were held in the city of Athens.

Plato 428/427 or 424/423 – 348/347 BC, was probably the better known of the three. He was a Philosopher in Classical Greece. Classical Greece was a period which lasted roughly two centuries, the 5th and 4th Centuries BC. Classical Greece had a major influence on the Roman Empire and helped lay the foundations of Western society that we know today. Plato is widely considered to be the most powerful figure in the development of philosophy in the western tradition. Along with all that talent and capacity for hard work that enabled Worgan to study the Greek Philosophers and Playwrights as well as tutoring, it was sad that his constitution couldn't cope with it. In tutoring Edward as well as Robert, he would have found that task exacting, as although Edward was older than Robert, he had the learning difficulties that Robert didn't have, and so that would probably have entailed extra work for the talented Worgan, because he was trying very hard to better himself before entering the church and wanted to carry out a good job for Dr and Mrs Jenner. However, when he became ill, Worgan lost much of his energy and was coughing incessantly. Mrs Worgan, John's mother came up from Bristol and took him back so that she could nurse him at their home which took a little of the pressure off Edward and Catherine while they battled to keep young Edward alive. When Jenner saw Worgan and his mother off in their carriage, he knew that he would never see the young man again, and it filled him with sadness that this exceptionally clever young man would be taken after such a short time with such unfulfilled talent being taken with him. What Jenner didn't know however, was which of the two young men would be taken first, John or his pupil, young Edward. To add to Worgan's misery, before he left 'The Chantry' to go home to Bristol with his mother, the fifteen year old boy had fallen deeply in love with a young lady but for whatever reason, his relatives disapproved of the match and any willpower that he had to fight his illness was eaten away. Worgan finally died on 25th July, 1809, five months before Edward junior. Worgan died leaving some poetry that he had written for the love of his life, and here is just one out of many that he left behind:

'No – to thy shrine no suppliant strains I bring,
Imaginary Queen of soft desires!

Nor shall my chords with lawless ardor sing
Of Cupid's Darts, and Passion's treacherous fires.
To pure affections holy shrine I bow,
There the fond feelings of my heart proclaim,
There for Eliza breathe th'unhanging vow,
While soften'd love inspires a mutual flame.
To thee, Omniscient Father! I resign,
Almighty Guardian of my doubtful way!
If such thy will, Oh make Eliza mine,
Yet – let my heart thy sov'reign doom obey.
And oh! How blissful shall our moments roll,
When Love inspires, and Heav'n directs the soul.'

Whilst Jenner grieved deeply for his son, he also felt almost as much grief for John Worgan, the exceedingly clever young man who had lived with the household for two and a half years. Worgan was not only clever, but like Edward junior, was possessed of a sweet and gentle nature and along with Mrs Catherine Jenner, was deeply religious. In fact, his religion was so strong that he had no fear of death, despite his youth, and embraced the thought of Heaven with great tranquillity, and worshipped God and Jesus Christ with great calm. His love for Doctor and Mrs Jenner was very great, and that love that he had for them matched his love of God.

Jenner had a very good friend in the Revd Thomas Pruen who he would confide in when spiritual matters took hold of his life. On the same day that John Worgan died, Jenner wrote a lengthy letter to his friend, part of which can be quoted here:

"I fear it is all over with my coming to Cheltenham this Season. Poor Edward's complaint which remained so long enveloped in obscurity, has at length shewn itself in a most alarming shape. Within this last fortnight he has been repeatedly affected with Haemorrhage from the Lungs… Death is a terrible visitor in whatever shape he approaches us, and this is a frightful one indeed. But God's will be done!"

Readers may notice that when informing both Henry Hicks and the Revd Thomas Pruen of young Edward's passing, he used the identical words to finish each letter off, namely, 'But God's will be done'. Although Jenner was a Christian and had his beliefs that gave him some comfort, it was almost certainly his wife Catherine's much stronger beliefs that helped him through the dreadful loss of the son that they both loved so much.

Jenner must have tried to take his mind off both Worgan and young Edward whilst both young men had attempted to fight off their illnesses and had tried to concentrate on his paper 'Distemper in Dogs' which was presented to the Medico-Chirurgical Society in March 1809 but it gave him little satisfaction as it was rather cobbled together from old notes that he had made. Also, he still had the deaths of John Worgan and young Edward to face regardless of any other work that he had carried out.

Needless to say, this had hardly any effect on the dark cloud that hung over Jenner's head. He felt like many people of his age, that his own death was easier to contemplate than the death of the young ones that he and Catherine loved so dearly. On hearing of Worgan's death, Jenner wrote:

"It must be some consolation to his surviving relatives and friends that his name will not be forgotten, and greater still to those that were most dear to him that his long indisposition awakened in him those sentiments in all their purity from which alone can spring true happiness at any period of our existence, but particularly at the awful hour of death."

A small book of his poems was published by John's friends in an attempt to keep his memory alive, but a book of poems by an unknown poet was never going to be successful in a situation like that. If he was unknown at his death, it would be unlikely that people would buy such a book, but in the event it didn't matter. John Worgan was remembered by those that mattered, namely his friends and relatives and they would never forget the young man who was both sweet and gentle and was taken at such a young age.

Around this sad period in his life, a little light shone through when his great friend and future biographer, Dr John Baron travelled down to Gloucester, settled there and set up in general practice in order to be near his friend in his time of crisis. Baron's admiration of Jenner actually went further than close friendship, he really hero-worshipped Jenner and this was proven as in later years, he had to put a great deal of Jenner's chaotic affairs in some sort of order before he could even begin to start Jenner's biography. During the years that Jenner was hard at work promoting and defending his ideas of vaccination throughout the world, scores of letters from all over the globe reached him at 'The Chantry'. Jenner was totally incapable of filing them, let alone answering them. It was an amazing feat for someone as busy as Baron must have been in running his own practice and looking after his patients, but Baron sat down and got on with the job in a very methodical way and in a way that Jenner could never have managed. The resulting biography was a massive piece of work which is a tribute to Baron, but sometimes it is difficult to be even handed when your subject is so well loved by the author and the subjects failings are often left out if they were ever recognised before. At this time, Jenner's health, both mental and physical, was not in good shape. He was unable to make any diagnosis of his own condition as the physical side of his health would almost certainly have been caused by the grief that he felt over recent losses. Added to that was the possibility that the dreadful ordeal that he went through when he was treated for smallpox in his youth might well have come back to haunt him. Some of the symptoms that he was now suffering from, namely, very bad digestive problems, noises in his head, and a lack of energy during the day causing his sleep pattern to be disturbed, always seemed to come to him when he was agitated about something and only since that barbaric treatment for smallpox earlier in his life.

He thought that it would be a good idea to spend some time in Bath. When all of the regular treatments had been tried and found not to be helping, Bath was thought to be the cure for all ills. Quite how this idea came about is not clear, but maybe a few people did feel better after staying in this lovely city which meant that people possibly regained some of their health due to some placebo effect. If that was the case, it didn't really matter as long as some cure was effected. If people went to Bath who were suffering from the result of overeating, then they would expect a cure and it didn't seem to matter what the problem was. It seems ludicrous to us today as that particular problem should surely be cured by simply staying where you lived and watched what it was that you were eating. Excessive drinking, low fevers, gout, losses at cards, anxiety, and even a broken heart all added to the lunacy of the idea. Many people today hear that a friend is suffering from gout and find it funny, believing it to be the prerogative of extremely fat and alcohol riddled 18th century men. Whilst that may have been the case at this time, in actual fact, it is difficult to cure even in the 21st century. The disease is very painful and causes inflammation, especially of the joints. Nothing in Bath helped Jenner, and he wrote to his friend, John Baron, and said: "I have been cupped, calomeled, salted, &c. &c. and I think the cascades do not roar so loud in my ears as they did, nor my head feel so heavy; but still all is far from right…I feel right from breakfast-time till about ten o'clock, when the acidity in my stomach is the signal also for nodding. For six days my only drink was water…"

Soon after that he went to London to see his long term friend, Henry Hicks, but his visit was brief because he was asked to see Augustus, the Duke of Sussex, (1773–1843), the fifth son of King George III and Queen Charlotte, which was the reason that he returned to Berkeley in such a hurry. On 15th September, 1810, Jenner wrote: 'Went to Gloucester with Lord Berkeley to visit his R.H. the Duke of Sussex. Spasm; Asthma, opium and ipecac.' Two days later the Duke was better and well enough to travel to Berkeley Castle and a day or so later, Jenner attended him again and eventually the Duke recovered. Jenner hadn't had a great deal to be happy about lately, but whilst he was naturally concerned that the Duke was unwell, he was a Royalist as most of his contemporaries were and it cheered him to be chosen to administer to a member of the Royal Family. He wrote to his friend, the Rev Thomas Pruen: "There was certainly an honour in being called to visit His R.H. the Duke of Sussex. Had the Paragraph in the Gloster Herald or Journal, just added this simple sentence, 'I should have been fully satisfied, his R.H. was attended by Dr Jenner.'" He asked Pruen to make such an entry in the Chronicle and finished the sentence with the words: 'but do not puff me higher'. Jenner continued: "The Duke of Sussex is now here and much better. He was so extremely ill at Gloster that he was about to send an Express to Town for his Physician just as I arrived. By the end of the month, the patient was well enough to leave the castle. He has been having a grain of ipecacuanha two or three times a day and occasionally the extract of Colocynth comp." Jenner then added in his notebook, "He smokes three or four pipes of Turkish tobacco daily."

The Duke was obviously pleased with the treatment that he received, as he recovered and on returning to London, sent Jenner a hookah, which is an oriental pipe in which smoke is drawn through water and a long tube. Jenner enjoyed smoking, although he did not do it to excess, but it calmed his nerves. It seems extraordinary to us in the 21st century that a doctor should encourage a patient to smoke, and not only that, but to smoke himself, but in those days, all medical knowledge was of the opinion that breathing in smoke actually cleared the lungs and this was common thinking right up to and including the 1950s. In actual fact, film stars or other famous people would appear on television smoking as late as the 1970s and public opinion had no problem with that scenario. In fact, there was the dreadful experience of Dr Thomas Richard Allinson (1858–1918) who was struck off the list of doctors who were allowed to practice by the General Medical Council as he said that smoking was injurious to people's health. He also recommended that people exercise, not work too hard and get overtired, and to reduce their intake of salt and tobacco. He went on to say that it would be better if people were teetotal, should become vegetarians, and not to drink tea and coffee too late in the evening. Dr Allinson founded the bakery that bears his name today. It was a tragedy that the man was so far ahead of the rest of society when any of the above advice would be given to the public in the present day.

It was during the time that Jenner had been looking after the Duke when he was made a magistrate. On 18th September, 1810, his nephew, the Revd William Davies made an entry into his diary:

"In the morning at an adjourned Quarter Sessions of the Peace, at the White Lion, Berkeley, when the oaths of Allegiance, Qualifications etc were severally administered to Dr Jenner and me by the Earl of Berkeley, the Chairman, to enable us to act as Magistrates for the County of Gloucester."

Jenner had become sick of London and London politics and this appointment meant that he was totally committed to Berkeley and its small population. This post was the symbol of authority and only landowners and members of the clergy could be magistrates.

To be appointed a Magistrate, one had to be a communicant, or putting it another way, one who receives communion and they would be required to take Holy Communion shortly after their appointments. George Jenner administered the sacrament to both cousin, William Davies, and his uncle, Edward Jenner. Two days after this, William and Edward travelled to Gloucester to take their magisterial oaths.

Returning to the Duke of Sussex who Jenner had been administering to, no sooner had the Duke recovered from his illness, then an illness that the Earl of Berkeley had been suffering from for some time took a turn for the worse and Jenner was summoned and was so concerned that he waited on the Earl on a daily basis. So concerned was he in fact, that he asked his long-term friend, Caleb Hillier Parry whose practice was in Bath for his help. Parry wrote: "It will give me great pleasure to hear your pathological theories, because, without flattery, I highly respect them all, and have no hesitation in saying that it is your own fault if you are not still the first pathologist existing."

The Earl was facing death and whilst lying in his sick bed, thought only of the wrongs that he had committed against his wife, the Countess, originally plain Mary Cole who he had married twice. The first marriage took place on 30th March 1785 at Berkeley Church and that marriage produced four children, the first being named William Fitzhardinge (1786–1857). The other three children are detailed in chapter 3 so we do not need to name them again. There had always been doubt as to whether this first marriage was in fact legal and there was a long legal dispute as to whether the first born child from the first marriage of the 5th Earl (William Fitzhardinge) should inherit the title or whether it should be the first child from the second marriage (Thomas Moreton, 1796–1882) which was of course, the couple's fifth child. The 5th Earl died on 10th August 1810, a troubled man, not knowing who would inherit his title as the case did not reach the House of Lords until March 1811, several months after his death. The late Earl had wanted the first marriage to be declared legal so as to right the wrong that he had committed against the Countess, whilst the Countess wanted the same status to be accorded to the first marriage in order that her first four children should be deemed legitimate. As it happened, it was deemed Thomas Moreton, the first child from the second marriage should be the 6th Earl, but he refused to accept the title out of respect for his older brother, William Fitzhardinge, the first born from the first marriage. The reader may wish to return to chapter 3 where the details of the Berkeley family and the dispute as to who should inherit the 5th Earl's title are laid out in more detail.

After the Earl's death, the Jenner family travelled to Cheltenham and soon after their arrival, they were informed of the sad news that Jenner's sister, Mary (1730–1810) had died at the age of eighty. Her surname was Black as she had married the Rev G.C. Black in 1757 although he died in 1776 leaving her a widow for the last thirty-four years of her life. It seemed that deaths were coming thick and fast in the Jenner circle, and sadly, it did not stop with Mary. Later in 1810, a Mr Fuller prepared a bill which he wished to put to Parliament that inoculation with smallpox be made illegal but before he did so he sent a rough draft to Jenner. Jenner was unhappy with much of it and returned it to Fuller with several amendments. Fuller duly presented it to Parliament and it was rejected out of hand. It seemed that Fuller had not incorporated any of Jenner's alterations which makes one wonder why he bothered to send the rough draft in the first place. Jenner had prophesied that the bill would be rejected if his amendments were not included but he felt little satisfaction to be proven right. As Jenner thought, the bill was rejected in its entirety with the result that his ever loyal friend, Caleb Hillier Parry (1755–1822), wrote to him: 'The great business is accomplished, and the blessing is ready for those who choose to avail themselves of it, and with those who reject it the evil will be on their own heads'.

The letter, whilst supportive of Jenner and had been written by one of his oldest friends, nevertheless did little to cheer him up. It was of no consequence how well vaccination with cowpox was doing if doctors were still variolating patients with smallpox which meant that the deadly disease would never be conquered. However, whilst no new law was introduced stopping variolation with smallpox nationally, it was stopped locally in Gloucestershire because of how well known Jenner was and how well thought of he was in the area. Because of the vaccination process that was used in Gloucestershire ever since Jenner had first started practicing with it, the area was free from smallpox. Cheltenham, where Jenner had also been practicing vaccination, was also clear except there were a few cases that had been brought in by a few travellers, but that was all.

The local doctors were naturally impressed by this, and with help from two of Jenner's oldest and faithful friends, his future biographer, John Baron (1786–1851), and Charles Brandon Trye (1757–1811), the doctors decided to form an association which finally decided that local medical men would stop practicing smallpox inoculation (variolation) completely. This was a great start to enable Jenner to make the practice of variolation illegal throughout the country, but it was obviously going to take a lot of time and patience and Jenner was growing weary through age generally, but also the constant battle for the vaccination remedy to be used legally throughout the country and for Parliament to put a bill through to that effect. The fight to make vaccination with cowpox the standard treatment which would in time eliminate smallpox instead of variolation was far from over. However, although Jenner realised that it would never happen in his life time, several Acts of Parliament were put in the statute book in the beginning of the 19th century, and the main two were as follows:

1804 – Act passed to make variolation illegal.

1805 – Act passed to make vaccination compulsory.

Jenner was exhausted but thrilled at the same time. What he had worked for nearly a decade had at last come to pass, although his dream of wiping smallpox from the world was obviously going to take longer and there were still people who needed convincing.

-oOOo-

Chapter 15

Setback in the Treatment of Smallpox by Vaccination, Further Deaths with Family and Friends

The constant battle over the years to enable the process of vaccination to become the universal treatment to wipe smallpox from the world had exhausted Jenner and must have undermined his immune system.

Jenner's physical resources were drained but after a brief unspecified illness, became well again and was able to travel to London in the spring of 1811 and soon after arriving, was pleased to learn that he had received an honour from the National Institute of France to mark the vaccination of the King of Rome. This august body had conferred on him the honour of being Foreign Associate. However, Jenner's joy was short-lived as in the same month, he was confronted by what seemed a failure in the smallpox vaccination. On 26th May, 1811, the Hon. Robert Grosvenor contracted a serious bout of the disease despite the fact that Jenner had vaccinated him along with two siblings when he was an infant, ten years before. The boy in question was heir to an earldom so the situation was a serious one for Jenner. Robert was attended by distinguished physicians, Sir Henry Halford (1766–1844) and Sir Walter Farquhar (1738–1819), both men believing that the disease was very likely to end in the boy's death. Halford was Physician Extraordinary to King George III between the years 1793 until 1820 when the king died, and was Physician in Ordinary to King George IV, William IV, and Queen Victoria. Farquhar was an eminent Scottish Physician who looked after the Prince of Wales before he became King George IV, and also Prime Minister William Pitt the Younger. The National Vaccine Establishment undertook an investigation and came to the conclusion that it was a much milder form of disease than people had suspected, due in fact to Jenner's earlier vaccination. Robert recovered fairly quickly whilst the two siblings didn't in fact catch the disease at all. The outcome seemed a happy one and Jenner felt vindicated but unfortunately the story had spread to London and the faith in vaccination that Jenner had built up over the years vanished and he was almost back to square one. Apart from worrying about the children, he was distraught that his reputation could have been finished in a short space of time. Mothers who had had their children vaccinated by Jenner set about ruining Jenner's reputation which if they had cause, no one could have blamed them. However, although the good news about the child's recovery took a while to reach London, it did eventually and Jenner's reputation recovered all though not overnight. However, recover it did in time but it was a while before the fuss died down and that confidence in smallpox vaccination was gradually accepted.

Jenner wrote to various people about the incident, and one of these was a Miss Calcraft, who was probably a friend as well as a patient. Jenner wrote: take a wide comprehensive view of Vaccination and then ask yourself what is this Case? You will find it a speck, a mere microscopic speck, on the page which contains the History of the Vaccine discovery…now this single, solitary instance has occurr'd, all my past labours…are forgotten, and I am held up by many, perhaps the majority of the higher classes, as an object of derision and Contempt…' The letter thus far is reasonable as he attempts to explain why this isolated outbreak takes place, but later in the letter, he states the following: 'the safest and best test is re-vaccination'. This letter confuses the issue of vaccination. The first quote says that however good a system of a smallpox cure that is being practiced, there is always a chance, however slight, of an occasional deviation from the norm, but that a single vaccination should however last a lifetime. However, in the second quote, he deviates from that which he has always claimed, and recommends a later vaccination for those who have been vaccinated before. It seemed that this very rare case had temporarily in any rate, slightly shaken Jenner's confidence. Luckily, the fuss died down and the passage of time plus continued success with vaccination allowed Jenner to eventually have his confidence and his reputation restored.

Jenner's mood darkened however in July of 1811 as Catherine's brother, Thomas Kingscote was dying and it was a slow lingering death. That, along with Catherine's own poor health plunged him into a deep depression. Catherine's health had always been delicate and the strain of looking after Edward Junior during his illness caused a huge strain to be put on the physical side of her health, whilst she was now experiencing the grief that only a mother could feel when mourning a much-loved son. Her dying brother's condition only added to her unhappiness.

October, 1811 came, and once again Jenner heard some bad news concerning a possible loss looming from one of his friends and family. This time, it was his great and long-standing friend, Charles Brandon Trye. On 3rd October, Jenner travelled from Cheltenham to Gloucester as he heard that his great friend had been taken ill with cholera. However, Trye's illness was over very quickly and he died only four days later, on the 7th October, 1811, and at the time when he was the senior surgeon at the Gloucester Infirmary. The friends had known each other from their younger days when they were students at Cirencester and the friendship had continued throughout their lives ever since. Trye had enjoyed a brilliant career in medicine and readers can remind themselves of what he did by looking back in the first chapter of this book. It is a nice touch that there is a monument to Trye in Gloucester Cathedral which at the time of writing is very close to the statue of Jenner. The words on Trye's monument are also recorded in the first chapter and it is fitting that the two friends are celebrated in the cathedral nave. They are not buried near each other however. Whilst Jenner rests in the altar of Berkeley Church along with members of his family, Trye is buried in the grounds of the Church of St Mary de Crypt, which is situated in the centre of Gloucester. Jenner was very depressed as it seemed that so many of his generation, be they friends or family were dying, but he turned to his long-standing friend, John Baron for support and Baron, whose admiration for Jenner bordered on hero worship did not let Jenner down. Jenner was doing what a great many people entering their later years did, and made friends with people from a younger generation, and in Jenner's case, Baron, who was born in 1786, thirty-seven years after Jenner, certainly fitted the bill.

Three months later, in February 1812, Edward and Catherine returned to Berkeley. They had only been home a matter of days when on the 12th, Jenner told his friend, the Rev Thomas Pruen, that he 'was again seized with the influenza which has handled me much more severely than on the first attack'. Although vaccination was back in favour and should have cheered him, the loss of his friend, Charles Brandon Trye took away some of the pleasure and Jenner suddenly took a dislike to Cheltenham. Again he wrote to the Rev Pruen:

'I have no longer a relish for Cheltenham – on the contrary I nauseate it. At the instigation of a man who is under considerable obligations to me, a building has been erected on the corner of Pacey's Garden, close to my front door on St G. Place. It bears all the appearance of a necessary House (a public lavatory), though used as a Tailor's Shop. Not a Creature could step forward and tell me anything about it till it was finish'd; but when they want the Money to expend on the improvement of the Town, then I can hear from them fast enough.' Jenner's mood darkened even further when he realised how ill his sister, Anne Davies (1741–1812) was. In 1766 she had married the Revd William Davies (1740–1817) who at this time was the Rector of Eastington. She had suffered several severe strokes, the first one being on 7th August and although she was under the care of Mr Darke of Eastington, Jenner nevertheless visited her on that day and again on the 19th, and again on the 27th. However, Anne died a month later on 25th September and her husband, the Rev William Davies, noted that he had lost 'My dearest Friend'. From the note her husband left, she appeared to have been very warm hearted and kindly woman and kept a house that people were welcome to call in at any time. The loss to Edward and Catherine was great, as she was the last of Edward's sisters to have died, and along with that, she and Catherine got on very well and liked each other very much.

When writing about Edward Jenner and his great achievements, it is usual to keep the events of his life centred around his years of work in his herculean events over many years to change the way that smallpox was treated. The events of the Napoleonic wars are briefly touched on but not in any great detail. In any book that is written concerning Jenner, his work revolves around Berkeley, Cheltenham and to a degree, London. However, during the period that Jenner was facing up to the deaths of friends and family, a cataclysmic event happened in Parliament, the very heart of government that had never happened before, and thankfully has never happened since, but no record of Jenner's reactions can be found. The shock and sudden death is looked at in the following chapter.

-oOOo-

Chapter 16

Two More Major Deaths, One a National Figure, Although Virtually Unknown to Jenner, the Other, the Tragic Loss of a Beloved Wife

Although most of the deaths recorded are of friends and members of the Jenner family, one of the most dreadful and sudden deaths that happened was to a man who Jenner had almost certainly never met, and yet no doubt read all about his work in all the major newspapers of the day. It affected him as it did most of his generation. That was the assassination of the Prime Minister of the day, Spencer Perceval on the 11th May 1812, in the lobby of the House of Commons, and the only serving Prime Minister to have met his death in this manner whilst in office. Perceval was a small man in physical stature, but in the role that he played in Great Britain, was one of the most powerful men in the land. He combined the role of the Chancellor of the Exchequer with that of Prime Minister, or the more formal title of The First Lord of the Treasury which the Prime Minister of the day was known as, and these two roles made him exceedingly powerful, but produced a workload that would be unheard of today where the posts of Prime Minister and Chancellor are always held by different people.

Spencer Perceval (1762–1812) was a British statesman who was born on 1st November, 1762 in Audley Square, the seventh son of John Perceval, the 2nd Earl of Egmont and was the second son of John Perceval and his second wife, Catherine Compton. Spencer Perceval himself grew up and married Jane Wilson in 1790 and the couple went on to have thirteen children. He had enjoyed a good parliamentary career and was the only Solicitor-General who became Prime Minister. He became Prime Minister from October, 1809 until the day of his death which was on that fateful day of 11th May, 1812. He had been educated at Harrow School and from there he continued his studies at Trinity College,

Cambridge. He studied law at Lincoln's Inn Fields and practiced as a Barrister before becoming a King's Counsel in 1796 at the age of 34 years. He then entered Parliament as the member for Northampton.

Although the two main parties were Tories and Whigs, Perceval was definitely a Tory although members did not always describe themselves by their party. The political parties did not have the same way of operating nor did the MPs have to blindly follow what the whips instructed them to do as they do today.

Members in the 18th century were often swayed by a good speech from another member and often continued to follow that person. Like other members, Spencer Perceval followed the Prime Minister of the day who was William Pitt the Younger (Prime Minister from 1783–1801 and again from 1804 until 1806 when he died) as his speeches were often mesmerising and could last two hours being delivered with no notes. Spencer Perceval supported the war against Napoleon which Pitt was conducting and again like Pitt, he was completely against the slave trade which William Wilberforce (1759–1833) and Oloudah Equiano (1745–97) was working for its abolition along with others such as Thomas Clarkson (1760–1846) and many others who were from the Quaker religion such as the writer Hannah More (1745–1833). The trafficking of slavery was abolished in 1807 whilst slavery itself was finally abolished in 1833.

On that dreadful day in 1812, Perceval was on his way to the Chamber and on reaching Parliament made his way up the stairs to the House of Commons chamber at a few minutes past five o'clock when a tall man stood in his way. Perceval was running late as he had been due in the chamber at 4.30pm, but ever the courteous gentleman, said a few words to the man, possibly asking him politely if he could let him pass, when the man pulled a gun from the inside breast pocket of the brown coat that he was wearing. The weapon that he was carrying was small and over a distance of more than five yards was totally inaccurate, but the would-be killer had no intention of hurting anybody other than Perceval. Without uttering a word, the man whose name was John Bellingham, pushed the gun straight at the Prime Minister's chest and fired, shooting him at point blank range. Perceval was said to have shouted, "I am murdered, murdered." whilst Bellingham was grabbed by Henry Burgess, a Mayfair solicitor and a large man by the name of William Jerdan, a journalist who wrote for the British press'. They both grabbed Bellingham's arms and took the pistol from him. In the meantime, Spencer Perceval was carried into another room where he died a few minutes later. Two men had been in conversation close by, one being William Smith, the MP for Norwich and a fervent supporter of the movement to end slavery, and Francis Phillips, another MP who was also in the anti-slavery lobby. A detailed description of what happened was given by William Smith at the Coroner's inquiry and it went as follows:

'Almost at the same instant a person rushed hastily from among the crowd, and several voices cried out, "Shut the door," and "let no one escape." The person who came from among the crowd came towards me, looking first one way and then another, and as I thought at the moment, rather like one seeking for shelter than as the person who had received the wound. But taking two or three steps towards me as he approached he rather reeled by me, and almost instantly fell upon the floor, with his face downwards… When he first fell I thought he might be slightly wounded, and expected to see him make an effort to rise, but gazing at him a few moments, I observed that he did not stir at all; I therefore immediately stooped down to raise him from the ground, requesting the assistance of a gentleman who stood close by me for that purpose. As soon as we had turned his face towards us, and not till then, I perceived it was Mr Perceval.'

Phillips and Smith knelt down beside Perceval and saw the bullet hole which was just above the heart and seeing that it was angled downwards swiftly came to the conclusion that although Perceval was still breathing, the wound would prove to be fatal especially as the bullet was still lodged inside Perceval's chest. The two MP's held the body upright and taking an arm each, carried the stricken Prime Minister to an office which was used by the Speaker's clerk as it was the nearest room. Phillips said afterwards that before the two men could lay Perceval down, his body suddenly went limp which indicated that the Prime Minister had died.

The assassin made no attempt to escape and the gun was taken from him without him giving any undue resistance. Bellingham freely admitted his guilt although at his trial, which was held at the Old Bailey a few days later on 15th May, his barristers attempted to prove that he was insane to save him from the death penalty. There were witnesses for both sides of the argument and in the end it was decided that he was not insane and Bellingham was found guilty. The summing up of the proceedings had been delivered by Sir James Mansfield, S.L., K.C. (1734–1821), who was judging the case. Sir James had no family connection with Lord Chief Justice Mansfield whose rulings went a great deal towards Britain ending the barbaric slave trade. Sir James Mansfield nonetheless had a good career. He became King's Counsel in 1772 and his ability was recognised by Lord North who was Prime Minister between 1770 and 1782. Mansfield entered Parliament in 1779 as the member for Cambridge University and was Solicitor-General twice before serving as Chief Justice of the Common Pleas from 1799 until 1814 when he resigned due to ill health. The post that he held was one of the highest judicial officials in England. When speaking to the jury, Bellingham had virtually no chance when Sir James Mansfield said to the jury the words that were reported in the Old Bailey Sessions Papers:

'Gentlemen of the jury, you are now to try an indictment which charges the prisoner at the bar with the wilful murder (here the learned judge was so hurt by his feelings, that he could not proceed for several seconds) of Mr Spencer Perceval, (in a faint voice) who was murdered with a pistol loaded with a bullet; when the prisoner mentioned the name of (here again his lordship was sincerely affected, and burst into tears, in which he was joined by the greatest portion of the persons in court) a man so dear, and so revered as that of Mr Spencer Perceval, I find it difficult to suppress my feelings.'

The inevitable verdict of guilty meant that Bellingham was duly executed on 18th May, 1812, one week from the assassination of the Prime Minister, the Right Honourable Spencer Perceval. The jury had come to their conclusion after a mere fourteen minutes of discussion although Sir James Mansfield, whose remarks to the jury left them in no doubt as to which verdict he wanted was surprised that they took as long as fourteen minutes to arrive at their decision.

The second death was completely different for Jenner. The loss to the country of the Prime Minister, Spencer Perceval, was devastating but the man himself was little known to members of the British public on a personal level. The second death however was quite the opposite of Perceval in as much as she was largely unknown to the general public but was the love of Edward Jenner's life, his beloved wife Catherine. On 1st September, 1815, Edward and Catherine Jenner were residing in their house in Cheltenham, not by choice as Berkeley had always been their favourite place and 'The Chantry' their favourite house, but by necessity as Catherine, who never enjoyed good health suddenly became ill. During the spring she was unwell, but Jenner was not too worried as she was to all intents and purposes holding her own, and both she and her husband were looking forward to the summer when Edward thought that there was bound to be an improvement. However, when June came, Catherine caught bronchitis and Jenner became uneasy and much less confident that Catherine would fully recover. He stayed with her constantly but there was nothing that he could do. He wrote to his friend, the Revd Thomas Pruen: 'Poor Mrs Jenner who has been much better in some respects is labouring (sic) under a dreadful depression of spirits'. Jenner's great friend and future biographer, John Baron, travelled to see Jenner both as a friend and a doctor and arrived on the 12th. Catherine, despite the fact that she had two eminent doctors looking after her, one a loving husband and one a great friend of her husband's, was sadly beyond help, and she succumbed to her illness soon after Baron had arrived, and she passed away at 12.30 am on the morning of 13th September, 1815. Baron clearly didn't stay long because only a day or so after Catherine's death, Jenner wrote the following letter to Baron:

My dear Baron,

I know of no one whom I should like to see here better than yourself; and as often as you can find a little leisure, pray come and exercise your pity. I am, of course, most wretched when alone; as every surrounding object then the more forcibly reminds me of my irreparable loss. Every tree, shrub, flower, seems to speak. But yet no place on earth would at present suit me but this, and I trust my friends will not endeavour to take me away; for, strange and contradictory as it may seem, the bitter cup has a kind of relish in here, which it could afford nowhere else.

Give me a task and I will execute it as well as I can. Tell me which subject you want first, put it down on a slip of paper when you come. I mean a list of what I promised you. God bless you.

Sincerely yours, E. Jenner

The funeral was held on 21st September, one week after Catherine's death, by the vicar at that time, the Revd Caleb Carrington and was buried in the chancel of Berkeley Church on 21st September. Jenner virtually retreated from general society and for the first few months after the funeral lived permanently at 'The Chantry' hardly ever leaving the place although he carried on visiting a few patients. About a month after losing his beloved Catherine, Jenner wrote to his friend, the Revd Thomas Pruen:

"My whole frame is thrown into derangement. What a severe shock have I received. It was the more severe as it was unexpected. Poor dear Soul, but little more than a fortnight before, we walk'd together about the streets of Cheltenham and took a ramble in Mrs Williams's garden. Never sufficiently attentive to herself, tho' ever mindful of the wants of others, she was inadvertently exposed to a cold current of air from the North, which brought on an inflammation of the Lungs, too violent for her tender frame to sustain. Her departure was mark'd with that sweet serenity, which I believe ever attends the last hours of those who have spent an (?) in life. Hers is a bless'd gain; mine an irreparable loss. The privation is not to be describ'd."

Catherine died from pulmonary tubercle. It is a sad irony that this great man, whose tireless work saved millions of lives throughout the world, could not save the lives of the two people who he loved the most, his eldest son, also called Edward, who died in 1810 aged just twenty one years, and his wife Catherine who passed away five years later, in 1815.

The death of Catherine was a desperate blow to Edward and a blow that he never really recovered from. He left the house in Cheltenham which he only purchased as a house for Catherine and himself to visit each summer for her health, and made no future plans to visit London again. He retired to 'The Chantry' and whilst he saw friends and a few patients from time to time, never left Berkeley again.

-oOOo-

Chapter 17

Life After Catherine

After the death of his wife Catherine, Jenner turned to the man who although much younger than him, had been a true friend for many years, and who Jenner knew would give him the support that he needed after the death of Catherine. The man was John Baron who would eventually write his mentor's biography. Shortly after Catherine's death, Jenner wrote to his trusted friend which is the letter that is printed at the end of the previous chapter and true to form, Baron visited Jenner whenever he was able.

Most people can understand the feeling of being lonely despite the fact that they may be surrounded by people. Jenner was in that position. He had two surviving offspring, Catherine (1794–1833), and Robert (1797–1854). Catherine was twenty-two years old when her mother died and Edward had her in Berkeley for another seven years until she married John Yeend Bedford in 1822 and moved to Birmingham. Robert was seventeen but was little use to his father. They were completely different people and, in any event, Robert was keen to leave home anyway and wished to go to Oxford and then join the army. There was his nephew Henry (1767–1851), the son of Edward's brother, also called Henry (1736–98) who had proved unreliable when in his younger days he had helped his uncle with his projects. When his aunt Catherine died Henry (1767–1851) was forty-eight years old and was a middle-aged man but his uncle still had no high regard for him. He had married Susan Pearce (1766–98) in 1792 and they produced eight children, three boys and five girls. We know the years of each child's birth but not the year of each of their deaths so we have no record as to how many of them lived until adulthood. Henry (1767–1851), Edward's nephew was in partnership with a young physician named Henry Shrapnell, a Gloucester physician and between them continued the practice in Berkeley. Henry Shrapnell should not be confused with WF Shrapnell but as the former was friendly with Henry, Edward's nephew, and the latter friendly with Edward himself, it could be that they were father and son, although it has proved very difficult to obtain any information on either of them.

There were more family members who could provide potential support. His brother in law, the Revd William Davies (1740–1817) had married Edward's sister Anne (1741–1812), but she had died in 1812, three years before Catherine, whilst the Revd Davies only lived for two years after Catharine died. It was unlikely that Edward was on his own very often, but that did not mean that he was not lonely. He had lost the love of his life and she was always on his mind.

Indeed, although not related to Jenner, Henry Shrapnell was very helpful to Jenner, unlike his partner, Edward's nephew Henry. When not working in the practice that he shared with Jenner's nephew Henry, Shrapnell busied himself in his study, sorting out and labelling specimens that Jenner had collected over the years. Jenner had been good when collecting specimens but hopeless when trying to sort them out which may have simply been pressure of work and the categorising of them therefore not a priority. However, this was odd as most books on Jenner will include the time in 1771 when he spent many months carefully categorising the thousand plus plant specimens that the botanist Joseph Banks (1743–1820) had brought back from his three-year world voyage with Captain Cook (1728–1779). This was outlined in chapter two of this book; indeed, Jenner's work had been so good that Banks offered him a job as part of his team that would be going on a second voyage with Captain Cook. Jenner turned it down as after spending the years 1770 until 1773 studying under Dr John Hunter (1728–93) in London, he simply wanted to return to his beloved rural Berkeley. Most people probably thought he was mad as sailors had come back talking about the exotic South Sea island people and the beautiful islands such as Tahiti and Fiji that they had visited. Indeed, many of the sailors had formed relationships with the island women and it was down to the strength of Cook's character that he was able to stop wholesale desertion. Having said all that however, Jenner was born and brought up in the country and was eager to go back, set up his own practice and start his work on curing the dreaded disease of smallpox which even as a young doctor, he had started to think about.

Having said all that about Jenner's lack of administrative skills however, he had his own unique way of cataloguing specimens by putting them down in verse. As said earlier in the book, although Jenner's work and indeed his whole career was of a scientific nature, he possessed great talent as he could also straddle both science and art which is why he got on so well with Anne Hunter (nee Home), the wife of his former teacher and mentor John Hunter who was also artistic. Jenner, who played the flute and violin, also like Anne Hunter wrote lyrics, and the following lines were written by Jenner in order to catalogue the specimens in his museum. The verses are entitled 'Berkeley Fair'.

'There's an encrinite's head, a cornu ammonias,
And marquisites fit to adorn an Adonis;
Fine corals, all fossil, from Woodford's grand rock;
And granites from Snowdon in many a block;
Alcyonites, too, we have joined to our stock;
Hippopotamus' bones, and a great alligator,
And things most surprising thrown out of a crater;
All changed into flint are an elephant's jaws,
The mammoth's vast teeth, and the leopard's huge paws:
There are beautiful agates washed up by the fountains,
And crabs that were found on the tops of the mountains;
Asbestos, chert, chrysolite, quartz, hermatitis,
Madrepore, schistus, basalt, and pyritis,
Oolites, zoolites, graphites, a store,
Pentacrinites, chlorites, and many things more.'

A rather eccentric way of recording details of his collections, but nevertheless effective in its own way.

There were still more friends that Jenner could call on for support in this time of loneliness. His very good friend, Edward Gardner, was very close by and would ride to Berkeley from Frampton on a regular basis. Another long-standing friend was Henry Hicks who was at Eastington and he too saw Edward on a regular basis. Dr Caleb Hillier Parry (1755–1822) who lived with his wife at Bath and had run a practice there used to come over along with Matthew Baillie, John Hunter's nephew. He had bought a house near Cirencester and although still running a practice, came over when he could. Along with all of these, the Countess of Berkeley would pay visits, her late husband, the 5th Earl having died in August, 1810, and her sons would also visit. There were more, but it is unnecessary to write them all out as the point has already been made that he had a great deal of support in these difficult times. However, kind though all his friends were, and generous with their time for their friend, it couldn't take away the sadness and loneliness he felt without his beloved Catherine and would feel like that way until his own death eight years later. Having said that, with the love and support of his many friends, he made the best of things and was able to make a tolerable life for himself without her.

Although desperately sad, Jenner did make some sort of life for himself without Catherine. Although retired, he would still ride out to visit patients, and never refused a request to come out when asked. Sometimes he would have to hear rambling accounts of their illnesses, real or imaginary, and always did his best for them although it would test the patience of a saint. Still, he was keeping active and with his friends and relatives visiting him, he often had someone to talk to, even though their monologues were not always to his taste. Despite all the support he had from friends, many of them slipped away to return to their own lives and Jenner, like any other bereaved person, found himself having no one to talk to on some days. With none of the modern appliances we take for granted today such as telephone, radio and television, the lengthy silences must have been dreadful. However, it must be said that the ever-loyal John Baron (1786–1851) was a very good friend. Jenner found him a little dull, but that trait in his character was more than compensated for by his loyalty and kindness and Jenner loved him very much. However, on the days that he was completely alone, he would adopt regular routines, getting up at eight o'clock, a walk of about a mile before having breakfast and then two miles before dinner and then he would walk around his garden afterwards. Fresh air and exercise would not bring Catherine back, but that and his friends along with being needed by a few patients helped him to cope.

In September, 1810, Jenner had been made a magistrate and now that he was going to be permanently in Berkeley, he was made Mayor in 1815, which earned him a small amount of money but had minimal duties, and was also made Justice of the Peace which carried no salary at all. He found the latter post not to his liking whatsoever. Being Mayor was fine, and admirably suited to a man who was retired and wanted a post that gave him few worries. However, being a Justice of the Peace suited him not one iota. Amongst a hubbub of noise that his one assistant was completely unable to control, he found that he had to listen to tales of drunkenness, thieving and any amount of lawless behaviour, as well as poverty, and all this coupled with many having a complete inability to write were brought in front of him. He wanted a quiet retirement and this was certainly not that. Jenner wanted something done about it. He wrote: 'Is not this too bad? I am the only acting magistrate in this place and I am really harassed to death. I want the Lord Lieutenant to give me an assistant, and I have applied for my nephew, but without success.' Eventually, the Revd William Davies did indeed become his assistant and Jenner's son, Robert a magistrate so his circumstances improved, but he was never entirely happy in the post. He almost certainly took the post in the first place as he thought that it would help fill the huge void in his life with Catherine gone, but there were times when he longed for a quieter life. He wrestled with the problem in his mind because if he had left the post and had his quieter life, his loneliness would become unbearable again. It was a sad situation and whatever decision that he would make would not necessarily lead to further his happiness.

Farmers were suffering a bad year in 1815 which resulted in an increase in poaching. There were two reasons for this; firstly and most obviously, to obtain more food but also to send a message to landlords that they, the farmers, were at the end of their tether because of the way landlords were charging very high rents. The poaching became such a huge problem that landlords took to protecting their property and they weren't too fussy about how they went about it. One of the landlords, Lord Ducie, started to use spring guns and after one night of poaching, it was used and a farmer from Totworth was killed. From a legal point of view, it was actually murder, but the jury sprang a surprise when they returned an open verdict. Perhaps they thought that if the farmers were poaching, then they had put themselves outside of the law and therefore the supposed illegality of the killing was not subject to the protection of the law. In any event, they were also almost certainly sympathetic to the farmer's case. Not unnaturally, the farmers were outraged; not only had one of their kind been killed, but the killer had got away scot-free. They took matters into their own hands and organised poaching raids with large numbers of farmers along with their sons. A fight ensured with gamekeepers at Catgrove which was on the Berkeley Estate. It started with fists but tragically things got out of hand and guns came into the fray and a gamekeeper was killed along with another half a dozen being wounded. Now the boot was on the other foot and it was the landlords who were angry. Colonel Berkeley mustered a party of his people to find the men who they suspected had killed the gamekeeper and, in the process, beat up a farmer by the name of Allen along with his servant. Farmer Allen's servant was absolutely terrified and gave the names of the poachers and their leader, who as it turned out, was Farmer Allen himself. They were tried at Gloucester Assizes and Farmers Allen and Penny were hanged and the remaining nine were transported to Australia. The severity of the sentences caused Jenner a great deal of stress as he knew a great many of them and some of the sons had been pupils at his wife's Sunday school. However, he was powerless to change the sentences and there was nothing he could do or say that would alter them in any way.

In the 18th century, convicts were transported to the Americas because there wasn't nearly enough room to house prisoners in Britain. However, since America won their independence from Britain in 1783, a new place had to be found and there was a great deal of discussion in Parliament as to where this could be. In 1770, Sir Joseph Banks (1743–1820), the great botanist, had briefly visited Australia with Captain Cook (1728–79) during the latter's first of his three great voyages round the world and suggested Botany Bay in 1784 as a replacement place for offenders. Because of the distance between Australia and Britain, the idea was initially turned down but when it was realised that there was no other suitable place, New South Wales was chosen. The place was barren and the new settlers had a very tough few years before they were able to farm it properly but eventually the area just a little way north was cultivated and is now the great city of Sydney that we know today. The city was named after Lord Sydney (1733–1800) who was Home Secretary at the time. Sydney entered the House of Commons in 1754 as Thomas Townshend and supported the Whig party. When Lord North resigned as Prime Minister in 1782 for his part in Britain losing the American War of Independence, Townshend stepped up to the House of Lords where he became Home Secretary and hence became Lord Sydney.

Returning to Jenner, he was visited by his great friend John Baron when they watched the trial in Gloucester, and Baron returned to Jenner's house in the summer of 1816 and whilst there, developed a serious bout of tonsillitis and pharyngitis. Baron wanted to go home but fortunately for him, Jenner managed to persuade him to stay. This was just as well, as Baron grew very ill indeed and his throat was completely congested. Jenner decided that the only way to save Baron was to perform a tracheotomy which is exactly what he did with complete success. A tracheotomy involves cutting open the windpipe and without an anaesthetic, was probably very painful. This was the least of Baron's problems however, and Jenner almost certainly saved his friend's life.

Glad that he had almost certainly saved Baron's life, before he had time to be pleased, another person to whom he had been close for many years became ill having suffered an apoplectic seizure. This was his great friend, Dr Caleb Hillier Parry (1755–1822) who lived and worked in Bath. Jenner lost no time in going to see him and was distressed to see his great friend in such a bad state. Parry was conscious, but was unable to speak – all Jenner could see was that his friend was in a very bad way indeed. It looked for all the world that he would die very soon, but in fact he lived for another five years although he was practically an invalid dying in 1822. Jenner was getting more and more depressed as he realised that he was at an age where all his friends, some, including Parry, going back to his schooldays, were dying off.

However, there were two things that he did to combat this depression, the first being, although officially retired, he never stopped working, quite literally until the day that he died. The other thing that kept him going were the new friends in his life, one of the obvious ones being John Baron, who were younger than him, and he was kept all the happier for it.

It was at this time that Jenner started working with a man called Sir Stamford Raffles (1781–1826) and it was in time to lead to the formation of the London Zoo. Raffles had been Lieutenant-General of British Java from 1811 until 1815 when Java was returned to the Dutch under the terms of the Anglo-Dutch Treaty of 1814. Raffles was out of a job until he was appointed Governor-General of Bencolon in 1817 and held that post until 1822. It was when he was between these two posts that he returned to England and visited Jenner. Raffles had been involved in the capture of Java and when it became under British rule he placed restrictions on the slave trade in Java and this made him unpopular with the East India Company. However, the mood concerning slavery was changing throughout the world, not least because of the lengthy campaign lead by the great anti-slavery campaigner, William Wilberforce (1759–1833), and the passing of the act in the British House of Commons on 23rd February 1807 which outlawed the trafficking of slavery. However, it was not until 26th July 1833, that slavery was abolished completely by the British Parliament. Raffles was a family man having been married twice. He married Olivia Marianne Devenish in 1805 but she died in 1814. Three years later in 1817, he married his second wife, Sophia Hull, and they remained husband and wife until Raffles died suddenly on 5th July, 1826 of a brain tumour. The following day would have been his 45th birthday. He lies buried in St Mary's church, Hendon, London.

When Raffles was Lieutenant-Governor of Java, he set aside lands that were specifically used for vaccination posts and when he told Jenner that smallpox in that region had been eliminated then that naturally pleased Jenner a great deal. Raffles had a great interest in zoology and shared his interest with Edward who described Sir John Hunter's (1728–93) interest in the subject. He went on to describe the way that Hunter kept wild animals in captivity. Some of the ways that they were held may not seem too bad to us today such as sheep grazing together in meadows along with buffaloes and goats, and with various types of fish in ponds, but keeping snakes in cages along with the way he kept leopards would be unthinkable today. Jenner enjoyed the visit of Raffles very much and not only did he learn a great deal, the conversations that they had brought back happy memories of Hunter who Jenner always referred to as 'The dear man'. Jenner had started to feel stimulated again, and with those feelings he became much happier, although he still missed his Catherine.

He and Gardner were in touch again, and arranged to go on a fossil-hunting expedition which again was a boost to Jenner's pleasure as he had collected fossils when younger. However, they had to postpone it due to poor weather but it inspired Jenner to write some poetry, a hobby that he had neglected in recent years.

'The hollow winds begin to blow,
The clouds look black, the glass is low.
The soot falls down, the spaniels sleep,
The spiders from their cobwebs creep.
Last night the sun went pale to bed,
The moon in haloes hid her head.
The boding shepherd heaves a sigh,
For see! a rainbow spans the sky.
The walls are damp, the ditches smell,
Clos'd is the pink eye-pimpernel.
Hark how the chairs and tables crack.
Old Betty's joints are on the rack;
Loud quack the ducks, the peacocks cry;
The distant hills are looking nigh;
How restless are the snorting swine,
The busy flies disturb the kin
Low o'er the grass the swallow wings;
The cricket too, how loud it sings!

Puss on the hearth with velvet paws,
Sits smoothing o'er her whiskered jaws.
Through the clear stream the fishes rise,
And nimbly catch the incautious flies.
The sheep were seen at early light,
Cropping the meads with eager bite.
Through June, the air is cold and chill;
The mellow blackbird's voice is still.
The glow-worms numerous and bright,
Illumed the dewy dell last night.
At dusk the squalid toad was seen,
Hopping and crawling o'er the green.
The frog has lost his yellow vest,
And in a dingy suit is dressed.
The leech, disturbed, is newly risen,
Quite to the summit of his prison.
The whirling winds the dust obeys,
And in the rapid eddy plays.
My dog, so altered in his taste,
Quits marrow-bones on grass to feast.
And see, yon rooks, how odd their flight!
They imitate the gliding kite,
Or seem precipitate to fall,
As if they felt the piercing ball.
'Twill surely rain, I see with sorrow,
Our jaunt must be put off tomorrow.'

Jenner still mourned his beloved Catherine, but had reached a stage whereby he had adjusted to his new situation and was able to lead a life that gave him some pleasure, notably when his friend John Baron came to visit him. However, if he was ill, then even Baron could not cheer him up and he seemed to be under the weather quite often and worried about his health. During his recovery from one such episode, he wrote to Baron who was by this time, certainly his best friend, and told him in great detail what his symptoms had been and how he was feeling. Jenner wrote:

Having just heard that a person is going from hence to Gloucester tomorrow morning. I write to tell you that our stern alarms will soon be changed to merry meetings.

I am in every respect better. The pain in my head gone; my respiration easy, the expectoration lessened; but there is now no impediment to the separation of the mucous from the membranes. Still, however, there is that susceptibility that a single inhalation of air colder than the temperature of my bedchamber instantly makes me hoarse. I took several doses of the squills, but have omitted it from its singular effects. It called to my remembrance the terrible consequences of the dose of cayenne, by giving a glow that almost called up pyrosis. The difference, however, was as great as one to fifty. But does this not indicate a state of stomach that calls for some repairs? I mentioned to you that eating or drinking anything hastily produced palpitation, and that this has been the case with me for some time past. The palpitation entirely ceases when digestion has gone on to a certain extent. Flatus in the stomach has the same effect. It first came on some years ago from a fright, but I think I have felt more of it within these last twelve months than usual; much of it depends on the state of mind. Depression is sure to produce it, and spontaneous exhilaration (not wine) take it off. We must talk a little of this on a future day. I did not leave my bed till yesterday afternoon, and had no conception I should have suffered such a diminution of muscular strength. Today, I feel a great increase of strength, but was excessively faint until I took a little animal food and a small quantity of wine, largely diluted with water.

I am thinking of taking some infusion of columba with soda as a tonic for such a stomach as mine. But perhaps I shall see you are long. I am tired, so adieu, my dear Baron.

With best affection, truly yours,

E. Jenner

Although Jenner had reached a stage in his life where he was more or less content to live his remaining days peacefully and gently, his peace of mind was somewhat disturbed when a rumour reached England that an epidemic of smallpox had broken out in Europe. Unfortunately the rumour was true and it then reached London which meant that those doctors who lived and practiced in the capital and were quick to point out that vaccination was not infallible began to make their voices heard as well. The smallpox then reached Cheltenham where

Jenner had practiced for so many years, and finally reached Berkeley. Jenner did not want to have to fight his corner for the vaccination process as he felt that his record over many years had proved him right. He wrote to his friend, the Revd Dr Worthington who had been involved with Jenner in the early days of vaccination:

'We have at last imported the disease into this place. Henry Jenner, who although he has seen nearly half a century fly over his head has not yet begun to think, perched himself in the midst of a poor family pent up in a small cottage. It was the abode of wretchedness, had the addition of pestilence not been wanting. He was infected, of course, and his recovery is very doubtful. I am told today that he is very full of an eruption, the appearance of which stands midway between smallpox and chickenpox.'

Henry Jenner (1767–1851) was the bane of his uncle's existence. Jenner found his nephew almost impossible to teach, and the fact that Henry approved of vaccination with great enthusiasm, Jenner found that Henry's support was not necessarily a positive addition to the numbers that supported Edward. Jenner did not think that Henry would survive this bout of smallpox but not only did he survive, he lived to the ripe old age of eighty four years and in 1838 wrote a pamphlet entitled 'On the Proper Management of Vaccination' which claimed that he had never come across a person who had been vaccinated that had not been free from smallpox. This was not quite true as there had been a very few who had succumbed despite being vaccinated but whether Henry had made this claim out of his complete support of his uncle's work or whether his memory was at fault we cannot be sure.

This latest unwelcome spread of smallpox made Jenner think of James Phipps, the little boy who he had performed the first vaccination on all those years ago on 14th May, 1796 just days before Jenner's forty seventh birthday. At the time, Jenner had taken great pains to find someone who he knew was in good health and he selected young James as he was known to Jenner, there being one of two reasons why this was the case. Some biographies say that it was his gardener's son whilst others name the gardener as being a man by the name of John Jones and that James was working under him. Either way, it took a man of courage and confidence to carry that procedure out. The process was over with very quickly but the result of that experiment carried out in a village called

Berkeley nestling in the heart of Gloucestershire changed the health of the whole world.

Meanwhile, the latest epidemic meant that the battle had to be fought again but Jenner was old, tired and enjoying being semi-retired and taking life at a slow pace – he simply didn't have the energy any more. However, someone came along called Sir Gilbert Blane (1749–1834), the President of the College of Surgeons and Physician-in-ordinary to the Prince of Wales (1762–1830), the wayward son of King George III. Apart from his work with vaccination in the navy, it is also claimed by some that he introduced lime juice to the navy to ward off scurvy which was a bigger killer of seamen then all the casualties caused by war. The claim that it was he who first tackled the massive problem of scurvy could well be disputed however, as Captain Cook (1728–79) used lime juice along with fresh vegetables as early as 1768, which was the year that the first of his three great voyages round the world started. Before that of course, there is the great James Lind (1716–94) who wrote his brilliant 'Treatise of the Scurvy' which was published in 1753 but which was ignored by the navy at the time causing thousands of unnecessary deaths and suffering. Its findings were finally accepted by the navy in 1795, the year after Lind's death and is now regarded as a medical classic. However, there is no disputing the fact that Blane was a highly respected physician who had looked after health for the navy and whose writings were included in the 'Transactions of the Medico-Chirugical Society'. It is also beyond dispute that Blane was responsible for the navy accepting that vaccination was the best way of treating smallpox. Jenner wrote to thank him with enthusiasm:

'I dashed at your paper the moment I opened it, and I should set no value on my feelings if I could not with truth assure you that its perusal afforded me the highest gratification. It is exactly the thing the public wanted. A statement so clear and so decisive cannot fail to make a beneficial impression even in its present state of confinement; but if I may be allowed to burst the blue walls of its prison-house, I would, with yours and the consent of the Society, set it free and give it the liberty of ranging the world over.'

Meanwhile, James Phipps had been very ill with what Jenner feared was pulmonary tuberculosis and Jenner thought that he may die. The cow called Blossom from where the original strain of cowpox came via the milkmaid Sarah Nelmes and which was inserted into the young James Phipps' arm on 14th May, 1796, had been granted an honourable retirement and some of her hide is now on display at The Chantry which now houses the Jenner Museum. Jenner was very worried about James and thought that he too should receive some reward for being the first ever person who was officially recognised as being the first to be vaccinated with cowpox.

Jenner himself drew up some plans for a cottage and had one built for Phipps who loved living there, and not only did he survive this illness but went on to live to a very ripe old age. We do not know quite how old he was when he died, but Dorothy Fisk, in her excellent book 'Doctor Jenner of Berkeley' first published in 1959 says that there were one or two people living at that time in Berkeley who remember Phipps as an old man. Given what happened after that first vaccination with cowpox, it was a fitting present for him to live in comfort in his old age.

-oOOo-

Chapter 18
The Death of Edward Jenner

During the summer of 1820, Jenner felt healthy and well, and he went to visit his friend Dr Matthew Baillee (1761–1823) who was the nephew of Jenner's mentor, Dr John Hunter (1728–1793) at Duntisbourne for several days. They went out riding together, once to London where Baillee was still in practice, and to Gloucester and also the lovely little town of Cirencester. John Baron joined them for a day and listened intently whilst the two doctors talked about the Hunter Brothers, William and John, and their early days in London.

Jenner enjoyed his trips out with his friend, Matthew Baillee, but Baillee was twelve years younger than Jenner and he had difficulty keeping up the pace set by his younger friend, Matthew. Jenner was pleased that he was back at The Chantry and he could return to his slower pace of life. However, when he was out in his garden one evening and suddenly feeling giddy, sat down on the gravel path to rest but despite his efforts, for a short time, he lost consciousness but still fighting what he thought could be his death, he struggled up and managed to get back into the house and sank into the couch. He was vaguely aware of Henry and his business partner, William Shrapnell looking down at him. They bled him and eventually he began to relax and found that he could move his limbs which was a huge relief as he had feared that he might be paralysed. John Baron naturally came over to sit with him and listened patiently while Jenner contemplated death which Baron assumed could not be far away. However, eventually, Jenner rallied and slowly returned to the semi-retired existence that he had enjoyed before; the slow pace of life, the occasional visit to some patient who might need him, and the pleasure of meeting friends from time to time. This pattern of life continued and he felt more like his old self again. King George IV, previously the Prince of Wales who ruled as Regent from 1811 to 1820 which was when King George III had finally died and his son had just been crowned King, was in Cheltenham and whilst Jenner was not that keen in revisiting the town, he went and was honoured to be appointed the King's Physician Extraordinary. This honour, although given to Jenner a little bit late in the day, nonetheless cheered Jenner and gave him more energy. He started visiting a few patients more often and also returned to vaccinating the poor of Berkeley for free from the hut that was in his garden. The hut had been built for Jenner years before by a friend, the Reverend Robert Ferryman (1753–1837) and it still stands proudly in the gardens of The Chantry to this day, although extensive repairs were carried out on it in the early part of the 21st century. Ferryman was a remarkable person who had not entered the priesthood until 1796 by which time he was forty-three years old. We do not know how he and Jenner met, but it is thought by some that it was possibly Admiral Berkeley who had introduced them. Ferryman had gone to sea with the admiral in 1795 and as Jenner knew the Berkeley family well, both as friend and as physician, it was highly likely that it was these events that brought them together. Ferryman returned from sea and settled in Gloucester and in July, 1789 he opened the Museum of British Quadrupeds and Birds in Berkeley Street which is opposite the grand building of Gloucester Cathedral. All the specimens had been collected and preserved by Ferryman and according to the Gloucester Journal, the following year, the Duke of Gloucester along with Richard Beadon (1737–1824), visited the museum. Beadon was the Bishop of Gloucester between 1789 and 1802 and had been Master of Jesus College, Cambridge from 1781 until 1789 and was then appointed Vice-Chancellor of the university along with his appointment as the Bishop of Gloucester. Sometime after he was admitted to the priesthood, Ferryman had stayed with the Duke of Bedford at Woburn Abbey where he vaccinated three hundred people. Ferryman was a bit of a maverick but his charm won him over to the members of the aristocracy although it has to be said that Jenner was rather less enamoured with him and after he had known Ferryman for thirty years, he summed him up as follows:

"I have just got a letter from Ferryman. He says that if he could get a curacy he would relinquish his post at Halifax.

"What a strange jumble of intellect does this unfortunate man possess. How much he has mistaken himself, and put that in front which should have been in the background. He is a preeminent (in my opinion) as a Landscape Gardener and by pursuing that for the benefit of others, he might have enriched himself –

but he must become an architect and be hanged to him, ruin himself and those who were heedless enough to employ him."

Apparently, Ferryman had taken a post in Halifax, Nova Scotia, and many thought that he had done this to escape his wife. After marrying and raising a family together they had gone their separate ways and were not on the best of terms. To help both his friend and his daughter Catherine who by now was married, Jenner had written to a friend of his daughters that Ferryman would do a good job for her as an architect as she was thinking of building cottages just outside of Birmingham where Catherine now lived with her husband, John Yeend Bedford. Jenner's recommendation that Ferryman would do his daughter's friend a good job as an architect seems to contradict his opinion of Ferryman in the previous paragraph. Perhaps he thought that designing the cottages would be an easy job that even Ferryman couldn't mess up, that, plus the fact that Jenner wanted to help his friend who was probably in debt may have been the reason.

Returning to 1822, because the position of Physician Extraordinary to King George had given Jenner renewed energy, and still not liking his own company, he had set about mixing with friends again and he spent some weeks with his nephew, Edward Davies, the son of Jenner's sister Anne (1741–1812) and her husband, the Revd William Davies (1740–1817) at Ebley. Many of his friends wanted him to have his portrait painted as although it had been done before, it had been ten years since Sir Thomas Lawrence (1769–1830) had painted him and over the years, Jenner had put on some weight and so any new portrait would look very different from the Lawrence portrait. Jenner had also been painted by James Northcote (1746–1831) and John Raphael Smith (1751–1812) so he agreed to sit for William Armfield Hobday (1771–1831). The details of the lives and careers of Northcote, Lawrence and Smith have already been dealt with earlier in the book so a few details of Hobday should be looked at here.

We're not sure of the exact date that he was born, but we know the year, 1771. William showed great promise at an early age and he was sent to London when still a boy and articled to an engraver by the name of William Barney and was with him for six years whilst at the same time studying to gain a place at the Royal Academy schools. The Royal Academy of Arts (R.A.) had been established in 1768 to create the promotion of creativity, the approach of visual arts through exhibitions along with education and debate. Later on he became well known as a portrait painter and his clients included royalty and in particular, King George IV, the famous Rothschild family, and of course Edward Jenner amongst many others. He constantly exhibited at the Royal Academy and was a very successful portrait painter and miniaturist. During his career he made a great deal of money and in 1831 married Maria Pearce in Exeter although he sadly died on 13th February of that same year.

Although still mourning Catherine, Jenner was able to enjoy life to a degree and he was often searching out some of his old friends. He visited John Phillimore Hicks, the son of his very long-standing friend, Henry Hicks. Father and son were now partners in the cloth mill but like many fathers and sons who were in partnership together, there were tensions as to how it should be run and where the business was heading to in the future. Son John wanted to introduce new methods, but Henry could not agree. It was difficult for John. He wished to respect his father's views but not to the degree which would cause the business to collapse. John kept a diary and one entry reads as follows:

'A day never to be remembered without regret from having been betrayed into a violent dispute with my father on the subject of the business. May God grant me pardon for this and many other acts of undutiful behaviour, and dispose my heart to bear the reproof of my parents (however unjust or harsh) with meekness'.

We don't know whether it was Henry, the father, who was holding things up or his son John who being younger might have wanted to try new methods. All logical thought must be that it was Henry who being the older man, was reluctant to try the new methods. However, the waters are a bit muddied on this as Henry had proved himself open to new ideas as he was one of the first to support Jenner when he initially introduced the vaccine idea to the world. However, it is useless to speculate as we shall probably never know.

Jenner still wanted to work as without Catherine, he needed a reason for being. Many years before, he had started a paper on bird migration, a pastime that had always made him feel relaxed. He would lie awake in the early morning listening initially to the robin, followed by the lark. After that all the birds were singing and he was reasonably content as it meant the dawn of a brand new day, a new day that he had once dreaded when he first lost Catherine, and whilst he still missed her dreadfully, he was in that happy state of semi-retirement which meant that he could still partake in seeing some of his friends but also could work when and if he felt like it. An inveterate nature lover, he listened to all the sounds of the birds and decided to write about them all. He was determined to write to the best of his ability and with his quill pen at the ready, started to write the following. Even the first few words told many people of something they had probably never known:

'First the robin, and not the lark as has been generally imagined, as soon as twilight has drawn the imperceptible line between night and day, begins his lonely song. How sweetly does this harmonise with the soft dawning of the day! He goes on till the twinkling sunbeams begin to tell him his notes no longer accord with the rising scene. Up starts the lark; and with him a variety of sprightly songsters, whose lively notes are in perfect correspondence with the gaiety of the morning. The general warbling continues, with now and then an interruption for reasons before assigned, by the by the transient croak of the raven, the screaming of the jay and the swift, or the pert chattering of the daw. The nightingale, unwearied by the vocal exertions of the night, withdraws not proudly by day from his inferiors in song, but joins them in the general harmony. The thrush is wisely placed on the summit of some lofty tree, that its loud and piercing notes may be softened by distance before they reach the ear; while the mellow blackbird seeks the inferior branches. Should the sun, having been eclipsed with a cloud, shine forth with fresh effulgence, how frequently we see the goldfish perch on some blossomed bough, and hear his song poured forth in a strain particularly energetic, much more sonorous and lively now than at any other time; while the sun full shining on his beautiful plumes, displays his golden wings and crimson chest to charming advantage. The notes of the cuckoo blend with this cheering concert in a perfectly pleasing manner and for a short time are highly grateful to the ear; but sweet as this singular song is, it should tire by its uniformity were it not given in so transient a manner. At length the evening advances, the performers gradually retire, and the concert softly dies away. The sun is seen no more. The robin again sets up his twilight song, till the still more serene hour of night sends him to the bower to rest; and now, to close the scene in full and perfect harmony no sooner is the voice of the robin hushed, and night again spreads a gloom over the horizon, than the owl sends forth his slow and solemn tones. They are more than plaintive and less than melancholy; and tend to inspire the imagination with a train of contemplations well adapted to the serious hour.'

Beautiful words that paint a vivid picture and clearly written by a lover of nature. 'All very well' Jenner must have thought. However, there were very few people who would read this descriptive piece and he had more pressing and practical things to think about. His daughter, Catherine (1794–1833) was acting as her father's hostess cum secretary and she had been happily carrying out these duties for nearly seven years but Jenner knew that she must find a husband who will look after her when he is gone. So many of his friends had died, and Jenner knew that he couldn't go on forever. The problem was that in those days, if the father died, then the estate would go to the eldest surviving son, in this case Robert (1797–1854). If Edward died therefore, it mattered not that Catherine had been living there for years, she would have to leave, and Robert, the surviving son would inherit The Chantry. It was grotesque but in 1822 that was how the legal system worked. Many people even in those days could see that it was unfair and Jane Austen tackles the subject very well in two of her books, 'Sense and Sensibility' and 'Pride and Prejudice'. It was all extremely unfair, but that was the law of the land and there was nothing that they could do about it. The only way that Catherine would have been able to stay was if Robert had never married and Catherine had stayed on as hostess. As it happened, Robert never did marry but Jenner and his daughter could not know that and on 7th August, 1822, Catherine married a man named John Yeend Bedford and they left Berkeley to set up home in Edgbaston, Birmingham where Catherine's new husband worked as a solicitor. Although Edward was heartbroken at the fact of her not only leaving home, but leaving Berkeley to live in Birmingham, he was nonetheless relieved that her future was secured. Like any father in his position, he was distraught at losing his daughter, not only from his home, but from the village he loved so much, and later in the evening of the marriage, he turned to his friend Baron and wrote: 'Pray do not desert this forlorn cottage, but come sometimes to chase away my melancholy hours'.

Baron responded quickly as Jenner knew he would, but others helped out as well. Various relatives came, especially Jenner's great nieces, Susannah and Caroline, who were the twin daughters of Jenner's nephew Henry (1767–1851) and his wife Susannah (1766–98) who were born in 1794, although we do not know how long each of the sisters lived. They were very pleasant girls and not only came to give their great-uncle companionship, but also helped him with his correspondence, probably putting some of it in order as it is doubtful that Jenner ever made much of a job in ever getting round to tackling the job himself. In that year of 1822, the autumn saw Baron publish his book entitled 'Tuberculous Diseases', and the title page recorded Jenner's latest position of which he was immensely proud, that of being Physician Extraordinary to King George IV.

Nevertheless, despite all the support he was getting, given his age and the fact that so many of his friends had died, he was thinking a great deal about his own mortality and he could not get the thought of his wife Catherine out of his mind. He wondered whether he would see her again. Her own deeply held Christian beliefs enabled her to face her death far more easily than Edward could because although a great deal of her Christianity rubbed off on him, without her physical presence he was not quite so sure. He wondered why so many people who were good and kind should have to suffer. He was probably thinking that in general terms but he must also have been thinking of the early deaths of his beloved sweet natured son, Edward (1789–1810) and the remarkably talented John Worgan who tutored young Edward along with his brother Robert (1797–1854). Why did the nature loving Edward who his father worshipped die at barely twenty-one years of age whilst his rakish brother live until he was fifty-seven which was a reasonable age in the 18th century? With these thoughts in mind he sat down and wrote:

"May those sacred truths, revealed by Him who did condescend to assume a human form, and appear among men upon the earth, be so engrafted in my mind that I may never lose sight of these Thy divine mercies, and thus, by my faith and practice when it may please Thee to send my body to the grave, may my imperishable soul be received into Thy habitations of eternal glory."

What he did with these written words is not clear, but a safe bet is to guess that they were simply his thoughts as laid down for himself and not necessarily for anyone else to read. Be that as it may, his reasonably active life continued in the same way until the morning of the 24th January 1823. The weather was freezing and Jenner sat down and wrote what was to be his last letter to his great nephew, William Davies, who was the son of Rev William Davies, Jenner's nephew, and his wife Sarah who he had married in 1810:

My dear William,

I hear by your father that you will return in a few days to Bristol. Be assured you will take with you my best wishes and affections, which I present to you with greater delight than at any former period, because you are more entitled to them, for I am happy to certify that that no boy could behave better than you did during your stay with me at 'The Chantry'. Pursue this line of good conduct, my dear William, and you will be happy yourself and make your father and everyone who loves you happy.

Your affectionate uncle,
Edward Jenner

When the letter was finished, he walked briskly over to Cam, about a mile and a half away to take charge of the distribution of fuel to the poor. He returned to the house which was still freezing, as was he, and he spent the afternoon pottering round keeping himself busy in an attempt to disguise the fact that he was unable to get warm. The date was Friday, 24th January 1823, and in the evening, Jenner was walking in the garden when his butler came to him and told him that Mr Joyner Ellis, the Berkeley coroner had been taken very ill and asked if Jenner would come out to see him. Jenner never refused anyone who requested his time and his skill, nevertheless, he would be less than human if he liked the thought of riding out on a freezing evening to see a patient. His great nephew, Stephen Jenner (1793–?), son of Henry (1767–1851) and the late Susannah Jenner (1767–98) was there and remained at the house until Jenner returned. When at last he arrived home, he went straight to bed partly because of the cold and partly because it had been a long day and he was very tired. He would write up his notes the next morning.

The next day, convinced that Mr Ellis was going to die very soon, Jenner went straight to his study and wrote the following:

'Mr Joyner Ellis, from long exposure to severe cold, the thermometer being many degrees below freezing point, was so benumbed that he was brought home after a long journey, chiefly in an open carriage, in a state of paralytic debility; the harmony of all his vital functions seemed disturbed, and of some he had seemed quite deprived. Being moved he appeared to feel pain about the chest; and as his breathing was short and laborious, Mr H. abstracted about 16 ounces of blood from the arm, but without relief. There was that peculiar effort in breathing that is not really stertorous, but approaching to it; so that my prognostic was as unfavourable as it could be.' Jenner was correct in his fears about Mr Joyner Ellis as the Berkeley Coroner died two days later.

When he had finished writing, he put down his pen and thought about his morning walk with little enthusiasm as he felt so tired. He decided to lie down on the couch and rest until the next mealtime. He woke after a while, but still exhausted, retired to bed where he went straight to sleep. Jenner's nephew Henry Jenner (1767–1851) usually came to see Jenner at 8 o'clock each morning when they would breakfast together and the next morning was no exception. He arrived at the usual time and was told by his son Stephen that Jenner had not come down yet. Henry called Jenner's servant to go to Jenner to tell him that breakfast was ready. This was the morning of Saturday, 25th January and the servant found Jenner in the library unconscious on the floor and after placing him on the sofa immediately went to Henry to see if he could do anything for his uncle. Henry Jenner was convinced that his uncle had had an apoplectic seizure accompanied with paralysis on the right side. Henry then bled him and applied blisters to his feet. He then sent for Henry Hickes, the Berkeley surgeon, and despite his and John Baron's best efforts, it was to no avail. Nothing more could be done for Edward Jenner and he remained unconscious until the early hours of the next day when he finally died at 2am on 26th January 1823.

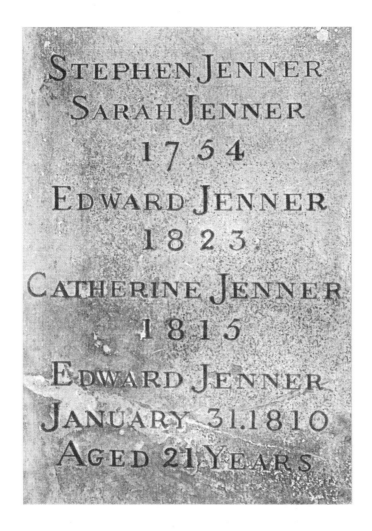

STEPHEN JENNER
SARAH JENNER
1754
EDWARD JENNER
1823
CATHERINE JENNER
1815
EDWARD JENNER
JANUARY 31.1810
AGED 21 YEARS

In terms of Jenner's stated aims to bring about the end of smallpox, it had not been reached at the time of his death, nor could it have been, but the tide of public opinion had changed towards Jenner's ideas making the acceptance that vaccination was the only known effective cure for smallpox. He has left us with an incredible legacy which will always be with us and in 1853, vaccination was made compulsory and in 1980, the World Health Organisation announced that the scourge of small pox was wiped from the face of the earth. It had taken over 150 years from his death but all those who had doubted or even ridiculed him were finally shown to be wrong. Jenner had achieved what he had set out to do in his 1801 paper, 'The Origin of the Vaccine Inoculation' in which he had claimed that it was inevitable that smallpox would be wiped out.

Jenner was totally unselfish and also very brave. He could have kept his ideas secret and made a great deal of money by so doing. Instead, he made his ideas known to the whole world, and even invited his own country's ire by allowing France to understand vaccination even though it meant that more soldiers of the French army would be fit to fight against Britain. As a result, Napoleon had a very high regard for Edward and when the English country doctor used to write to Napoleon to obtain the release of an important prisoner-of-war, Napoleon never refused Jenner.

In all the work that Jenner carried out, he wished only to serve his country and a letter that he wrote demonstrated this very well. We do not know who the recipient was, but the meaning is clear:

"Shall I, who even in the morning of my days sought the lowly and sequestered paths of life, the valley and not the mountain, shall I now my evening is fast approaching, hold myself up as an object of fortune and for fame? Admitting it as a certainty that I obtain both, what stock should I add to my little fund of happiness? And as for the fame, what is it? A gilded butt, for ever pierced with the arrows of malignancy." So there we have it, Jenner never sought fame as such but it seems inexplicable today as to why he never received a knighthood. Today's world of popstars receiving knighthoods makes our current world seem shallow. It makes even less sense when we know that Jenner was Physician to the Prince Regent, later to rule as George IV. Perhaps it was due to the prolonged illness of George III, George IV's father that stopped him taking rational decisions although that shouldn't have stopped the Prince Regent, later to rule as George IV to have given Jenner the much-deserved title. As we have already read, George III ruled from 1760 until 1820 when he died, although he became too ill to rule from 1811 onwards so that the Prince of Wales ruled as Prince Regent from 1811 until 1820 which is when he became King as George IV. George III first became ill in 1788 before Jenner carried out the first vaccination and this illness nearly caused a constitutional crisis. On the one hand, there was the Prime Minister, William Pitt the Younger who was desperate for the King to recover and was forever using stalling tactics against the Prince of Wales who was on very good terms with Charles James Fox along with the other members of the Whig party and who had their own agenda with the Prince of Wales desperate to become Regent. The situation was saved for Pitt when his Regency Bill, which he was eventually forced to bring out and present to the House of Commons on 5th February 1789, and again to the Lords on 16th February was beaten by a bulletin dated the next day, the 17th February from the King's doctors saying that the King had recovered and was fit to rule. It was extraordinary timing but Pitt was off the hook and both he and the King remained in power whilst Charles James Fox and the Whig opposition could do nothing about it.

The King ruled during the time that Jenner was performing his work on smallpox, but the erratic nature of the King's health over a prolonged period of time may have caused Jenner not to have his knighthood which must have disappointed him although he remained the modest man that he always had been, and if he was disappointed about it, he never expressed any sorrow.

However, regardless of the reasons why Jenner never received a knighthood, there were probably many others who shared the same fate and there was certainly one, who, like Jenner, was cruelly passed by for an honour and he was the brilliant self-taught watchmaker, John Harrison (1693–1776), who spent virtually the whole of his working life attempting to solve the problem of calculating the longitude at sea. Sailors understood how to calculate latitude but without longitude, it was almost impossible to work out at any one time where exactly the ship was when it was at sea.

Matters had come to a head when in 1707, Admiral Sir Cloudsley Shovel (1650–1707), a highly regarded naval commander, was bringing his fleet home from battle when Shovel miscalculated their exact position and the entire fleet was wrecked and 2,000 lives, including that of Shovel's were lost through drowning. As a result, the government created a Board of Longitude in 1714 offering a reward of £20,000, a huge amount in today's terms, for anyone who could solve the problem. Harrison did solve the problem but only after a protracted battle with the various members of the Board of Longitude and then only after the government stepped in was the balance paid in full. This must have happened to a great many men over the years which is shown by the biblical quotation (Mark 6/4) that says: 'A prophet is not without honour, save in his own country'. It was a bitter lesson for both Jenner and Harrison.

It is almost certain that Jenner's great friend and future biographer, John Baron, would have liked his mentor to have had a state funeral followed by a burial at Westminster Abbey, but Jenner would not have wanted that. Instead, he was laid to rest in the chancel of Berkeley church alongside his wife, Catherine, his parents Stephen and Sarah, and his beloved son, Edward. All of them together in the quiet countryside of Berkeley, exactly how Jenner would have wished.

His legacy, sadly, unknown to so many who owe their lives to him, is still recognised the world over but not recognised so much in his own country. We have two statues of him, one in Kensington Gardens, London, whilst the other resides proudly in Gloucester Cathedral. Situated as it is in the west side of the nave near the south porch entry, the statue is virtually the first monument that visitors to the cathedral, whether they be local people or visitors from abroad, actually see, although many do not know who he is which is so sad.

The first statue is the one that is in Gloucester Cathedral. It was fashioned by Robert William Sievier F.R.S. (1794–1865), the English sculptor and engraver. Sievier showed promise in drawing and studied under John Young and Edward Scriven before attending the Royal Academy School in 1818 where he specialised in portrait engravings. However, despite being excellent at what he was doing, he decided in 1823 to cease work on engravings to concentrate on sculptures and he worked on many famous subjects. Apart from Jenner, he sculpted Prince Albert of Saxe-Coburg (1819–1861), the husband of Queen Victoria and also Sir Thomas Lawrence, P.R.A., F.R.S. (1769–1830), a leading portrait painter who was also the fourth President of the Royal Academy. Sievier exhibited at the Royal Academy from 1822 until 1844 and amongst his works during that time were busts, figure subjects, gravestones and monuments. The statue in Gloucester Cathedral is not the only work completed by Robert William Sievier that is placed in that beautiful building. Sievier also sculpted a beautiful monument for the great prison reformer, Sir George Oneisiphorus Paul (1746–1820), and although Paul died three years before Jenner, Seivier completed the two monuments at the same time, 1825.

The difference between the two monuments could not be greater. The inscription on the Edward Jenner statue spells out the single word 'JENNER', whilst the wording on Paul's monument is as follows:

'To the memory of

Sir George Onesiphorus Paul, Baronet

Who died Jan 16th 1820 aged 74 years.
A man
Endeared to his friends by many virtues
Both public and private

But who claims this mark of local respect

By having first reduced to practice

The principles which have immortalised

The memory of Howard

For to the object of this memorial it is to be ascribed

That this county has become the example and model

Of the best system of criminal discipline

In which provident regulation has banished the use of fetters

And health been substituted for contagion

Thus happily reconciling humanity with punishment

And the prevention of crime with individual reform.'

Sievier worked from his studio, the first being situated in Southampton Row, London, and in 1837, he relocated to Henrietta Street and on top of that, he also had a studio in Upper Holloway. He died suddenly in his studio on 28th April 1865 and was laid to rest in Kensal Green Cemetery. There is a post script to Sievier and his work in Gloucester Cathedral in the form of an entry into the diary of the Cotswold parson, the Reverend F. E. Watts (1783–1854). In November, 1825, he was visiting Gloucester and entered his thoughts on R. W. Sievier in two entries made when he was visiting the town. He clearly had a great deal of admiration for Sievier. These are the two entries:

November 9th 1825.

Mr Sievier is the Sculptor employed to design and execute the two monuments now erecting in the Cathedral to Sir G. Paul and Dr Jenner. He was, I am told, bred up as an engraver, and has only of late turned his talents to the art of sculpture. He has obtained great credit for a celebrated bust of the Lord Chancellor, which he has most felicitously conceived, and has it in charge now to engage in some elaborate works of art, to be placed in the new palace about to be erected on the site of Buckingham house. I found him a very unaffected, well informed, agreeable man; his mind has not been exclusively applied to the study of fine arts, as he seems by his conversation deeply versed in mechanics and chemistry. The Committees for the erection of the two monuments named above entrusted the execution to Mr S. both under the persuasion, that his talents and skill were of a high order, and because the artists anxiety to distinguish himself by some great works place in a public situation would tempt him to forgo that large profit, which Chantry and other established Sculptors of eminence insist upon.

The second entry was just three days later before his departure from his visit to Gloucester:

November 12th 1825

Before leaving Gloucester, I went to the Cathedral to take a last look at Sievier's two Monuments, the erection of which is nearly completed. They reflect the highest credit on his talents and execution. That to the memory of Dr Jenner is a marble statue. It is placed at the west end of the nave, immediately before the first pier on the south side. Dr Jenner is represented in the appropriate academical costume of a Doctor of Medicine of the University of Oxford, that body having conferred on him an honorary degree: the gown gives a fine display of drapery, so arranged as to render unobtrusive the ungraceful forms of modern costume, and at the same time to impart to the figure a degree of height and dignity, which it might otherwise have wanted. In his right hand, which crosses the body, and supports a fold of the gown, he holds a scroll, and in his left, which drops carelessly on the side, the appropriate academical cap. The whole figure is beautiful, distinguished by classical elegance and simplicity: the inclination of the head is peculiarly graceful. It cannot be called a correct resemblance of Jenner; but at any period of life, his was a very unsuitable study for a sculptor; the figure, broad, thickset, clumsy; and the countenance coarse, though very intelligent, when lighted up by the talent within.

A fine tribute to a sculpture by a local clergyman who must have seen many such sculptures. However, in reverting to the statues purely of Jenner, the above only covers the first statue of Jenner, the one by Sievier which resides in Gloucester Cathedral.

The second statue of Jenner was sculpted by William Calder Marshall, RA, (1813–1894), a Scottish sculptor, who was born in Edinburgh on 18th March, 1813. He attended the Royal High School before entering Edinburgh University and in 1834, he enrolled at the Royal Academy where he was taught by Sir Frances Leggat Chantry (1781–1841), a leading portrait sculptor of the Regency period which would put him in the early part of the 19th century, and Edward Hodges Bailey, R.A., F.R.S. (1788–1867), also a leading portrait sculptor.

In 1844, Marshall participated in an exhibition in Westminster Hall to determine how to decorate selected articles for the rebuilt Palace of Westminster which had been burnt down on 16th October, 1834 and was finally rebuilt in 1870. His statue of Edward Jenner was placed on a plinth set up in the south west corner of Trafalgar Square in central London in 1858 and it was inaugurated with a ceremony attended by none other than Prince Albert, husband/consort to Queen Victoria. However, it was only there for four years before being moved to Kensington Gardens in 1862 much to the disgust of the British Medical Journal who wrote an article expressing their feelings on the matter. They then wrote a further article which included the acidic comment: "…had been banished even with ignominy from those honourable neighbourhood of men esteemed great because they had killed their fellow creatures whilst he had only saved them."

The statue is still in Kensington Gardens where it continues to rest today. In 2010, a movement was set up in order that it could return to its original home in Trafalgar Square, and despite a great deal of support from both the medical world and the general public, it remains where it is at the time of writing (2019).

William Calder Marshall died on 16th June, 1894 at his home in 115, Ebury Street, Chester Square, London and is buried in Kensal Green Cemetery, London.

Jenner never received a state funeral and he wasn't buried at Westminster Abbey, and if that wasn't enough, he was not given the knighthood that he surely deserved as mentioned before. On top of that, he was criticised more in his own country than in anywhere else in the world where his name was lionised, especially in France despite the fact that we were at war with that country from 1793 until 1815. Instead, this humble man turned down a three-year voyage around the world to the Pacific Islands with the great botanist, Joseph Banks as well as refusing a lucrative practice in London along with his mentor Sir John Hunter so that he could return to Berkeley and practice his medicine there.

We, who inhabit the world must always be aware that he saved us all from a most lethal disease but despite this, he had a simple family funeral where no one from the medical world attended. However, admirers of Jenner can be rest assured that a simple funeral followed by being laid to rest in Berkeley Church next to his beloved Catherine was almost certainly what this modest man would have wished for. We can at least be grateful that he got his wish although there were many who would have agreed with Jenner's biographer and friend, John Baron, who thought that he should have had a state funeral and should have been laid to rest in St Paul's Cathedral or Westminster Abbey. We who live in Gloucestershire can be grateful that his statue is still with us and the least that the rest of the world can give him is our eternal gratitude and that we must never forget him.

-oOOo-